ALS

Advances in Life Sciences

Tropical Forests in Transition

Ecology of Natural and Anthropogenic Disturbance Processes

Edited by
J.G. Goldammer

Birkhäuser Verlag
Basel · Boston · Berlin

Editor's address:

Dr. Johann Georg Goldammer
Max Planck Institute of Chemistry
Biogeochemistry Department (Mainz)
Fire Ecology and Biomass Burning Research Group
c/o University of Freiburg
Bertoldstr. 17
D-7800 Freiburg
Germany

Deutsche Bibliothek Cataloging-in-Publication Data
Tropical forests in transition: ecology of natural and anthropogenic disturbance processes
/ ed. by J. G. Goldammer. – Basel ; Boston ; Berlin : Birkhäuser, 1992
(Advances in life sciences)
ISBN 3-7643-2601-8 (Basel...)
ISBN 0-8176-2601-8 (Boston)
NE: Goldammer, Johann Georg [Hrsg.]

© 1992 Birkhäuser Verlag
        P.O. Box 133
        4010 Basel
        Switzerland

Printed from the authors' camera-ready manuscripts
on acid-free paper in Germany
ISBN 3-7643-2601-8
ISBN 0-8176-2601-8

Contents

VI

Preface

In evolutionary time scales natural disturbances have affected the vegetation on Earth. During the Quaternary the forest biomes of the tropics were subjected to manifold disturbances. Climate changes and climate oscillations were associated with changing precipitation and drought regimes, flooding, siltation, landslides, etc. The prehistorical forest was also influenced by the effects of large wildlife populations. Large-scale catastrophies in the forest biomes were mainly caused by abiotic environmental alterations, the small-scale disturbances were and still are related to both biotic and abiotic processes. Both the large- and the small-scale disturbances have played a significant role in shaping distribution, dynamics, structure and composition of the paleoforest.

After the expansion of hominids and early humans, and later, by modern humans, the anthropogenic influences on the tropical forest began to overlap natural disturbances. Today's anthropogenic impacts on the tropical forests differ qualitatively and quanitatively from the natural disturbances. The speed of tropical deforestation and savannization is dramatically increasing. The physical and chemical impacts of forest conversion and biomass burning add to other anthropogenic influences on the atmosphere and climate. The expected anthropogenic climate change will also have considerable impacts on the tropical flora and fauna.

The book on "Tropical Forests in Transition" synthesizes information on changing environmental conditions and human impacts on the tropical forest by looking back to the paleoecology, analyzing the impact of modern human populations and modeling the future of the tropical forest in a changing environment. The aim of the book is to strengthen multidisciplinary thinking in disturbance ecology.

Acknowledgements

The contributors to this book convened at the University of Freiburg (Germany) under the sponsorship of the German Society of Tropical Ecology and the Fire Ecology and Biomass Burning Research Group[*]. Financial support was provided by the Deutsche Forschungsgemeinschaft (DFG) and the Ministry of Science and Arts of the State of Baden-Württemberg. Valuable assistance was given by the University of Freiburg, particularly by the Institute of Forest Zoology, the Institute of Biology I and the Faculty of Forest Sciences. The editor is indebted to Doris Spitzer, for preparing the camera-ready manuscript of the book, and to Jennifer Johns, for a final critical linguistic review of the contributions.

Freiburg (Germany), January 1992   Johann Georg Goldammer

---

[*] The Fire Ecology and Biomass Burning Research Group is a Subdivision of the Max Planck Institute of Chemistry, Biogeochemistry Department (Mainz, Germany), and is located at the University of Freiburg, Institute of Forest Zoology

Tropical Forests in Transition
J. G. Goldammer (ed.)
© 1992 Birkhäuser Verlag Basel/Switzerland

Tropical Forests in Transition. Ecology of Natural and Anthropogenic Disturbance Processes - An Introduction

Johann Georg Goldammer[*]

Abstract

Recent paleoecological, biogeographical, atmospheric and climatological findings have revealed that general conceptions of the assumed ageless stability of today's tropical forest ecosystems can no longer be supported. Pleistocene climatic changes and Holocene climate oscillations have caused significant fluctuations in tropical forest biomes, which leads to the conclusion that patterns of distribution and species composition of today's tropical forest formations are closely related to the relatively short period of modern climate conditions.

In addition to the impact of climate change, other forces such as anthropogenic forest disturbance, the ecological feedback mechanisms of deforestation and other human-induced environmental changes, determine the present and the possible future development of the tropical forest biota. A predictive assessment of tropical forest development requires detailed knowledge of interacting ecological processes, that is, the coupling of small-scale impacts (e.g. timber extraction, shifting cultivation, grazing, fire) with large-scale feedback mechanisms (e.g. atmospheric changes, meso- and macro-climate change).

A thorough understanding of paleoclimate and forest changes and the coupling of terrestrial ecology with atmospheric sciences will be imperative to predict the possible development of tropical forests in transition to a new climate-supported equilibrium. The introductory paper to this volume gives some selected examples of past and present natural disturbance processes in the tropical forest biota. The possible impacts of anthropogenic disturbances on present and future ecosystem processes are highlighted.

---

[*]Fire Ecology and Biomass Burning Research Group of the Max Planck Institute of Chemistry, Biogeochemistry Department (Mainz, Germany), at the Department of Forestry, University of Freiburg, Bertoldstr. 17, D-7800 Freiburg, Germany

Introduction

During the past decade the growing threat to the world's tropical forests by the impact of human civilization has received increasing attention on public and political levels. The demand for a reliable scientific base and for information on the state of the global tropical forest reserves and on the ecological impacts of the utilization, the degradation and the destruction of the tropical forest has been increased accordingly. The warning signals directed to the public by an increasing number of tropical forest ecologists cannot be overheard - and the relevant publications and political statements are becoming countless.

It is not the intent of this paper and of this volume to add to the various attempts to explain and to quantify the destruction or conversion rate of the world's tropical forests; the interested reader is refered to synoptic summaries such as the state-of-knowledge report on the protection of tropical forest resources by the German Parliament (Deutscher Bundestag 1990).

The aim of this volume is rather to highlight and to elaborate on a multidisciplinary interpretation of the disturbance (or "interference") ecology of the tropical forests (1) along a broad time scale, ranging from the Pleistocene to the $2xCO_2$ climate, (2) by developing an objective approach that would explain the functional role of disturbances, and (3) by relating the impacts of anthropogenic disturbances to natural disturbances by avoiding subjective valuation of contemporary forest destruction. This approach was based on following considerations:

- It is generally accepted that during evolutionary time scales tropical forests were subjected to manifold disturbances related to abiotic and biotic stresses. This especially refers to the Pleistocene climate changes during which the tropical forest underwent dramatic reduction in distribution and changes in species composition. An overall comparison of the suggested distribution of the tropical forest area during the last glaciations with the extent of today's forest cover reveals that at present the tropical rain forests occupy a considerably larger area (cf. syntheses by Flenley [1979] and Prance [1982]).

- It is widely recognized that small- to large-scale disturbances, e.g. in the equatorial rain forest, are key processes in the diversification (speciation) and specialization of species, thus being responsible for the richness of species in the tropical forest biota. From a phylogenetic point of view, these disturbances must have played a role that could be explained as a functional task in evolution (cf. syntheses by Pickett & White [1985] and Platt & Strong [1989]).

- The regular influence of natural and anthropogenic disturbances, such as fire, have created unique seral forest ecosystems that may be valued - from a socio-ecological point of view - to be highly sustainable and productive (cf. Goldammer [1990]).

While it is evident that natural climate changes or climate oscillations play a key role in the development and changes of forests, it becomes increasingly clear that supra-regional or even global interference processes other than climate patterns also have considerable impacts on forest ecosystems. One of the most striking examples is the recent finding on the injection of Saharan dust into the forests of the Amazon basin through mass exchange of air between the two continents. According to Swap *et al.* (1991) c. 190 kg ha^{-1}yr^{-1} of Sahara dust are deposited in the northeastern Amazon basin. Deposition of trace species, such as phosphate, associated with this dust ranges from 1 to 4 kg ha^{-1}yr^{-1}. The authors of this remarkable and somewhat revolutionary study conclude that part of the productivity of the Amazon rain forest is dependent upon critical trace elements contained in this soil dust. They believe that dependence of one large ecosystem upon another separated by an ocean and coupled by the atmosphere to be fundamentally important to any view of how the global system functions. A discussion whether this phenomenon would be designated or valued as a "disturbance" or simply as an "interference" seems quite redundant.

Other aspects of the disturbance ecology of the tropical forest are the possible feedback mechanisms. What are the impacts of natural and anthropogenic disturbances on regional and global systems ? One of the major phenomena linked to natural shrinking of forest cover or to human-made forest conversion is the transfer of carbon from a terrestrial ecosystem into the atmosphere. In the context of anthropogenic global climate change this phenomenon has received extensive scientific attention (cf. Esser, this volume). There are, however, other processes linked to the problem of deforestation, e.g. the impacts of emissions from plant biomass burning on regional processes (see below).

While the apparent complexity of processes related to tropical forest disturbances cannot be explained entirely in this volume, the introductory chapter highlights some selected examples of disturbance ecology and finally discusses the consequences for research in tropical forest ecology.

Long-Term Forest Disturbances: A Paleoecological View

Hierarchical disturbance processes affecting the forest region range from short-term gap-phase dynamics on a local scale to increasingly long-term regional and large-scale disturbance processes (paleoclimatic and tectonic disturbances) (Haffer 1991).

The most recent large-scale paleoclimatic disturbance dates back to the Wisconsin-Würm ice age. The global atmospheric and climatic changes during the last glaciation as recorded in the Vostock ice core (Barnola *et al.* 1991) brought dramatic pressure on the world's tropical forests. A generally cooler and drier tropical environment forced the pre-glaciation rain forest biota to retreat to refugia in which the unfavourable climate conditions could be compensated by topographic, hydrological and micro-climatic particularities of the terrain. Despite the incompleteness of evidence of the geography of the refugia and the controversial discussion on their shape and extent (cf. synthesis by Prance [1982]; Brown [1987]; Flenley [this volume]) it is undebated that the refugia must have played an important role as islands of diversification.

While the climatic condidtions were the primary driving force of the retreatment of forests into the refugia, other disturbance effects may have played a role. In a generally drier and probably distinctly seasonal climate the forest refugia were surrounded and separated by savanna-type vegetation subjected to seasonal droughts and, most likely, to frequent natural fires (lightning fires). It has been suggested that the isolation of the forest refugia was enforced by the regular occurrence of fires between the refugia (Goldammer 1991). The functional contribution of these "fire corridors" to evolution was to reduce the gene flow (seed dispersal, pollination, migration) between the refugia.

This hypothesis is supported by modern observations of rain forest islands occuring in some Western African savannas. These islands (ecological characterization cf. Mühlenberg et al. [1990]) show very distinct boundaries (fire-induced and fire-maintained edges) to the savanna vegetation, which has been and still is being shaped by the long-term influence of regularly occuring man-caused and natural fires.

The paleoecological evidence of prehistoric changes in vegetation cover is largely dependent on palynology (Flenley 1979, this volume). The palynological base, however, is still weak because of the lack of sufficient suitable sites in the lowland rain forest biota for obtaining pollen cores. Soil charcoal is another source of evidence of forest disturbance. Besides recently raised doubts on the reliability of ^{14}C ages older than 9000 yr BP (Bard et. al. 1990), there is one major obstacle in interpreting charcoal occurrence: It is not always clear whether soil charcoals are remnants of early human activities - hominids were able to use fire for at least the last 1.5 m yrs (Brain & Sillen 1988) - or an indirect expression of long-term climate changes or short-term climate oscillations.

This refers especially to the time frame of the Pleistocene-Holocene transition period. The ^{14}C ages of charcoal recovered in the northern Amazon basin, ranging between Present and c.6000 years BP (Sanford et al. 1985), and in Southeast Venezuela of up to c.3500 years BP (Fölster, this volume) may be testimonies of natural wildland fires favoured by climate fluctuations or early human activities.

Quaternary rain forest fires in East Kalimantan (Borneo) which were dated back to the period of the peak of the last glaciation (up to c. 17,500 years BP) are a more drastic example of disturbance and recovery potential of the tropical lowland rain forest (Goldammer & Seibert 1989, 1990). These rain forest fires are the result of a unique interaction of cyclic droughts and a natural fire source. Recurrent droughts in insular South Asia (and in the Western Pacific region in general), related to the El Niño-Southern Oscillation (ENSO) event, periodically cause drought stress and induce the exceptional flammability of the rain forest vegetation.

During the 1982-83 ENSO drought large-scale wildfires in East Borneo (Indonesian Province of East Kalimantan, and the Malaysian Provinces Sabah and Sarawak) affected a total c. 5×10^6 ha of forest land; a smaller area was affected during the 1987 ENSO. While most of these fires originated from slash-and-burn agriculture and other forest conversion fires, another permanent source of drought-triggered forest fires was identified. It was observed that during the 1987 ENSO drought a rain forest fire was started at a burning coal seam in East Kalimantan (Fig.1). Thermoluminescence dating of soil materials baked by the heat of the burning coal seams which stretch at or near the surface of the forest revealed that these fires have been active at least since the last ice age. While on the one hand the ^{14}C ages of charcoal samples from rain forest sites revealed that fires had occurred repeatedly between c.17,500 years BP and today, the lowland dipterocarp forest was and still is being considered as a valuable "undisturbed" forest community. In fact, in the description of that particular forest region in this volume (Riswan & Abdulhadi, this volume; cf. Riswan 1982) the term "primary forest" is applied.

The recovery process of the lowland mixed dipterocarp rain forest after a surface wildfire (which, in its effects, differs considerably from the impact of fire applied by the slash-and-burn agriculturist) is not yet entirely clear (Goldammer & Seibert 1990; for the neotropical forest cf. Kauffman & Uhl [1990]). However, as underlined by Goldammer & Seibert (1990) and indirectly supported by Riswan & Abdulhadi (this volume) a variety of studies show an unusual abundance of Bornean Ironwood (*Eusideroxylon zwageri* T&B), one of the few fire-adapted tree species. The relatively high occurrence of this species is an indication of ancient fire influence.

Fig.1. Surface fire in a lowland dipterocarp rain forest in East Kalimantan (Indonesia), September 1987. During the drought of 1987 many of the evergreen species shed their leaves due to the extraordinary drought stress. This led to the build-up of a highly flammable litter layer which carried the fires over large rain forest areas which in average moist years would not burn. During the 1982-83 ENSO-related drought forest fires occurred on an area of c. 5 million hectares of forest land on the whole island of Borneo. Paleofire data suggest that fire disturbances have occurred in long intervals during the Pleistocene (cf. text). Photo: Goldammer

Patterns of forest disturbance by fire or by wind (cf. below) may also be traced by examining the larger fire- or hurricane-induced mosaics inside of large closed forested tracts. Wildfires, for instance, usually burn in irregular patterns which create a mosaic of burned and unburned patches. This phenomenon has been extensively explored in the temperate and boreal zone and explains the existence of forest landscapes composed of a complex mosaic of species composition and stand ages. Again, the shape and boundaries of "islands" of unburned and burned forest sites may have persisted for a long time and may have played a relevant evolutionary role.

Another paleoecological aspect of the tropical forest dynamics is related to the influence of the fauna. The role of megaherbivores in the ecology of forest disturbances is receiving increasing attention (W.Schüle, this volume; cf. also Schüle 1990). Before the end of the last glaciation the megafauna had a considerable impact on vegetation through the effects of trampling and feeding that created openness and patchyness of the vegetation. Much of today's closed forest lands may have been much more open or "savannized" due to this effect. W.Schüle (this volume) in a synoptic interpretation and a *gedankenexperiment* highlights the possible and potential impacts of the Pleistocene megafauna on the structure of forests and the subsequent feed-back mechanisms on the climate.

One of the postulated explanations of the mass extinction of megaherbivores at the end of the Pleistocene refers to the impacts of the changing climate. Another theory envisages the dramatically increasing impact of hunting by early humans at that time (cf. Owen-Smith 1987, 1989; Martin & Klein 1984). According to what we know today about the impact of large megaherbivore populations (e.g. elephants) on tropical vegetation, this sudden and large-scale reduction of the Pleistocene megaherbivores must have contributed to the progressive development of the vegetation cover at the beginning of the Holocene. More assumptions may be added in the context of the refugia theory and the prevailing savanna vegetation at that time. Did the large megafauna populations somewhat contribute to the refugia patchyness of the tropical rain forest ? It may be assumed that during the peak of the last glaciation three major elements may have interacted, the seasonal climate with pronounced droughts, the impacts of megafauna on the spatial structure and flammmability of vegetation, and, consequently, the effects of recurrent fires.

Altogether it seems consequent to follow the interpretation of pollen data by Flenley (this volume) who reminds us that the glacial climates, which on the whole were more arid than the present one, occupied ca. 80% of the last two million years. Flenley suggests that it could therefore be more appropriate to think of the savanna species (and savanna communities) as occupying refugia during the present interglacial climate, while the rain forests are enjoying an unusual expansion (cf. Whitmore *et al.* 1982).

Conclusions to be drawn from this paleoecological view will be discussed in the end of this chapter.

Short-Term Forest Stressors: Natural and Anthropogenic Interferences

Considering the inherence or origin of natural forest disturbances, two "types" may be distinguished, intrinsic (or endogenous) and extrinsic (exogenous) disturbances. Tree-fall gaps caused by biotic or abiotic triggers are typical intrinsic disturbances which play a vital role in survival of species and in maintaining ecosystem diversity (cf. syntheses by Pickett & White [1985]; Remmert [1991]). Tree falls, however, may be also caused by extrinsic and less predictable forces, such as cyclonic storms. The interpretation of the role of fire as disturbance factor may serve as an example of controversial views whether this element is an endogenous factor or not (Shugart & Noble 1981; Christensen 1985). While in general fire is considered to be a typical extrinsic interference factor, Mutch (1970) suggested that in plant communities, which are maintained by regular burning, natural selection may favour plant traits that increased flammability. This would imply that fire cycles may be under intrinsic genetic control.

The origin of recently described stand-level dieback in Pacific forests may take an intermediate position between the endogenous and exogenous disturbances (Mueller-Dombois 1991).

Waide & Lugo (this volume) demonstrate the need of long-term studies for a better understanding of the functional role of disturbances (or stressors) that operate at many scales, frequencies, and intensities. This view must be supported because of the interactions and the possible interdependencies between two or more intrinsic and extrinsic stressors that may occur at different levels of impact sizes and severities, and return intervals.

The contemporary disturbance pressure on tropical forest biomes is increasingly being dominated by anthropogenic (= extrinsic) interferences, ranging from timber extraction and small shifting cultivation plots to larger-scale forest conversion activities. These anthropogenic impacts on forest structure and dynamics are often less predictable once they mix with natural phenomena, e.g. cyclonic storms and droughts. Many events of this kind have received public attention because of their devastating or "catastrophic" nature. Deforestation in the tropical mountain regions, for instance, has generally been leading to severe downstream impacts of cyclonic storms; the recent events in Thailand and in the Philippines have demonstrated the magnitude of multiple-factor disturbances. Vice-versa, human impacts on naturally disturbed forest ecosystems may dramatically interfer with successional processes. Again, the large-scale human-caused forest fires affecting Borneo's rain forests after being desiccated through the ENSO-related drought of 1982-83 may serve as a good example. The extended rain forest fires of 1989 in Yucatan (Mexico) were also the result of a chain of disturbance events: Hurricane "Gilbert" in 1987 opened the closed forests and increased the availability of unusual amounts of fuels. The downed woody fuels were then desiccated by the subsequent drought of 1988-89, and the whole of the forest area was finally ignited by escaped land clearing fires. None of these single three factors, the cyclonic storm, the drought, or the ignition sources, if occuring alone, would have caused a disturbance of such severity and magnitude on an area of c. 90,000 hectares.

While large-scale forest disturbances may have detrimental impacts on the welfare of rural societies, regularly occuring forest disturbances often are the prerequisites for human habitability and sustainable development of the tropical forest landscapes. This does not only refer to the slash-and-burn agricultural systems. Open vegetation types, e.g. tree, brush and grass savannas, often provide higher carrying capacity for human populations than does the closed, undisturbed forest. A great part of tropical savannas and "savanna forests" are in a seral (pre-climax) stage which is maintained by a variety of disturbance factors. The impacts of wildlife and domesticated animals on the savanna vegetation, through grazing, browsing, and trampling, are in strong interaction with the impacts of regularly occurring fire (Figs.2 and 3). Species composition of some seasonal broadleaved and coniferous forest types are maintained by regular fire influence, e.g. the highly sustainable and productive teak (*Tectona grandis*) and sal (*Shorea robusta*) forests of continental South Asia (Stott *et al.* 1990; cf. Fig.4), or the fire climax pine forest all over the tropics (Goldammer & Peñafiel 1990). However, there is no doubt that fire plays a dual role in vegetation development of the tropics. There is a critical threshold between the "positive" or at least "tolerable" amount of fire needed to maintain the productivity of a fire ecosystem, and the initiation of fire-induced ecosystem deterioration. This threshold is often trespassed, either because it is not recognized or because it is simply not possible to do anything about it.

Figs.2 and 3. The photographs, taken in the *Sclerocarya birrea* tree savanna biome of the Kruger National Park (South Africa), may demonstrate the effects of regular disturbance by fire on the density of the treee and shrub layer. The experimental plot shown above (Fig.2) was not burned between 1955 and 1988 (year of photograph). The photograph below (Fig.3) shows the same vegetation type, but burned annually in August. The visual differences between the plots show two completely different habitats. Fire exclusion from savannas which may serve as wildlife reserves or livestock rangelands may greatly reduce the carrying capacity. Photo: Goldammer

Fig.4. Pure stand of sal (*Shorea robusta*) in Southern Nepal. These highly productive and valuable forests are the result of regular disturbance by surface fires. These fires are set by the rural population for improving the utilization of non-wood forest products (Goldammer 1988). Without fire influence the fire-tolerant sal trees are replaced by other tree species which grow more vigorously without fire. During the regeneration phase fire should be excluded from these stands. Heavy soil erosion is often associated with regular burning. Photo: Goldammer

Impact of Modern Anthropogenic Forest Disturbances on Large-Scale Ecosystem Processes

With the pantropical acceleration of anthropogenic forest conversion into other land uses, and with the overall tendency of savannization of tropical wildlands, the impacts of small-scale disturbances accumulate to such an extent that they become measurable on regional or even on global scales. While the consequences of physical land surface changes on changing climate patterns cannot yet be separated from the "background noise" of natural climate variability, the atmospheric chemical impacts of anthropogenic vegetation disturbance by fire are already traceable.

A recent estimate of tropical plant biomass burned in shifting agriculture, permanent deforestation, and savanna fires revealed that the prompt (=gross) release of carbon into the atmosphere from these fires may range between 1 and 3.4 Pg (Crutzen & Andreae 1990). Andreae & Goldammer (1992) estimated that c. 2.2 Pg of carbon is being emitted annually to the atmosphere from these tropical fires. The amount of carbon remaining in the atmosphere (net release) is not known exactly. It is generally accepted that the net release of carbon into the atmosphere from plant biomass burned for permanent conversion of tropical forest into other land uses ("deforestation") amounts to c. 1 Pg yr^{-1}.

There is still uncertainty on the amount of plant biomass combusted in savanna fires. Although it is generally agreed that the great part of *prompt* carbon release into the atmosphere is from savanna fires (Crutzen & Andreae 1990; Hao *et al.* 1990; Andreae & Goldammer 1992), no exact figures are available on the land area affected by fire and the plant biomass burned annually. Own global estimates (unpubl. data of Weiss [1990] and Weiss and Goldammer 1990; cf. Goldammer 1991) of the worldwide size of tropical savannas, the aboveground biomass loads, theoretical fire frequencies (fire return intervals) and available fuels show that out of the estimated total area of tropical savanna biomes of ca. 2.6×10^9 ha, an area of c. 1.5×10^9 ha is potentially ready to burn each year. According to these estimates a total of c. 3.6 Pg carbon would be released (prompt release) if all of the 7.9 Pg aboveground biomass (dry matter of cured grass layers) of these savanna biomes would be consumed by fire. The pantropical fire mapping also reveals that a total of up to c. 12 Pg plant biomass (dm) may be burned in all tropical vegetation fires, theoretically releasing up to c. 5.5 Pg carbon into biogeochemical cycles. This number, which is considerably higher than other estimates (e.g. Crutzen & Andreae 1990; Andreae & Goldammer 1992), resembles the total global carbon emission from fossil fuel burning of c. 5.2 Pg (Bolin *et al.* 1986).

The amount of carbon released and remaining in the atmosphere from tropical wildland fires, especially from its largest fraction, the recurrent burning of savannas, is not known exactly. This gap of information is due to the lack of reliable knowledge on (1) the extent of net deforestation, (2) the extent of shifting agriculture, (3) the extent of fire-induced savanna degradation and its consequences on a lowered capability of taking up atmospheric carbon by post-burn regrowth of vegetation (increase of net release of carbon), and (4) the formation and deposit of elemental carbon (increase of a net sink).

Crutzen & Andreae (1990) pointed out that, although the emissions from biomass combustion are dominated by CO_2, many products of incomplete combustion that play important roles in atmospheric chemistry and climate are emitted as well. Much of the burning is concentrated in limited regions and occurs mainly during the dry season, and results in levels of atmospheric pollution that rival those in the industrialized regions of the developed world. Photochemical reactions, for instance, in the plumes of biomass fires may be responsible for as much as one third of the global input of ozone into the troposphere. Recent observations of dramatically elevated levels of tropospheric ozone in some tropical regions, particularly over the southern tropical Atlantic Ocean between South America and Africa, led to the hypothesis that emissions from tropical wildland fires and subsequent photochemical processes may play an important role in atmospheric chemistry over that large region of the Earth (Figure 5; cf. final remarks in this chapter).

The environmental consequences of tropical fires demonstrate that this natural force, increasingly induced by humans, is influencing ecosystem processes on a scale that goes far beyond the site where the fire is being applied. The accumulated effects of small-scale disturbances, as mentioned before, may trigger processes that may either reinforce or mitigate the occurrence and severity of the disturbance mechanisms. They may also lead to other feedback mechanisms that cannot yet be predicted. The reliability of quantitative assessments of tropical ecosystem disturbance by fire, however, is still weak, and further investigations are required (Levine 1991; Crutzen & Goldammer 1992).

Looking into the Future: A Challenge for Modeling Disturbance Regimes

With increasing knowledge of the complexity of disturbances, modeling becomes an inevitable tool for determining the processes involved. The reason for modeling disturbance processes is not only because of the enormous amounts of information to be linked, but also because of the projected time spans. Long-term field observations in tropical forests, e.g. over several decades, in many places are difficult if not impossible. The contributions to this volume by Waide & Lugo, Schäfer et al., and A.Schüle demonstrate the usefulness of demographic process models in places where in situ field observations would not accomplish this task.

Another application of disturbance modeling is related to global change scenarios. Global climate change, as induced by anthropogenic change of the chemical composition of the atmosphere, is partially a consequence of human-induced forest disturbances and is, at the same time, an expected stressor of the forest ecosystems. The contributions of Esser and Smith et al. (both this volume) reveal that the expected changes of forest ecosystems in response to a human-induced $2 \times CO_2$ atmosphere are far from being entirely predictable.

An example of the dimension of uncertainty in predicting the forest environment in a $2 \times CO_2$ climate would be the comparison two different models, the modeling of the response of tropical vegetation to climate change (Smith et al., this volume), and the modeling of drought occurrences (Rind et al. 1990; Fig.6). By anticipating changes in moisture availability (ratio of potential evapotranspiration/precipitation) in the $2 \times CO_2$ climate, as predicted by various Global Circulation Models (GCM's), and by application of the Holdridge life-zone classification to climate change, Smith et al. (this volume) predict a poleward shift of all forest zones. Within the tropics some GCM's predict a decrease in the areal coverage of deserts, with a corresponding increase in the extent of grassland and forest ecosystems (for more details on GCM's applied and modeling results cf. final chapter of this volume).

SEASONAL DEPICTIONS OF
TROPOSPHERIC OZONE DISTRIBUTION

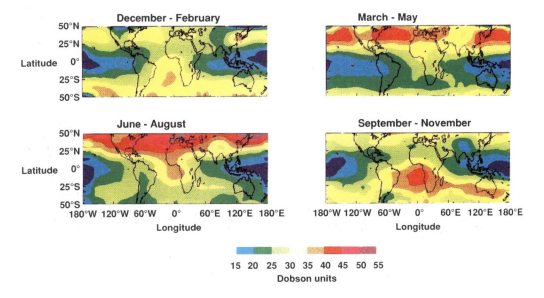

Fig.5. Distribution of tropospheric ozone residual derived from data between 1979 and 1989 for three-month periods. Tropospheric O_3 levels are obtained by subtracting the amount of O_3 in the stratosphere (derived from the Stratospheric Aerosol Gas Measurements [SAGE]) from the concurrent measurement of the total O_3 measured by the Total Ozone Mapping Spectrometer (TOMS). Measurements are in Dobson Units (1 DU = 2.69 x 10^{16} molecules of O_3 per cm^2). The tropospheric data show a well-defined maximum of O_3 of greater than 45 DU off the West coast of Southern Africa during September-November. Most likely the high O_3 concentration over the tropical South Atlantic is due to the extended wildfires during the Southern Hemisphere dry season. The magnitude of the accumulated impacts of numerous man-made forest and savanna fires in the tropics on atmospheric chemical composition is comparable with the ozone pollution over the industrialized regions of the Northern Hemisphere during the Northern summer (Fishman 1991 [*Environ. Sci. Technol.* **25**: 612]; Fishman *et al.* 1991 [*Science* **252**: 1693]). The Southern Atlantic O_3 concentration is in the focus of an upcoming research campaign under the umbrella of IGBP/IGAC in which the impacts of tropical fires will be investigated by interdisciplinary research approaches (cf. text). Graphics: Courtesy J.Fishman, NASA

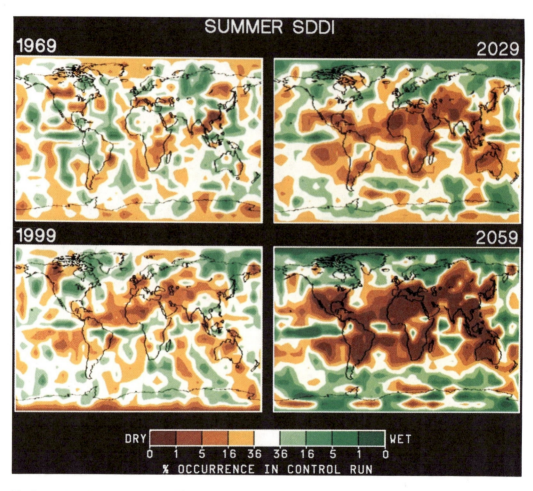

Fig.6. SDDI for June-August in the GISS climate model simulation for trace gas scenario A (Rind *et al.* 1990; cf. text). The color scale is set by the frequency of occurrence of a given drought index in the 100-year control run which had 1958 atmospheric conditions. Results show that between 1969 and 2059 extreme droughts (dark and red color) increase dramatically (dark red or 1% means: Extreme drought conditions occurring less than 1% of the time in the control run increase in frequency during the next century to close to 50% by 2060 (for details cf. Rind *et al.* 1991 [*J. Geophys. Res.* **95**: 9983]). Graphics: NASA/GISS

By looking at the relationship of precipitation and potential evapotranspiration in a $2 \times CO_2$ climate (Goddard Institute for Space Studies [GISS] GCM, trace gas growth scenario "A" in which radiative greenhouse forcing continues to grow at an exponential rate [Hansen *et al.* 1988]), Rind *et al.* (1990) generated a new "Supply-Demand Drought Index" (SDDI), i.e., the difference between atmospheric supply of and demand for moisture. The results are vizualised in Figure 6 and show the June-August SDDI for four years, 1969, 1999, 2029, and 2059. In 1969 there is an equal distribution of wet and dry regions, with extreme occurrences randomly distributed and infrequent. By 1999, very dry conditions begin to occur over some tropical and subtropical land masses. In 2029 the dry regions have expanded, especially in most of tropical and subtropical Africa and the Caribbean, and the tropical West Pacific region. By the model year 2059 extreme drought covers most of the tropical and subtropical regions of the globe.

What are the conclusions to be drawn from these models? Are their findings contradictory, or can they be used to elaborate on a more comprehensive model of tropical vegetation development, which would include human demographic and interference (or disturbance) components, and which finally would result in a "real world" scenario ?

As Smith *et al.* (this volume) point out, the results of tropical vegetation changes in a $2 \times CO_2$ climate have several sources of uncertainty. One major uncertainty is in the fact that the model results represent equilibrium solutions for both climate and vegetation dynamics. In reality, the vegetation would most likely be unable to track the true transient climate dynamics. The increasing probability of droughts, as predicted by the SDDI scenarios, would probably be the most important limiting factor in a smooth transient vegetation development. Droughts and the presence of human interferences, which are likely to grow in future, will result in an increasing proportion of seral vegetation types, which are shaped by multiple stressors, among which wildfires may play a predominant role. The growing amount of fire-induced savannas and other fire climax forests occurring on sites and under climatic conditions that would support rain forest vegetation is already being observed today. Figure 7 summarizes the possible feedback mechanisms between anthropogenic interference by fire and tropical vegetation development in a changing climate.

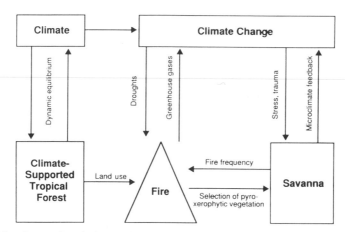

Fig.7. The role of disturbance of tropical vegetation by fire and climate-feedback mechanisms (from Goldammer 1990)

The possible impacts of tropical climate warming on altitudinal shifts of vegetational zones deserve special attention through modeling. Paleoecological evidence on the biogeography of tropical vegetation may be helpful to predict basic patterns of change (Fosberg *et al.* 1990). Pollen evidence on the distribution of tropical vegetation between the last glacial maximum and the present climate indicate such altiduninal shifts. During the late Quaternary, the maximum depression of the forest limit in the New Guinea highlands amounted to c. 1000 to 1500 m below today's levels (Hope 1976; Flenley 1979). Tentative reconstructions of similar upward and downward migration of vegetational zones have been established for the Andes in South America (van der Hammen 1974; Flenley 1979). It is expected that a generally warmer climate in the tropics will lead to a further upward movement of vegetational zones in which two main processes will be involved (Fosberg *et al.* 1990). In those mountainous lands that are below the potential present forest limit, an upward zonal migration will result in a total loss of of species confined to the present upper vegetation zones. In those mountains that are higher than the present forest limit, the vegetation will be affected less severely. However, snow fall in high elevations and perennial snow pack will be reduced. These effects on altered hydrological regimes may have severe downstream effects. One of the potential effects would be the reduction of continuity of perennial water supply to lowland aquifers and water bodies. This would have considerable impacts on lowland water tables, fish life, riparian forests, and swamp ecosystems.

Conclusions and Outlook: New Approaches in Tropical Ecosystem Research

As it is the aim of this volume, this introductory chapter highlights the abundance and complexity of factors and processes involved in tropical forest disturbances. Being aware that the tropical forest is now entering a new phase of transition toward a changed natural and human environment, it is timely that we look at tropical forest development from a highly multi- and interdisciplinary point of view. Synthesizing paleoecological, biogeographical, modern biological, ecological and biogeochemical information, and the socio-economic and -cultural aspects related to disturbance processes, may help to obtain the knowledge relevant for developing strategies to save the ecological and genetic function of the tropical forest biota affected by multiple environmental stresses. Most challenging is the exploration of paleoecology and history of the tropical forest. For instance, prehistoric and historic records on tropical climate and forest changes may give answers on the most critical questions arising in the context of global change. A clarification of the evolutionary and ecological role of rain forest refugia during the Quaternary may provide guidelines and strategies to maintain and save the genetic potential of the rain forest biota into the next millenia.

This volume, although a compilation of contributions from various disciplines of tropical ecology, aims to stimulate interdisciplinary thinking in tropical disturbance ecology. Some highly interdisciplinary research programs are, however, already underway. Tropical forest ecology has become a part of the research efforts under the International Geosphere-Biosphere Program (IGBP) which is operational on the level of experiments, e.g. under the umbrella of the International Global Atmospheric Chemistry (IGAC) Programme which, among other subjects, addresses the tropics and their changes due to human activities (Galbally 1989). One of the IGAC projects is "Impact of Biomass Burning on the World Atmosphere", which, in its first phase, is focussing on the tropics. In 1992 this project will be operational in an international set of experiments in which the impacts of forest conversion and savanna fires in South America (Brazil) and southern Africa on biogeochemical cycles and especially on the phenomenon of high tropospheric ozone concentrations over the southern tropical Atlantic region (cf. Fig.5) will be investigated. The intercontinental network of simultaneous experiments involves more that 50 research groups or individual scientists from a variety of disciplines, e.g. tropical forest and savanna ecology, biogeochemistry, atmospheric chemistry, climatology, meteorology, and auxiliary sciences such as remote sensing (Hoell *et al.* 1991; Andreae *et al.* 1991).

One of the major obstacles in further developing interdisciplinary tropical ecosystem research is the lacking of research and educational institutions that would have the necessary capabilities. This volume may contribute to raise the interest on decision-making levels.

References

Andreae MO, Goldammer JG, Lindesay JA (eds.) (1991) Southern African Fire/Atmosphere Research Initiative (SAFARI). A subprogramme of the Southern Tropical Atlantic Regional Experiment (STARE). Research project outline. Mainz: Max Planck Institute of Chemistry (mimeo)

Andreae MO, Goldammer JG (1992) Tropical wildland fires and other biomass burning: Environmental impacts and implications for land-use and fire management. Abidjan Conference on West Africa's Forest Environment. Washington: The World Bank (in press)

Bard E, Hamelin B, Fairbanks RG, Zindler A (1990) Calibration of the ^{14}C timescale over the past 30,000 years using mass spectrometric U-Th ages from Barbados corals. Nature 345: 405-410

Barnola JM, Pimienta P, Raynaud D, Korotkevich YS (1991) CO_2-climate relationship as deduced from the Vostok ice core: a re-examination based on new measurements and on a re-evaluation of the air dating. Tellus 43B: 83-90

Bolin B, Döös BR, Jäger J, Warrick RA (1986) The Greenhouse Effect, climatic change, and ecosystems. SCOPE 29. Chichester, England: Wiley & Sons

Brain CK, Sillen A (1988) Evidence from the Swartkrans cave for the earliest use of fire. Nature 336: 464

Brown KS Jr (1987) Areas where humid tropical forest probably persisted. Conclusions, synthesis, and alternative hypotheses. In: Biogeography and Quaternary history in tropical America (TC Whitmore and GT Prance, eds.), pp 44-45, 175-196.

Christensen NL (1985) Shrubland fire regimes and their evolutionary consequences. In: The ecology of natural disturbance and patch dynamics (STA Pickett, PS White, eds), pp 85-100. Orlando: Academic Press

Crutzen PJ, Andreae MO (1990) Biomass burning in the tropics: Impact on atmospheric chemistry and biogeochemical cycles. Science 250: 1669-1678.

Crutzen PJ, Goldammer JG (eds) (1992) Fire in the environment: Its ecological, climatic and atmospheric chemical importance. Report of a Dahlem Workshop, Berlin 1992. Chichester: John Wiley (in prep)

Deutscher Bundestag (1990) Schutz der tropischen Wälder. Eine internationale Schwerpunktaufgabe. Zweiter Bericht der Enquete-Kommission des 11.Deutschen Bundestages "Vorsorge zum Schutz der Erdatmosphäre". Bonn: Universitäts-Buchdruckerei

Flenley J (1979) The equatorial rain forest: A geological history. London: Butterworth's

Fosberg M, Goldmmer JG, Rind D, Price C (1990) Global change: Effects on forest ecosystems and wildfire severity. In: Fire in the tropical biota. Ecosystem processes and global challenges (JG Goldammer, ed.), pp 463-486. Ecol Studies 84. Berlin-Heidelberg: Springer-Verlag

Galbally IE (ed.) (1989) The International Global Atmospheric Chemistry (IGAC) Programme. A core project of the IGBP. Commission on Atmospheric Chemistry and Global Pollution of the International Association of Meteorology and Atmospheric Physics

Goldammer JG (1988) Rural land-use and wildfires in the tropics. Agrofor Syst 6: 235-252

Goldammer JG (ed) (1990) Fire in the tropical biota. Ecosystem processes and global challenges. Ecol Studies 84. Berlin-Heidelberg: Springer-Verlag

Goldammer JG (1991a) Tropical wildland fires and global changes: Prehistoric evidence, present fire regimes, and future trends. In: Global biomass burning (JS Levine, ed.). Cambridge: MIT Press

Goldammer JG (1991b) Feuer und Waldentwicklung in den Tropen und Subtropen. Unpublished Manuscript, Department of Forestry, University of Freiburg, 245 pp

Goldammer JG, Seibert B (1989) Natural rain forest fires in Eastern Borneo during the Pleistocene and Holocene. Naturwissenschaften 76: 518-520

Goldammer JG, Peñafiel SR (1990) Fire in the pine-grassland biomes of tropical and subtropical Asia. In: Fire in the tropical biota. Ecosystem processes and global challenges (JG Goldammer, ed.), pp 45-62. Ecological Studies 84. Berlin-Heidelberg: Springer-Verlag

Goldammer JG, Seibert B (1990) The impact of droughts and forest fires on tropical lowland rain forest of East Kalimantan. In: Fire in the tropical biota. Ecosystem processes and global challenges (JG Goldammer, ed.), pp 11-31. Ecological Studies 84. Berlin-Heidelberg: Springer-Verlag

Haffer J (1991) Mosaic distribution patterns of neotropical forest birds and underlying cyclic disturbance processes. In: The mosaic-cycle concept of ecosystems (H Remmert, ed.), pp 83-105. Ecological Studies 85. Berlin-Heidelberg: Springer-Verlag

Hammen T van der (1974) The Pleistocene changes of vegetation and climate in tropical South America. J Biogeogr 1: 3-26

Hansen J, Fung I, Lacis A, Rind D, Lebedeff S, Ruedy R, Russell G (1988) Global climate changes as forecast by Goddard Institute for Space Studies three-dimensional model. J Geophys Res 93: 9341-9364

Hao WM, Liu MH, Crutzen PJ (1990) Estimates of annual and regional releases of CO_2 and other trace gases to the atmosphere from fires in the tropics, based on the FAO statistics for the period 1975-1980. In: Fire in the tropical biota. Ecosystem processes and global challenges (JG Goldammer, ed.), pp 440-462. Ecological Studies 84. Berlin-Heidelberg: Springer-Verlag

Hoell JM, Fishman J, Kirchhoff VW, Krishnamurti TN (eds.) (1991) Transport and Atmospheric Chemistry Near the Equator - Atlantic (TRACE-A). Proposal for a study. Hampton: NASA Langley Research Center (mimeo)

Hope GS (1976) The vegetational history of Mt.Wilhelm, Papua New Guinea. J Ecol 64: 627-663

Levine JS (ed) (1991) Global biomass burning. Cambridge: MIT Press

Martin PS, Klein RG (eds) (1984) Quaternary extinctions. A prehistoric revolution. Tucson: Univ. Arizona Press

Mühlenberg M, Galat-Luong A, Poilecot P, Steinhauer-Burkhard B, Kühn I (1990) L'importance des ilôts forestières de savanne humide pour la conservation de la faune de foret dense en Côte d'Ivoire.Rev Ecol(Terre Vie)45:197-214

Mueller-Dombois D (1991) The mosaic theory and the spatial dynamics of natural dieback and regeneration in Pacific forests. In: The mosaic-cycle concept of ecosystems (H.Remmert, ed.), pp 46-60. Ecological Studies 84. Berlin-Heidelberg: Springer-Verlag

Mutch RW (1970) Wildland fires and ecosystems - a hypothesis. Ecology 51: 1046-1051

Owen-Smith N (1987) Pleistocene extinctions. The pivotal role of megaherbivores. Paleobiology 13: 351-362

Owen-Smith N (1989) Megafaunal extinctions: The conservation message from 11,000 years BP. Conservation Biology 3: 405-412

Pickett STA, White PS (eds) (1985) The ecology of natural disturbance and patch dynamics. Orlando: Academic Press

Platt WJ, Strong DR (1989) Special feature: Gaps in forest ecology. Eology 70: 535-576

Prance GT (ed) (1982) Biological diversification in the tropics. Columbia University Press: New York

Remmert H (ed) (1991) The mosaic-cycle concept of ecosystems. Ecological Studies 85. Berlin-Heidelberg: Springer-Verlag

Sanford RL, Saldarriaga J, Clark KE, Uhl C, Herrera R (1985) Amazon rain-forest fires. Science 227: 53-55

Schüle W (1990) Landscapes and climate in prehistory: Interaction of wildlife, man and fire. In: Fire in the tropical biota. Ecosystem processes and global challenges (JG Goldammer, ed.), pp 271-318. Ecological Studies 84. Berlin-Heidelberg: Springer-Verlag

Shugart HH, Noble IR (1981) A computer model of succession and fire response of the high-altitude Eucalyptus forest of the Brindabella Range, Australian Capital Territory. Aust J Ecol 6: 149-164

Stott PA, Goldammer JG, Werner WL (1990) The role of fire in the tropical lowland deciduous forests of Asia. In: Fire in the tropical biota. Ecosystem processes and global challenges (JG Goldammer, ed.), pp 32-44. Ecological Studies 84. Berlin-Heidelberg: Springer-Verlag

Swap R, Garstang M, Greco S, Talbot R, Kallberg P (1991) Saharan dust in the Amazon basin. Tellus (in press)

Weiss KF (1990) Abschätzung der jährlichen Biomasseverbrennung und Kohlenstoffemissionen aus Wald- und Savannenbränden in den Tropen und Subtropen. Unpubl.Diploma Thesis, Department of Forestry, University of Freiburg

Whitmore TC, Flenley JR, Harris DR (1982) The tropics as the norm in biogeography? Geogr J 148: 8-21

Tropical Forests in Transition
J. G. Goldammer (ed.)
© 1992 Birkhäuser Verlag Basel/Switzerland

Palynogogical Evidence Relating to Disturbance and Other Ecological Phenomena of Rain Forests

John R. Flenley[*]

Abstract

The resolution in time and space of palynologically reconstructed paleoecology has greatly improved. As a result, palynologists can now offer help to ecologists in the following areas:

A   Disturbance or Disappearance: Pollen records show that rain forests have bcen disturbed or destroyed by people for thousands of years. This is associated with soil erosion and in some cases with decline of civilizations.

B   Diversity and Stability: Palynology has refuted the idea that rain forests are unchanging through time, and provides a means of testing the refugium theory.

C   Population Dynamics: Pollen is a surrogate measure of population, therefore pollen records can be analysed as population records.

D   Causes of Altitudinal Zonation: Palynological evidence is consistent with control of zonation partly by UV-B insolation.

E   Seral Changes: Pollen records can be used to increase the time-coverage of seral changes.

[*] Geography Department, Massey University, Palmerston North, New Zealand

Introduction

Rainforests, and especially tropical rain forests, have proved difficult for ecologists to understand. The combination of high species diversity, physical size of trees, longevity of many tree species, complexity of biological interactions, high biological productivity, and difficult logistic conditions have resulted in many problems being left unsolved. On the other hand, the need to conserve rain forests in the face of rapid economic development has made the desirability of understanding them ever greater. In this situation I believe that palynology (pollen analysis) has a great deal to offer. At one time it was believed that the results of palynology were 'necessarily generalized' (Muller 1980), but this has now been shown to be incorrect, for three reasons:

(a)   In suitable deposits, the time-resolution of palynology can be increased to the level where samples represent not just single years, but even seasons within years. This is the new 'fine-resolution palynology' of which the work by Green *et al* (1988) is a good example.

(b)   The spatial resolution of palynology has also been increased, because we now understand how pollen disperses. We know, especially from the work of Tauber (1965, 1967), Oldfield (1970) and Jacobsen & Bradshaw (1981) that the area from which the bulk of the pollen is derived is closely related to the size of the site of deposition. Large sites give us a regional summary of events; small sites give a local picture, which in extreme cases would approximate to the size of a single ecologist's plot.

(c)   Palynologists have at last escaped the statistical strait jacket of percentage data. Because they are not independent values, percentages could not be used to show real changes in population through time. In suitable deposits, however, it is possible to obtain sufficient 'absolute' dates (from radiocarbon or other dating methods) to estimate the sedimentation rate with reasonable accuracy. It is then possible to calculate *pollen influx values* in pollen grains/cm^2/year. These are independent values and can be used as a *proxy measure of population* for each taxon.

Development

Palynology is therefore now in a position to give evidence relating to many ecological problems in rain forests. Among these I have selected the following for consideration:

A   Disturbance or destruction.
B   Diversity and stability.
C   Population dynamics.
D   Causes of altitudinal zonation.
E   Seral changes in rain forests.

A   Disturbance or Destruction

The disturbance or disappearance of rain forest in the landscape often shows up rather clearly in pollen diagrams. Usually a reduction of primary forest taxa is accompanied by a rise of secondary forest tree taxa (forest ephemerals) and other elements of seral vegetation such as tree ferns and Gramineae. A good example is the replacement of *Nothofagus* forest by grassland evidenced in the pollen diagram from Sirunki (New Guinea Highlands) at about 4500 BP (Walker & Flenley 1979). The change is not always permanent, e.g. the records from Lakes Yaxha and Sacnab, show disappearance of forest during the Maya period of agriculture, followed by subsequent recovery (Deevey *et al.* 1979).

It is often difficult to demonstrate whether disappearance of forest is the result of human activity or climate change. In a few cases it has been possible to find pollen attributable to crop plants. A possible example is the *Arenga* (sugar palm) pollen at c.2000 BP in the pollen record from Lake Padang, Sumatra (Morley 1982). Another is the *Elaeis* (oil palm) pollen from Cameroon (Richards 1987). The occurrence of charcoal in the sediment is an indication of burning, and, in the absence of indications of climate change, may well suggest human activity (Clark 1983). Natural fires can, however, occur in rain forest regions, particularly near volcanoes, or in times of extreme drought (Goldammer & Seibert 1989).

Another accompaniment of forest disturbance is soil erosion. The eroded soil may accumulate in the sediment. For instance, in New Guinea a layer of grey clay in Kuk Swamp has been attributed to human activity before 6000 BP (Golson & Hughes 1976). Even if the eroded material is not visible in the sediment, its presence may well be detectable chemically. On Easter Island, for example, there are increases in most of the major cations in layers dating after the arrival of people (Flenley *et al.* in press).

The accumulated pollen and associated evidence now suggests that disturbance of rain forest by people may have been in process in the tropics for much longer than previously believed. In Africa this evidence goes back to c.3000 BP in the west and the east (Richards 1987; Morrison & Hamilton 1974). In the Americas it is similar, c.3000 BP in the Andes (van Geel & van der Hammen 1973) with clear evidence of maize cultivation in Inca times (van der Hammen 1962). In the Malesian region there is evidence of forest clearance from c.6000 BP in Sumatra (Newsome & Flenley 1988; Maloney 1981), and from at least 6000 BP and possibly 9000 BP in New Guinea (Golson & Hughes 1976). There is even charcoal abundant at 10,000 BP in Irian Jaya (Hope & Peterson 1976). Forest clearance is very clear in the records from Pacific Islands. On Taiwan it began at c.4000 BP (Tsukada 1967); on Fiji at c.5000 BP (Southern 1986); on Mangaia, Cook Islands about 1000 BP (Steadman & Kirch 1990) and on Easter Island c.1200 BP (Flenley & King 1984). In the last case, the evidence was particularly striking, and clearly associated in time with the megalithic culture (King & Flenley 1989). It appears that the island was completely deforested, and that not long afterwards the civilization collapsed. Easter Island may be a lesson in miniature for our present treatment of the Earth and its likely results (Flenley *et al*, in press).

B   Diversity and Stability

The legendary species diversity of rain forests is almost certainly a multivariate problem, but some elements which might contribute to it have been usefully summarised by Ricklefs (1973). The most obvious contribution of palynology here is in relation to the time factor. Palynology has indeed confirmed that many rain forest families, and even genera, have been in existence since the Eocene or earlier (Muller 1970). A good example is the genus *Nothofagus*, the distinctive pollen of which is found back to the Upper Cretaceous of New Zealand (van Steenis 1971). Of course, there can be no guarantee that the pollen came from a tree identical in morphology or physiology to the present *Nothofagus*, but there is sufficient support from macrofossils of various ages to suggest that it did.

Palynology has, however, been equally successful in refuting the idea that rainforests are exceptionally stable; i.e., that they have existed in the same places as nowadays, and with little change of composition, over very long periods. There are now over 100 Quaternary pollen records available from the tropics (Walker & Chen 1987) and almost all of them strongly suggest big changes in the last 15,000 years. In general, montane forests formerly occurred at lower altitudes, and lowland rainforests were often replaced by savannas. This does not mean, however, that the 'refugium' theory of diversity should be accepted - certainly not in the form originally proposed. As Livingstone (1982) pointed out, the attempt to locate refugia from present-day distribution is always hazardous, and it has recently been shown that those proposed for Amazonia are simply the areas of most concentrated collecting. When the refugium proposed for northern Venezuela (Meggers 1975) was investigated palynologically, it was shown to have been exceptionally arid in the Pleistocene (Salgado-Labouriau 1980). It has always seemed to me more likely that the refugia of Amazonia would have taken the form of gallery forests in individual river catchments, rather than the vague circles drawn on maps, which have no climatological probability. There is some evidence for catchment-speciation in *Macaranga* in Borneo (Ashton 1969). Evolutionists might find it helpful to remember that glacial climates, which on the whole were more arid than the modern one, occupied about 80% of the last two million years. It could therefore be more appropriate to think of the savanna species as occupying refugia during the present interglacial climate, while the rainforest species have been enjoying an unusual expansion. This should not, of course, be taken as a justification for felling rain forest, as we shall see later.

To be successful in explaining tropical diversity, a mechanism must be much more effective in the tropics than in temperate regions. I am not convinced that this is so in the case of refugium theory, for temperate regions also had refugia (e.g. Huntley & Birks 1983). Personally I have always leaned towards the 'pest pressure' idea of Gillett (1962), much developed by Janzen (1970). I am, however, informed by Peter Ashton (pers. comm.) that the effect, though present, is too weak to account for all the known diversity. Nevertheless it does seem to me that some mechanism like pest pressure, i.e. something which makes it *an advantage to be rare*, is probably important.

Perhaps, as usual in science, we need to ask the right question before we can advance. Possibly the question should not be 'Why are there so many species in the rain forest?' but 'Why are there so many *rare* species in the rain forest?'. The usual fate of rare species is to become extinct, when random fluctuations in their populations cause them to reach zero. In the rain forest something seems to prevent this happening. It could be pest pressure, or perhaps allelopathy (Webb *et al.* 1983).

C   Population Dynamics

Rain forest trees are not short-lived. *Nothofagus cf. carrii* in New Guinea lives for c.500 years (Walker 1963). Yet in a recent publication, rain forest studies covering more than three years were classified as 'long-term studies' (Sutton *et al.* 1983). This is ludicrous. Clearly what we need is a *proxy measure of population* so that we can study population changes on a scale of 10 to 1,000 years. Fine-resolution palynology can provide this, when it is done on small sites which reduce the spatial scale. The result is that a whole new subject - *paleo-population ecology* - is being founded.

At least two possible approaches have so far been tried. Walker & Wilson (1978), using pollen influx values to escape the statistical problems of percentage data, were able to carry out an analysis with likelihood statistics. It was thus possible to fit mathematical curves to the pollen changes, and thence to draw ecological conclusions (Walker & Pittelkow 1981).

An alternative is to apply *a priori* modeling, i.e. to model population changes according to first principles, and then to test these models against pollen data. One such possibility was adumbrated by Flenley (1985), and models have actually been applied to temperate pollen data by Bennett (1990). The possibilities for the study of rain forest dynamics are enormous.

D   Causes of Altitudinal Zonation

There has been a general assumption, but little evidence, that the altitudinal zonation on tropical mountains is controlled entirely by temperature or by phenomena such as cloudiness which are closely related to temperature. Other factors which vary with altitude, such as atmospheric pressure or ultra-violet insolation, receive little attention. Particular difficulty has been experienced in explaining the morphological features of trees of the Upper Montane rain forest: stunted growth, small leaves, thick leaves, presence of a hypodermis. Grubb (1977) has suggested that the frequent clouding of mountains results in reduced transpiration and thus inability to move nutrients from the soil. The soil itself is also suspected of being involved (Grubb 1971). The features have, however, not been demonstrated experimentally to be produced by these mechanisms. An alternative is the hypothesis of the late Francis Merton (pers. comm.) that UV-B is responsible. UV-B (i.e. insolation in the range 280-315 μm) is known to be higher at high altitudes (Caldwell 1971). It has recently been demonstrated (Teramura 1983; Murali & Teramura 1986) that various species of plants when subjected to high UV-B exhibit stunted growth, small leaves, thicker leaves and a hypodermis. These are exactly the peculiarities of the Upper Montane rain forest. They also occur in Southern hemisphere temperate rain forests, but UV-B is also higher in the southern hemisphere, partly because the earth is nearer to the sun during the southern summer, leading to 7% greater total insolation than the same latitude in the northern hemisphere.

I have tested this hypothesis so far only on a sub-tropical species, *Spartocytisus supranubius* from Tenerife. This plant is a leafless broom of upright habit, growing at c.2000 m on Mt Teide. It eventually forms a hemispherical bush. I grew it from seed in the greenhouse at Hull University Botanic Garden. Glass reduces UV-B. The plants were leafy, lax and of sappy growth, so that they were incapable of erect habit. They were almost unrecognisable as *S. supranubius*. Although this was not a controlled experiment (the temperature regime was dissimilar to that of the native habitat), the results do not conflict with the idea that UV-B is significant.

The contribution of palynology to this hypothesis results from the peculiar fact that, according to the pollen record, Upper Montane Rain Forest almost disappeared from the mountains of New Guinea during the Late Pleistocene (Walker & Flenley 1979; Flenley 1979). A similar disappearance of the Sub-Paramo (the uppermost shrub zone) is reported from the Andes at the same time (Salomons 1986). Since all forests were restricted to lower altitudes at this period, because of lower temperatures, it can be hypothesized that the Upper Montane Rain Forest and the Sub-Paramo, genetically adapted to high UV-B, were unable to compete effectively at altitudes below 3000 m where UV-B insolation is less intense. This hypothesis merits further investigation.

E   Seral Changes in Rain Forests

The great problem here is the time factor. In most ecological studies, ten years is regarded as long-term, whereas even secondary trees in the tropics live for 20 years, and primary trees for up to 500 years or more (Walker 1963). A ten-year study is therefore like trying to study succession in annual plants by a one-week survey. For a longer view, try the pollen diagrams from the peat-swamp forests of Borneo (e.g., Anderson & Muller 1975; Morley 1981). These records cover about 4000 years (the time since sea level reached its present position) and clearly show the origin as a mangrove swamp, and the succession through various phases, similar to, but not identical with, the zones occurring on the swamp today. The time-resolution here is about 200 years; the spatial resolution very small indeed, for Muller (1965) showed that surface pollen samples in peat swamps are dominated by the trees directly above. Closer sampling down the core would improve the time resolution.

For an example of a xerosere, the pollen falling into Lake Birip, Papua New Guinea, during the last c.2000 years may be used (Walker & Flenley 1979). Whether the basal clay is the ash from the original volcanic event which formed the lake, or whether it resulted from a later disturbance such as forest clearance by people, is uncertain. Clearly, however, there was an early phase of dominance by Gramineae, then a phase of dominance by secondary shrubs such as *Dodonaea*, and finally a rise of forest (*Castanopsis*). Before long this was disturbed by people, who removed the forest and instead planted *Trema* and *Casuarina*, which were still there in the 1960s. For a site of this size, the spatial resolution will be about the size of the crater, and the time resolution is again about 200 years, and could be reduced by closer sampling.

Conclusion

I conclude that the relevance of palynology to tropical ecology is great, and potentially much greater than expected now. Many people, I know, are put off by the rather laborious nature of the analyses needed, especially for fine-resolution palynology. Fortunately, help is on the way. Attempts at automation, by texture analysis of pollen images, have already begun (Langford et al. 1986, 1990; Witte 1988). Within a few years we may expect to have automated palynology, leading to rapid results, greater resolution in sampling, and perhaps finer determinations.

References

Anderson JAL, Muller J (1975) Palynological study of a Holocene peat and a Miocene coal deposit from N W Borneo. Rev Palaeobotan Palynol 19: 291-351

Ashton PS (1969) Speciation among tropical forest trees: some deductions in the light of recent evidence. Biol J Linn Soc 1: 155-196

Bennett KD (1990) Models of plant population growth and analogies with reaction kinetics. Rev Palaeobotan Palynol 64: 247-251

Caldwell MM (1971) Solar UV irradiation and the growth and development of higher plants. In: Photophysiology, Vol.. VI, A C Giese, Vol. VI, pp 131-177, New York, Academic Press.

Clark RL (1983) Pollen and charcoal evidence for the effects of Aboriginal burning on the vegetation of Australia. Archaeol Oceania 18: 32-37

Deevey ES, Rice DS, Rice PM, Vaughan HH, Brenner S, Flanney MS (1979) Mayan urbanism: impact on a tropical karst environment. Science 206: 298-306

Flenley JR (1979) The equatorial rain forest: a geological history. London, Butterworths, 162pp

Flenley JR (1985) Relevance of Quaternary palynology to geomorphology in the tropics and subtropics. In: Environmental Change and Tropical Geomorphology (I Douglas and T Spencer, eds.), pp 153-164, London, Allen & Unwin, 378pp

Flenley JR, King SM (1984) Late Quaternary pollen records from Easter Island. Nature, Lond. 307: 47-50

Flenley JR, King ASM, Teller JT, Prentice ME, Jackson J, Chew C (in press). The Late Quaternary vegetational and climatic history of Easter Island. J Quat Sci

Geel B van, Hammen T Van der (1973) Upper Quaternary vegetational and climatic sequence of the Fuquene area (Eastern cordillera, Colombia). Palaeogeogr, Palaeoclimatol, Palaeoecol 14: 9-92

Gillett JB (1962) Pest pressure, an underestimated factor in volution. Taxonomy and Geography, Systematics Association Publication No. 4, pp37-46

Goldammer JG, Seibert B (1989) Natural rain forest fires in Eastern Borneo during the Pleistocene and Holocene. Naturwissenschaften 76: 518-520

Golsen J, Hughes PJ (1976) The appearance of plant and animal domestication in New Guinea. IX Congress, Union International des Sciences, Prehistoriques et Protohistoriques, Nice, Proceedings

Green DG, Singh G, Polach H, Moss D, Banks J, Geissler EA (1988) A fine-resolution palaeoecology and palaeoclimatology from southeastern Australia. J Ecol 76: 790-806

Grubb PJ (1971) Interpretation of the 'Massenerhebung' effect on tropical mountains. Nature, Lond. 229: 44-45

Grubb PJ (1977) Control of forest growth and distribution on wet tropical mountains. Ann Rev Ecol Syst 8: 83-107.

Hammen van der T (1962) Palinologia de la Region de "Laguna de los Bobos". Historia de su clima, vegetacion y agricultura durante los ultimos 5000 anos. Revta Acad Colomb Ciene exact fis nat Vol XI (44), pp 359-361 + 4 plates + 1 fig

Hope GS, Petersen JA (1976) Palaeoenvironment. In: The Equatorial Glaciers of New Guinea (GS Hope, JA Peterson and U Radok, eds), Chapter 9, pp173-205 Rotterdam, A A Balkema, 244pp

Huntley B, Birks HJB (1983) An atlas of past and present pollen maps for Europe: 0-13000 years ago. 2 vols, 667 + maps, Cambridge, Cambridge Univ Press

Jacobson GL, Bradshaw RHW (1981) The selection of sites for paleovegetational studies. Quat Res 16: 80-96

Janzen DH (1970) Herbivores and the number of tree species in tropical forests. Am Nat 104: 501-528

King ASM, Flenley JR (1989) The Late Quaternary vegetational history of Easter Island. School of Geography and Earth Resources, University of Hull, Miscellaneous Series No. 31, 23pp

Langford M, Taylor GE, Flenley JR (1986) The application of texture analysis for automated pollen identification, pp729-739 in Proc. Conference on Identification and Pattern Recognition; Toulouse, *France, June 1986*, Vol. 2. Pub. Univ. Paul Sabatier

Langford M, Taylor GE, Flenley JR (1990) Computerized identification of pollen grains by texture analysis. Rev Palaeobotan Palynol 64: 197-203

Livingstone DA (1982) Quaternary geography of Africa and the refuge theory. In: Biological diversification in the tropics. Proceedings of the Fifth International Symposium of the Association for Tropical Biology. (G T Prance, ed.),Chapter 28, pp 523-536, New York, Columbia University Press

Maloney BK (1981) A pollen diagram from Tao Sipinggon, a lake site in the Batak Highlands of North Sumatra, Indonesia. Mod Quatern Res in S E Asia 6: 57-66

Meggers BJ (1975) Application of the biological model of diversification to cultural distributions in tropical lowland South America. Biotropica 7: 141-161

Morley RJ (1981) Development and Vegetation Dynamics of a Lowland Ombrogenous Peat Swamp in Kalimantan Tengah, Indonesia. J Biogeogr 8: 383-404

Morley RJ (1982) A palaeoecological interpretation of a 10,000 year pollen record from Danau Padang, Central Sumatra, Indonesia. J Biogeogr 9: 151-190

Morrison MES, AC Hamilton (1974) Vegetation and climate in the uplands of south-western Uganda during the Later Pleistocene Period. II Forest clearance the other vegetational changes in the Rukiga Highlands during the past 8,000 years. J Ecol 62: 1-31

Muller J (1965) Palynological study of Holocene peat in Sarawak. Symposium on ecological research in humid tropics vegetation, pp 147-156. Kuching, Sarawak, July, 1963. UNESCO Science Cooperation Office for Southeast Asia

Muller J (1970) Palynological evidence on early differentiation of angiosperms. Biol Rev 45: 417-450

Muller P (1980) Biogeographie, Ulmer, Stuttgart, 414 pp 8

Murali NS, Teramura AH (1986) Intraspecific differences in Cucumis sativis sensitivity to ultraviolet-B radiation. Physiol. Plant 68: 673-677

Newsome J, Flenley JR (1988) Late Quaternary vegetational history of the Central Highlands of Sumatra.   II Palaeopalynology & vegetational history. J Biogeogr 15: 555-578

Oldfield F (1970) Some aspects of scale and complexity in pollen-analytically based palaeoecology. Pollen et Spores 12: 163-71

Richards K (1987) A palynological study of the Late Quaternary vegetational history of Mboandong, a lowland lake in Cameroun. MSc Thesis, University of Hull, 160pp

Ricklefs RE (1973) Ecology. London Nelson 861pp

Salgado-Labouriau ML (1980) A pollen diagram of the Pleistocene-Holocene Boundary of Lake Valencia, Venezuela. Rev Palaeobotan Palynol 30, 297-312

Salomons JB (1986) Paleoecology of Volcanic Soils in the Colombian Central Cordillera (Parque Nacional Natural de los Nevados). The Quaternary of Colombia 13: 1-212

Southern W (1986) The Late Quaternary environmental history of Fiji. PhD thesis, ANU, Canberra.

Steadman DW, Kirch PV (1990) Prehistoric extinction of birds on Mangaia, Cook Islands, Polynesia. Proc Natl Acad Sci, USA, 87: 9605-9609

Steenis CGGJ van (1971) Nothofagus, key genus of plant geography, in time and space, living and fossil, ecology and phylogeny. Blumea 19: 65-98

Sutton SL, Whitmore TC and Chadwick C (eds) (1983) Tropical rain forest: ecology and management. Blackwell Scientific Publications, Oxford

Tauber H (1965) Differential pollen dispersion and the interpretation of pollen diagrams. With a contribution to the interpretation of the elm fall. Danm Geol Unders II Series, No. 89: 1-69

Tauber H (1967) Investigations of the mode of pollen transfer in forested areas. Rev Palaeobotan Palynol 3: 277-286

Teramura H (1983) Effects of ultraviolet-B radiation on the growth and yield of crop plants. Physiol Plant 58: 415-427

Tsukada M (1967) Vegetation in subtropical Formosa during the Pleistocene glaciations and the Holocene. Palaeogeogr, Palaeoclimatol, Palaeoecol 3: 49-64

Walker D (1963) Stratigraphy and Ecology of a New Guinea Highlands Swamp. Proc Symposium on Ecological research in Humid Tropics Vegetation, Kuching, Sarawak. July 1963, pp137-146

Walker D, Chen Y (1987) Palynological light on tropical rain forest dynamics. Quat Sci Revs 6: 77-92

Walker D, Flenley JR (1979) Late Quaternary vegetational history of the Enga District of upland Papua New Guinea. Phil Trans R Soc, B, 286: 265-344

Walker D, Pittelkow Y (1981) Some applications of the independent treatment of taxa in pollen analysis. J Biogeogr 8: 37-51

Walker D, Wilson SR (1978) A statistical alternative to the zoning of pollen diagrams. J Biogeogr 5: 1-21

Webb LJ, Tracey JG, Haydock KP (1967) A factor toxic to seedlings of the same species associated with living roots of the non-gregarious subtropical rain forest tree Grevillea robusta. J appl Ecol 4: 13-25

Witte HHL (1988) Preliminary research into possibilities of automated pollen counting. Pollen Spores 30: 111-124

Tropical Forests in Transition
J. G. Goldammer (ed.)
© 1992 Birkhäuser Verlag Basel/Switzerland

Holocene Autochthonous Forest Degradation in Southeast Venezuela

Horst Fölster[*]

Abstract

On marginally impoverished soils of southeastern Venezuela, forests have been degrading towards savannas at least since 3500 years BP. In an environment with a sparse human population, natural or man-made forest fires often represent the primary disturbing event. The degradation itself proceeds via successional stages with transitional patchy or individual die-back. Examples are described from two localities. The cause of this degradation is a low vitality and resilience of the forest vegetation conditioned by chemical and drought stress. The paper concentrates on the morphological and structural aspects of the degradation process.

---

[*] Institute of Soil Sciences and Forest Nutrition, University of Göttingen, Büsgenweg 2, D-3400 Göttingen, Germany

Introduction

The irregular distribution of forest and savanna in the moist and humid tropics of South America is a notorious problem of geobotany (Beard 1949; Rawitscher 1953; Eiten 1972; Sarmiento & Monasterio 1975; Sarmiento 1984; Huber 1987). The controlling factors have been discussed since a long time without satisfactory agreement. Specific site factors like episodically high ground water table or inundation may satisfactorily explain ocurrences of savannas in forest territory in some locations though the hydrological conditions that restrict forest growth do not seem to be constant, but rather depend on the nutritional quality of the site (Fölster & Huber 1984, 1991).

As to well drained soils, most investigators concord that irregular distribution or mosaics of forest and savanna seem to occurr only on nutritionally poor soils (Alvim 1954; Arens 1958; Goodland 1971; Goodland & Pollard 1973). An older concept which relates the frequency of savannas to climates with a prolonged dry season (savanna climates) has become obsolete but may have to be partially revived though within a different concept (see below). Preference is given today to concepts of dynamic disequilibrium which view the present distribution as a stage in a process of reforestation (refugium concept, see Haffer [1982]; Prance [1982]; Eden [1974]) or of forest degradation (Myers 1936; Hardy 1945; Rawitscher 1948; Ferri 1955, Fölster & Huber 1984). The time span considered for this change varies from recent, Holocene to Pleistocene (Cole 1960; Eiten 1972). For the extensive area of the Campos Cerrados, Eiten (1972) assumes a very early deforestation event or process. The refugium concept visualizes a reforestation during the Holocene, Fölster and Huber (1984) suggest a fluctuation during the Holocene, while Hardy (1945), Rawitscher (1948), Ferri (1955) and others consider recent human impacts - mainly by fire - as the main agent of deforestation.

These divergent concepts are not easily reconciled, and it may well be that regional differences have to be accepted. The extensive Cerrados of Brasil with their very specific vegetation cannot be compared directly with the also extensive grasslands of the Colombian and Venezoelan Llanos with their interspersed but vegetationally quite distinct forest patches, and these not with large scale forest-savanna mosaics.

Still, one cannot exclude the possibility of a basically common process. One of the problems seems to rest in the fact that, in most instances, forest patches within a savanna show very distinct boundaries and thus give no hints at the direction or the mechanism of the process involved. There are many studies of the soil conditions of the adjoining vegetation forms but they only indicate system differences and not causes responsible for the differentiation of the systems.

In the venezuelan Guayana, we encountered several instances of rather complex structures of the ecotones between forest and savanna which seem so provide a better understanding of the type and the direction of the process involved in the vegetational change. Fölster & Huber (1984) reported such a situation from the lowland piedmont bordering the Orinoco. Two different constellations shall be recorded in the present paper from the highlands of the Venezuelan Guayana.

The Distribution of Vegetation Forms in the Gran Sabana

South of about 7°N, humid forests (1700 to >3000 mm annual rainfall, 1-3 dry months) still cover most of the land surface of the Venezuelan Guayana. In quite extensive subregions of this sparsely populated territory one encounters different types of mosaics of high to low forest, shrublands and savannas. Some of them are restricted to very specific site conditions. The present paper, however, reports on mosaics of varying scales found on the common oligotrophic soils (Oxisols) of the region. The two localities (Fig.1) are situated in the southeastern corner of Venezuela (5°06'N, 61°01'W), a region called " Gran Sabana" which forms an elevated plateau (800 - 1400 m a.s.l.). The Gran Sabana is part of a more extensive *cuesta* landscape, including the famous table mountains, on the Precambrian Roraima formation. The soils of the study sites are derived from claystones, arcosic sandstones and jaspis, they tend to be rich in skeleton but have a clayey fine soil, they are acid and strongly impoverished in base cations, especially calcium.

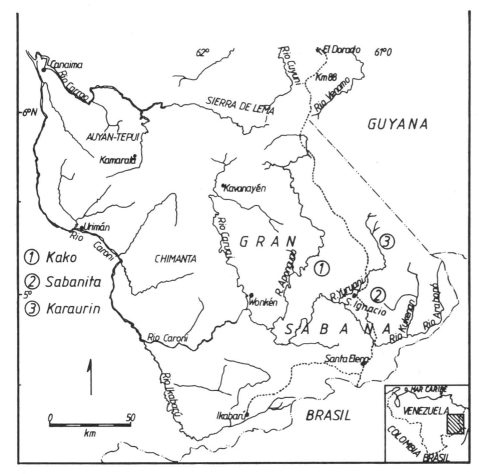

Fig.1. Location of the study area

The distribution of the vegetation forms which are components of the mosaic, is not related to chemical soil conditions. There are, however, abundant indications that hydrological conditions influence the frequency of the components. On soils very rich in skeleton as well as on hilltops, one is more likely to encounter low forests (8 - 15 m), dense shrub vegetation (*matorral*) or savanna. On a regional level (Fig. 2), one finds the most extensive savannas in the lower rainfall area to the west of the watershed which forms the present border to Guyana with the chain of table mountains which reduce the water load of the northeastern trade winds. The climate of this part (1700 to 2400 mm, 3 months dry season) would still be considered well capable of supporting a moist tropical rain forest but the increasing rainfall towards the west definitely furthers the dominance of the common medium tall (25 - 35 m) forest.

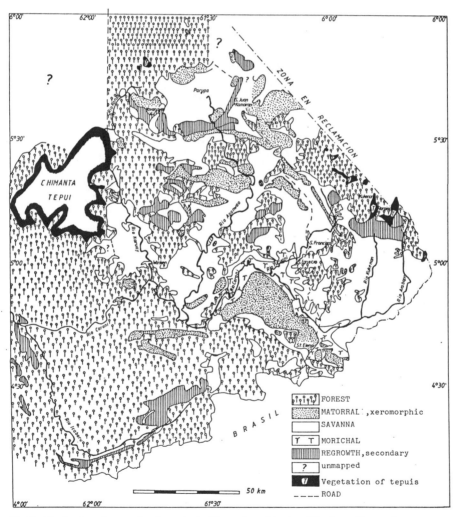

Fig.2. Distribution of vegetation forms in the Upper Caroni basin of Southeast Venezuela

Fig.3. Forest-savanna mosaic in the Gran Sabana

Fig.4. The impact of a single fire event (Upper Arabopo river)

Fig.5. The impact of repeated fire influence (Upper Kukenan river)

Fig.6. Secondary forest 50 years after the last fire occurrence (Kako)

Concerning these hydrological gradients, one should take note of two important facts:

a)   Drier climatic or relief and soil conditions do not induce the taller (evergreen) forest to change towards a seasonal evergreen forest but rather to an also evergreen low forests or matorral. Obligatory deciduous species do occurr patchwise in the tall forest but not on hill tops. Their possible affiliation to site factors cannot be defined.

b)   The impact of the relief factor is by no means consistent but can be described only by the rules of probability. This favors the interpretation of the mosaics as dynamic disequilibria.

One can observe a certain order in the spacial arrangement of the mosaic components. Within more extensive patches of taller forest, individual hill tops may carry a cover of low (single story) forest. The transition is gradual. A more complex mosaic may include a bush vegetation on the central part of the hill top, also with gradual transition to the low forest. This, however, is less frequent. More commonly, the boundary between (low or taller) forest and matorral is sharp or disperse with tree islands in the matorral.

The savannas are predominantly herbaceous without shrub elements. When they start to appear in more extensive forests, it is also on hill tops. With growing extension, they occupy more and more of the slopes. Where savannas dominate, forests may be encountered still on lower slopes and as galleries (Fig.3).

The border between forest and savanna is usually sharp. Occasionally, 10 to 50 m wide fringes of shrub savanna or fern vegetation intervene. Their origin can be clearly related to savanna fires entering the forest. Here, they change into ground fires smouldering in the omnipresent organic surface layer. Because of the preponderance of the fine roots in this layer, the fire impact kills most of the trees at once or within a few years depending on the intensity of the fire. Field observations (of the distributional pattern, comparison of actual with historical information from 15 years old air photos and eye witnesses as well as a follow-up of observed fire events) suggest that a fern vegetation forms the first successional stage. Its density strongly reduces the chance of tree seedlings to survive. Only vegetative regrowth has some chance. In a second stage, savanna herb species gradually take over. The thinning-out of the fern cover seems to be related to a gradual decrease of the humus content of the soil. The time span involved in this change has apparently to be expressed in decades rather than years.

The savannas are burned regularly every or every second year, without any economic motivation. However, from the frequency of these burnt fringes (as against clear cut boundaries) one can deduce that the overall effect of these fire attacks on a possible extension of the savanna area is probably rather limited.

Still, fire has to be considered a formidable agent in a process that obviously leads to a degradation of the forest. But these fires are singular events associated with exceptionally dry years and affecting much larger areas. Two such years have been eye-witnessed in this century, 1926 and 1940 (Röhl 1948), when even Puerto Ordaz, 500 km to the North, was hit by a prolonged smog impact. The areas affected must have been considerable though a clear and detailed assignment of certain areas to one of these events is rarely possible. Minor forest fires have also been recorded in other dry years. One can assume that many of these fires were man-made especially during hunting activities. The scope of natural fires will be discussed below.

In many of the affected areas one can still encounter trees of the previous forest stand, exclusively emergents with thick stems and usually dead. Trunks with smaller diameter rarely persisted, which means that low forests left hardly any trace. The density of standing dead emergents varies, possibly depending on the time elapsed since the fire but possibly also dependent on the dominant species among the emergents and their resistence to decay. Not all of them died imediately, and occasionally one can find survivers.

What happened to the affected areas after the fire? Results of studies from two localities will be presented. Before that, two photos from other localities may provide the reader with a first impression of the fire impact. Figure 4 shows the impact of a singular fire event with the clear cut boundary of the semicircular fire lines between the original forest and an obviously impeded regrowth, a mixture of matorral and tree islands. Figure 5 shows a large area apparently affected by fire for the first time 1926, and at least once more, probably 1940, because in one corner we encountered a continuous secondary forest. Today, most of the area is covered by a dense stand of fern.

Kako

A forest area 30 km northwest of San Ignacio de Yuruani of approximately 750 ha was burned as a consequence of severe drought during the years 1939 to 1941 . Dead emergents occur dispersed over the whole area except for the hill tops which obviously had been covered by low forests. The present vegetation is partly a low biomass secondary forest with a dominant stratum of about 15 m height (dominant dbh < 15 cm), and partly a shrub vegetation (matorral) of 2 - 5 m height. There are two varieties of matorral, open and dense. The difference is due to a thicker undergrowth of fern and grasses in the latter. The secondary forest may form a continuous cover (Fig.6) or occur as islands (50 to 100 m diameter) within the matorral. And parts of the denser matorral contain smaller tree islands of a few meters in diameter and 4 to 12 m height, with one or a few individual trees, frequently forming clusters of single species coppice regrowth. Figure 7 gives an overview of the transition between secondary forest island, denser matorral with tree islands and matorral.

In the modal transect of Figure 8, the dense matorral with the tree islands and a secondary forest island is called a transition zone between the open matorral and the continuous secondary forest. The spacial distribution suggested in the model, however, simplifies reality. Though the open matorral appears indeed to be restricted to the upper parts of the influves, the dense matorral can cover extensive parts of the slopes and even reach down to the valleys. In one small incised valley we found a remnant of the previous forest unburnt.

Fig.7. Transition of secondary forest to motorral (Kako)

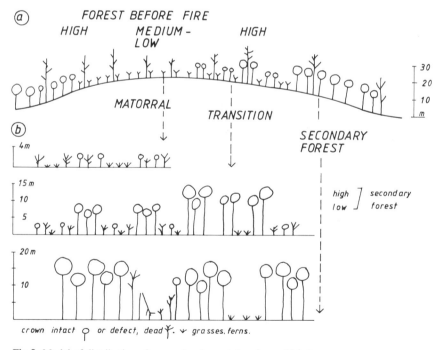

Fig.8. Model of distribution of successional vegetation forms (Kako)

Vegetation change

Table 1 (Heins 1990) shows the relative abundance of species in the tree stratum with dbh > 10 cm of the original forest remnant (KT1), various secondary forest plots and two plots from the transition zone comparatively rich in lower secondary trees (Ki4, KM4). No trees > 10 cm dbh are found in the matorral but all tree species registered in this vegetation form are present also in the secondary forest, also with larger diameters.

The information of Table 1 has its limitations, not only concerning the present stage of taxonomic knowledge. Because of the variable but usually limited extent of the vegetation patches, plot size is small and variable (125 to 800 m^2). In the original forest plot, 30 species were recorded in the >10 cm dbh stratum on 800 m^2. About the same number (33) were found in all secondary forest plots together (1080 m^2) though these represent samples from an area about 100 times larger. Though the affinity coefficient (Sörensen) of 28.6 % is still remarkably high, species composition in the secondary forest has to be considered simplified with some species reaching higher abundance values. However, there is only one species which might come close to a typical pioneer (*Dimorphandra macrostachya*) while most of the other species are widely distributed also in the upper stratum of the high forests that were studied in the region. The number of species decreases strongly from the secondary forest to the low tree transition zone (Ki4, KM4) with 8 species in 525 m^2.

In spite of the simplification of the species composition, it is obvious that both, secondary forest and matorral, are closely related to the previous higher and lower forest and represent successional stages. The differentiation of the two forms may imply depressed, stagnating regrowth in case of the matorral. Repeated fires have not been recorded, no indications (charred trunk bases or organic layers) have been found, and the distributional pattern of the components in the transition zone cannot be reconciled with a possible impact of fire lines. On the other hand, most woody plants of the matorral show considerable crown damages and high mortality which would support the interpretation of the matorral as an impeded regrowth constantly degrading due to loss of species. Even the present vegetation gives an indication of this change. While the main story still contains a considerable contribution of Tuponyek (*Myrcia* sp.), a regionally very common tree with dominant proliferation by seed distribution, the present undergrowth contains none and is supported only by vegetative regrowth.

What the earlier stages of the now degrading matorral looked like, is not known, at least not for the open matorral. In the transition zone, on the other hand, one can find strong indications that the matorral is replacing secondary forest via a process of unusual gap dynamics. Gaps are frequent throughout the secondary forest and forest islands. Their frequency increases towards the forest borders. Some were caused by falling dead emergents but most have no mechanical origin but open up after trees of the successional forest die. The most striking feature is the lack of a vigorous regrowth. Less seedlings are counted than under the forest canopy, and only few of them seem to be able to survive. The gap floor may be quite bare except when sufficient light intensity permits the development of a dense cover of fern. At the forest border, the fern gaps grade into dense matorral.

Tab.1. Relative abundance (%) of species (above 3 %) in the tree stratum with dbh > 10 cm, in a primary forest remnant (KT1), various plots of secondary forest, and two plots of low tree/dense matorral transition (Ki4, KM4).

Nr	Arten	Art	(Familie)	KT1	KA1/1	KA1/2	KC1	Ki1	Ki3	Ki5/1	Ki4	KM4
75	Sakariyek	Bellucia grossularioides	(Melastomataceae)	9								
11	Chipoyek	Protium sp.	(Burseraceae)	9								
34	Tekurenyek	n.b.	n.b.	11								
103	Akotayek	Dimorphandra macrostachya	(Mimosaceae)		20	42	28	57	44	17	38	36
140	Mukyek	Anaxagorea sp.	(Annonaceae)	5		16	7	3	8			
3	Tuponyek	Myrcia sp.	(Myrtaceae)	5								
26	Suruwarairayek	nb.	n.b.	5								
148	Pichinchupayek	n.b.	n.b.	5								
37	Chatoyek	n.b.	(Lauraceae)	3								
2	Wayamayek	Vismia guianensis	(Guttiferae)	3			7	3			8	18
20	Yuriyek	n.b.	(Lauraceae)	3								
89	Tabayeru	Retiniphyllum laxiflorum	(Rubiaceae)	3								
21	Matakyek	n.b.	(Lauraceae)	3								
197	Puruweyek	n.b.	n.b.	3								
52	Maikanvakuyek	n.b.	(Euphorbiaceae)	3	10							
48	Yaiyek	n.b.	(Araliaceae)	3	10					17		
33	Pounayek	Schefflera sp.	(Linaceae)	3	10							
85	Itoiyenayek (HG)	Ochtocosmus roraime	(Rubiaceae)				7					
58	Iwarkanakatapuyek	Duroia sp.	(Melastomataceae)		10	5	7		3			
23	Sakauyek	Miconia sp.	(Moraceae)			5			3			9
16	Wanaurayek	Ficus?	n.b.		10				3			
109	Suruwaiyek	n.b.	n.b.					3	3	33	8	18
7	Keparuanyek	n.b.	(Burseraceae)						3			
110	Balatakyek	Pithecellobium sp.	(Mimosaceae)						3			
46	Urayek	n.b.	n.b.					3	3			
9	Tukumanyek	Licania sp.	(Chrysobalanaceae)					3	3			
38	Tunyek	n.b.	n.b.					3	3			
13	Tanepureyek	Vochysia crasifolia	(Vochysiaceae)				14					
108	Saunanyek	Byrsonima sp.	(Malpighiaceae)				7					
59	Kapayek	Miconia?	(Melastomataceae)				7	3				
12	Kanwayaiyek	Tapirira guianensis	(Anacardiaceae)				7					
29	Pourekaurayek	Aspidosperma sp.	(Apocynaceae)		10							
5	Makariniyek	Hyptis arborea	(Labiatae)			11						
137	Pourekayek	Ocotea guianensis	(Lauraceae)			11						
10	Krishoyek	Panopsis sp.	(Proteaceae)					3				
8	Watakroyek	Clusia sp.	(Clusiaceae)	6								
104	Ishakyek	Caraipa tereticaulis	(Guttiferae)			5			3		8	9
95	Uruiyek	Myrcia sp.	(Myrtaceae)		10	5			5	17	23	
4	Itoiyenaiyek (HP)	n.b.	n.b.									
86	Shipanyek	n.b.	(Myrsinaceae)						5			
17	Kuipayek	Matayba sp.	(Sapindaceae)					8				
24	Morombouraiyek	n.b.	n.b.					3				
43	Toronyek	n.b.	(Rutaceae)					3				
54	Pokouyek	n.b.	n.b.					3				
111	Yachiyek	Zanthoxylum	(Rutaceae)					3				
112	Itewayek	n.b.	n.b.									
68	Manyek	Clusia sp.	(Clusiaceae)								15	9

Growth rates, mortality and replacement of the regeneration were registered in five vegetation forms from secondary forest to matorral in ten plots of 1 m² respectively during an observation period of three years (Tab. 2). The number of individuals shows little difference, the number of species drops from secondary forest to the matorral, and the percentage of survivers (during 3 years) falls from 73 to 29. The growth rate in three years is very slow. Its increase towards the matorral may only partially reflect the higher light incidence but is more likely due to the dominance of vegetative regrowth, at least in KM4 and KM2. The difference between mortality and replacement shows a strong negative impact of the (drier) second year, and an overall negative development under fern and especially in the open matorral. This generally low vitality of the regeneration supports the concept of a degrading change of the secondary vegetation.

Tab.2. Growth, mortality and replacement of regrowth plants (< 100 cm height) during 3 years in the Kako study area.

Ki 3:	secondary forest island
Ki 2:	shadowed gap in Ki 3
KH:	open gap with fern cover
KM 4:	dense matorral with tree islands
KM 2:	open matorral

	Ki 3	Ki 2	KH	KM 4	KM 2
a) Number of tree species (10 m²)	25	20	43	24	16
b) Number of individuals/m²	74	56	40	28	20
c) % of individuals surviving 3 years	73	74	43	69	29
d) 3 years height growth of survivers (c)	1.7	4.5	3.6	6.8	12.1
e) Differnce between % replacement and % mortality					
- 1. year	+4.5	+2.0	-8.2	+3.0	-18.1
- 2. year	- 6.1	- 1.4	-25.4	- 9.9	-42.0
- 3. year	- 3.0	+7.6	-8.6	+3.3	-20.3
- mean	-1.5	+2.7	-14.1	-1.2	-26.8

All this evidence suggests a swing from a slowing down forest regrowth to a degrading succession via bare gaps - fern gaps - dense to open matorral. In much of the transition zone, this swing must have occurred earlier in the life of the regrowing forest. Whether the tree islands represent stagnant remnants of this forest or later growth is unknown. Interestingly, a kind of gap structure is perceivable also in the dense and in the open matorral. In the former, these are patches of pure fern and grass cover, in the latter, they are almost bare. Figure 9 shows such a grass gap in an intermediate matorral.

Purely herbaceous savannas (dominated by *Trachypogon plumosus* and *Axonopus pruinosus*) surround the whole of the Kako forest but occur also as inlyers. The borders to the forest are sharp, those towards matorral gradual indicating a slow conversion of the matorral towards a herb savanna. An experiment of induced fire within two plots of open matorral showed that 50% of the trees were dead three years afterwards.

Karaurin

This site lies about 30 km northeast of San Ignacio de Yuruani (Fig.1), relatively close to the chain of table mountains shown in Figure 2. Between the Rio Karaurin and the upper Rio Yuruani extends a slightly elevated plateau with a vegetation pattern quite different from the rest of the Gran Sabana (Fig.10). The dominant vegetation form varies between a shrub savanna and an open shrub vegetation with interspersed islands of low forest and matorral. Borders between the mosaic components often follow the wide semi-circles characteristic of progressing fire fronts but there are many gradual transitions between matorral and the shrub vegetation.

The herbaceous stratum of the shrub savanna is dominated by *Axonopus pruinosus, Paspalum carinatum, Rhynchospora barbata* and *Scleria cyperina. Bonnetia sessilis, Phyllantus vacciniifolius, Ochthocosmus micranthus* and *Roupala montana* are the main components of the shrub stratum above which *Bonyunia minor* with, its very characteristic small crowns and thin stems, forms a tree stratum of several meters height. None of these dominant woody species occur in the forest-matorral complex though some of the subordinate species are common to both vegetation forms. *O. micranthus* is a new species, part of a highly differentiated complex of *Ochthocosmus* spp. endemic to the southeastern Gran Sabana (Huber 1990).

The complete absence of purely herbaceous savannas can probably be related to a much lower incidence of fires. According to R.Azuaje (pers.com.) the region is considered a taboo area not inhabited and normally not visited during hunting expeditions by the resident Pemon Indios. It is assumed that they withdrew from the grasslands of the Orinoco Llanos possibly under colonial pressure and maintained their habit of burning the grasslands. The taboo area might represent an old border against a former (replaced and now extinct) population. A low fire frequency may not only have permitted the development of a distinct plant community but would also explain the high incidence of common borders between matorral and shrub savanna. This is rare in the rest of the Gran Sabana because of the high fire susceptibility of the matorral.

Figure 11 shows the sequence of zones encountered along a transect through a forest-matorral patch studied. A represents the original low forest. The trees have a wide variety of stem diameters, and no charcoal can be found in or on the soil. All subareas B contain charcoal below the organic surface layer (formed under the present vegatation). Two samples from B 2/3 and B 5 were analysed by ^{14}C dating. The estimated dates of 320 and 245 years BP (Hv 15435, Hv 16195) respectively may or may not be identical considering the possibility of contamination and the variation in the life span of trees. In a similar case of charcoal sampled in a different locality at about 200 m distance within the same patch of still intact forest, the respective dates of 385 and 265 BP (Hv 15437, Hv 15438) were equally far apart but are unlikely to have resulted from different fire events.

With a certain probability one can, therefore, assume that it was one fire event which disturbed the original low forest. The following succession has reached the stage of an even-aged stand of trees with diameters not surpassing 20 cm (B1). It has survived only in part of the area and has been replaced in most parts by a matorral (B4-6) which, however, is not uniform but can be interpreted as a sequence of successional stages:

- B 2/3 represents a 20 x 100 m strip of advanced die-back of the secondary forest. About 2/3 of the trees are completely dead while on the remaining trees minor parts of the crowns still have leaves. The crowns of all trees have thinned out, and the ground is covered by dead branches and twigs. (Fig.12 provides a photo of such a die-back though not from the study area). Within the strip, one can differentiate two zones , without regeneration (B 2) and with a regeneration of about 1 m height (B 3).

- The next zone (B 4) represents a dense regrowth of about 2 to 4 m height still with some dead emergents.

- B 5 has already the character of a low forest though of limited height (< 10 m) and stem diameter (< 12 cm dbh). The most striking feature is a great variation in height and density which renders the forest very open and allows grasses and ferns to form an equally variable ground cover. The heterogeneity results from a high individual mortality. Very frequently one encounters clusters of successive coppice regrowth in which the oldest stem is dead, the next dying, the third alive and still younger shoots starting to sprout.

- In B 6, the character of the woody vegetation still equals that in B 5 but gaps have formed with denser fern and grass covers.

- B 7, the vegetation of B 6 passes gradually over to an open shrub vegetation by a further thinning out of the tree component and the appearance of species of the shrub vegetation.

Fig.9. Intermediate matorral with grass gap (Kako)

Fig.10. Shrub vegetation and shrub savanna with patches of low forest and transition matorral (Karaurin)

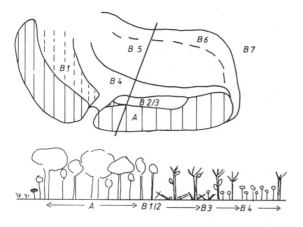

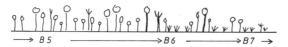

Fig.11. Plan and transect (about 150 m) of the study area Karaurin (description see text)

Fig.12. Dieback zone in older secondary forest (Upper Yuruani river)

In the study plot of the original low forest (400 m²) the tree stratum with dbh > 10 cm has a density of 15 individuals/ 100 m² and a mean dbh of 15 cm (10 - 26 cm). In B 2/3, 4 individuals/100 m² were still alive. Stem diameters varied between 10 and 19 cm (mean 12.7 cm). This was also the range in B 1. Stems with dbh > 10 cm turn up again in B 5 and B 6 with a density of 9 an 10 individuals / 100 m² respectively but they barely surpass the diameter class limit (mean dbh 11.6 cm). The structural change between the dense regrowth of B4 and the more differentiated advanced stage of B5/B6 is best expressed by the number of individuals with dbh > 1 cm/ 100 m², which is 264 in the former, 130 to 158 in the letter.

Between the low forests of the area around Kako and those of Karaurin one encounters a considerable shift in the species composition which seems to be related to the proximity of the chain of table mountains (L.Hernandez, pers.com.). On the other hand, low forest and the matorral stages seem to be very similar in their species composition. Of the 14 species registered in the study plot of the low forest with dbh > 5 cm, 8 occur in the matorral in the same stratum (3 plots of 100 m²). And of the 5 additional species which have been registered in this category in the matorral, 3 were abundant in the 1 to 5 cm category of the original forest. A certain change in relative abundance of species does occur and is to be expected. Some species important in the succession of Kako also turn up with a certain though reduced abundance. Nothing seems to contradict the interpretation of the two vegetation types as primary and secondary vegetations.

The zonation thus suggests the following succession: closed stand of secondary forest - patchwise die-back - a second regrowth with depressed development because of high individual mortality - gradual transition via gap formation and loss of tree components towards the surrounding shrub vegetation. The question remains unanswered whether part of the area B 5/6 was influenced by a second fire. If so it must have intervened during the earlier stage of regrowth. The fact remains that deforestation takes place, after a fire impact, as an autochthonous process, through a degrading succession.

Discussion

The processes described or inferred in this paper are not what one would consider as normal reactions of forests, and certainly reflect a low stability and equally low resilience of the forest ecosystem. The instability is basically explained by the generally shallow rooting of the forest. With 50% of the fine roots in the organic layer, and with hardly any roots below 20 cm depth of the mineral soil, the system becomes very susceptible to both fire and drought which explains the relative importance of the hydrological factor in the distribution of the mosaic components. The shallow rooting itself follows from the lack of nutrients, especially base cations, in the mineral soil which on the one hand attracts the roots to the organic layer where mineralisation takes place (Herrera et al. 1978). On the other hand does the shortage of Ca together with the prevalence of Al in the mineral soil give rise to toxic conditions which strongly affect the root system. Details of the chemical conditions of the soil solution and its impact on root morphology are recorded elswhere (Fölster 1986; Dezzeo 1990; Rettenmaier 1991).

Susceptability to fire cannot be very high in every dry season because otherwise savanna fires would penetrate into the bordering forests more frequently and deeper than they apparently do. One may relativate this conclusion to a certain extent because the more common constellation of forest occurring downslope of the savanna does not favor the entering of the fire, and as large but localized forest fires do occur in more than the exceptionally dry years. However, this may also be due to the fact that it is only in these years that the impact is equally strong in a large region while in other years, it varies locally (Fölster et al. 1987).

All field observations suggest that a direct, i.e. one-phase transition from forest to an open shrub vegetation or a shrub savanna requires more than one fire (see Fig.5) while singular fire events permit the regrowth of a secondary forest but may initiate multi-phase degradation processes like those described for Kako and Karaurin. How could this retarded impact be explained? The fire and the mineralisation of dead organic matter after the impact release nutrients. Because of the generally low vitality of the vegetation and its regeneration particularly, and because of the shallow depth of the zone in which nutrient uptake can take place, elements are easily lost from the system. In systems already short of essential elements, the reduced element store may be insufficient for the reconstruction of a new above ground biomass so that sooner or later, the supply of the growing stand with one or several elements falls below a critical level. This may force the plant to reallocate elements from existing to growing tissue thus destabilizing the former. The explanation is certainly very hypothetical but the morphological forms of the die-back supports such thinking. Often such die-back is associated not only with a break-down of the crown but a deformation and an attack by ants of the stems (see Fig.12). The consecutive decrease of the element store has been estimated by Dezzeo (1990) for Kako. The author could also demonstrate the loss of elements by flushes of base cations and NO_3 in the soil solution below the rooting zone in disturbed systems. However, the explanation as such has still to be considered a working hypothesis. Extending the results from the two localities to the region of the Gran Sabana, it seems inevitable to accept the operation of a process of deforestation in which fire plays the role of the initiating event but not that of the main agent. Two questions arise: Is fire always necessary or could drought alone suffice as initiating event, and is fire necessarily linked to human activity? There is no answer to the first question, only two observations: In Kako, gap formation by single tree mortallity seems to be more frequent near the border of the secondary forest, and in Karaurin, the die-back strip - located at the border between secondary forest and matorral - seems to have moved from the former border of the secondary forest towards the present position always representing a border situation, in which the drought impact could be expected to be more severe. In the other Guayana type locality mentioned above (Fölster and Huber 1984), no fire intervention seems to acompany the degradation process. It is likely, therefore, that fire is not essential in the process but will accelerate it.

The answer to the second question may possibly be similar. There are no direct observations as to whether or how frequently forest fires have been caused by lightning. There is no doubt that the actual frequency of fires is strongly influenced by the present Indio population. But forest degradation is a historically old process. The change from forest to open shrub or savanna vegetation is accompanied by a considerable increase of surface wash resulting in the accumulation of fine material, including charcoal, on the lower foot slopes. The base of these sediments is stratigraphically well recongnizable. ^{14}C-dates from charcoal collected at this discontinuity (Tab. 3) certainly underlines that deforestation is not a recent process but must have operated - at least intermittently - since a very long time. All but one dates are older than the suggested invasion of the present Pemon population. Though it seems most likely that the Pemon accelerated the process, they did certainly not initiate it. This does not prove the role of natural fires but augments the likelihood of their intervention.

Tab.3. ^{14}C-dates (years BP) from charcoal at the base of colluvial deposits indicating the initiation of forest degradation

Hv	15364	Agua fria	275	±	75
Hv	15436	Karaurin X24	1250	±	95
Hv	15360	San Ignacio 2	1360	±	55
Hv	15363	Urue	1815	±	55
Hv	15361	Mapauri	3470	±	55
Hv	15362	Sabanita B3	3540	±	75

The observations from the poor but quite extensive Guayana region of Venezuela suggest that the stability of tropical rain forests cannot be taken for granted even without the destabilizing human impact. Singular disturbing events which may be natural, can set off a chain reaction with degrading effect. Forest administrations should be aware that even careful exploitations may also play the role of an initiating event. As to the geobotanical savanna problem in South America, I believe that the concept developed in this paper may provide at least some background understanding of the dynamics involved. Considering the time scale indicated in Table 3, one would have to link the forest degradation process with the Holocene climatic fluctuations. Drier phases could have furthered the degradation process while humid phases might have retarded or locally even reversed it. The information about the regional climatic fluctuations is still too sparse to permit a detailed discussion of the ^{14}C-data but at least four of them fall into two drier spells (3900 to 2700 and 1700 to about 1000 years BP) encountered by Rull (1991) in a palynological study of several localities in the Gran Sabana.

Acknowledgement

The results are based on a common research project with the CVG-EDELCA, Venezuela. Financial support has been granted by the German Research Foundation (DFG).

References

Alvim PT (1954) Teoria sobre a formacao dos campos cerrados. Rev Bras Geogr 16: 96-98

Arens K (1958) O cerrado como vegetacao oligotrofica. In: Comptes Rendus du XIIIe Congrès International de Geographie 1: 308-319. Rio de Janeiro, 1956

Beard JS (1949) Brazilian campo cerrado: a fire climax or edaphic climax. Geogr Rev 39: 664-666

Cole MM (1960) Cerrado, caatinga and pantanal: the distribution and origin of the savanna vegetation of Brazil. Geogr J 126: 168-179

Dezzeo N (1990) Bodeneigenschaften und Nährstoffvorratsentwicklung in autochthon degradierenden Wäldern SO-Venezuelas. Göttinger Beiträge zur Land- und Forstwirtschaft in den Tropen und Subtropen 53. 104 pp

Eden MJ (1974) Paleoclimatic influences and the development of savanna in southern Venezuela. J Biogeogr 1: 95-109

Eiten G (1972) The cerrado vegetation of Brazil. Bot Rev 38: 201-341

Ferri MG (1955) Contribucao ao conhecimento de ecologia do cerrado e da caatinga. Bol Fac Fil Cienc Letr Univ Sao Paulo, Bot 12, 171 pp

Fölster H (1986) Forest-savanna dynamics and desertification processes in the Gran Sabana. Interciencia 11: 311-316

Fölster H, Huber O (1984) Interrelaciones suelos-vegetacion en el area de Galipero, Territorio Federal Amazonas. MARNR, Serie Informes Tecnicos, DGSIIA/IT/144, Caracas. 260 pp

Fölster H, Dezzeo N, Hernandez L, Huber O, Bareat F, Bareto A (1987) Informe Dinamica Bosque-Sabana, Gran Sabana (unpublished report)

Fölster H, Huber O (1991) Dynamics of a forest-savanna mosaic in the middle Orinoco region of southern Venezuela. Scientia Guayanae (in press)

Goodland R (1971) Oligotrofismo e iluminio no cerrado. En: III. Simposio sobre o Cerrado (MG Ferri, ed.), pp44-60. Editora da Univ de Sao Paulo, Sao Paulo

Goodland R. Pollard R (1973) The brazilian cerrado vegetation, a fertility gradient. J Ecol 61: 411-419

Haffer J (1982) General aspects of the refuge theory. In: Biological diversification in the Tropics (GT Prance, ed.), pp 6-24. Colombia University Press, New York

Hardy F (1945) The soils of South America. Plants and Plant Science in Latin America 2: 322-326

Heins R (1990) Autochthone Degradation eines tropischen Feuchtwaldes nach Brand, Gran Sabana, Venezuela. Diplomarbeit, Institut für Geobotanik. Universität Göttingen. 138 pp

Herrera R, Jordan CF, Klinge H, Medina E (1978) Amazon Ecosystems: their structure and functioning with particular emphasis on nutrients. Interciencia 3: 223-232

Huber O (1987) Neotropical savannas: their flora and vegetation. Tree 2: 67-71

Huber O (1990) Savannas and related vegetation types of the Guayana shield region in Venezuela. In: Las Sabanas Americanas. Aspectos de su biogeografia, ecologia y utilizacion. (G Sarmiento, comp.) Fondo Editorial Acta Cientifica Venezolana, 57-97

Myers JG (1936) Savanna and forest vegetation of the interior Guyana plateau. J Ecol 24: 162-184

Prance GT (1982) Biological diversification in the Tropics. Colombia University Press, New York

Rawitscher F (1948) The water economy of the vegetation of the "campos cerrados" in southern Brazil. J Ecol 36: 237-268

Rawitscher F (1953) Climax and pseudoclimax vegetation in the Tropics (South America). Proc 7th Intern Bot Congr, Stockholm, 1950, 616-618

Rettenmaier R (1991) Vegetationsdynamik und Chemismus in der Gran Sabana (unpublished report)

Röhl E (1948) Los veranos ruinosos de Venezuela. Boletin de la academia de ciencias Fisicas, Matematicas y Naturales 31. 23 pp

Rull V (1991) Contribucion a la Paleoecologia de Pantepui y la Gran Sabana: Clima, Biogeografia y Ecologia. Scientia Guayanae (in press)

Sarmiento G. Monasterio M (1975) A critical consideration of the environmental conditions associated with the occurrence of savanna ecosystems in Tropical America. In: Tropical Ecological Systems (FB Golley, E Medina, eds.) Ecol Studies 11: 223-250

Sarmiento G (1984) The ecology of neotropical Savannas. Harvard University Press, Cambridge, Massachusetts

Tropical Forests in Transition
J. G. Goldammer (ed.)
© 1992 Birkhäuser Verlag Basel/Switzerland

Vegetation, Megaherbivores, Man and Climate in the Quaternary and the Genesis of Closed Forests

Wilhelm Schüle[*]

Abstract

Plant biomass consumption by herbivores is a major influence on the structure of the vegetation canopy. In woodland and forests megaherbivores are most important. In the presence of dense populations of megaherbivores a multi-species fauna of smaller herbivores prevents the formation of a closed crown canopy. In the Tertiary and (outside the range of *Homo*) in the Quaternary there is always at least one species of megaherbivores on all continents and in all climates. Forests were generally more open and patchy, and while less carbon was stored in plant biomass, high herbivore biomass produced large quantities of methane.

In the tropics of the Old World, long coevolution of hominids and megaherbivores allowed some species to adapt to human hunting. Their population density, however, was reduced. As a consequence, with an increase of tree cover and canopy closure, more carbon was sequestered and less methane emitted. Since the Middle Pleistocene *Homo* proceeded into other climates and continents. There, all megaherbivores became extinct, and crown canopies of forested lands began to close. Since the Lower Pleistocene anthropogenic fire regimes shaped the vegetation cover outside the humid regions. It is suggested that anthropogenic changes, through extinction of megaherbivore populations and introductuion of large-scale use of fire, have changed the albedo and influenced carbon fluxes, thus triggereing climatic feedback processes of the Quaternary.

---

[*] Institute of Prehistory, University of Freiburg, Belfortstr. 22, D-7800 Freiburg, Germany

Introduction

Postulated concepts of "climax" or "potential natural vegetation" have been based on the assumption that composition and structure of the vegetation cover are essentially, if not exclusively, determined by pedologic, hydric and climatic conditions. The fauna, particularly the vertebrates, is neglected in these models or is considered a mere consumer of plant biomass which exerts little influence on the structure of the vegetation (Clements 1916, 1936; Ellenberg 1986; Remmert 1985; Walter 1984; Walter & Breckle 1983). The species composition of the fauna is more or less considered a result of the vegetation cover: Prairie animals inhabit prairies, forest animals inhabit forests, few or no large mammals inhabit rain forests. It is largely anticipated that habitat competitors and predators maintain population densities of herbivores at levels where possible disturbances of the vegetation cover are negligible. Only if this "natural balance" were disturbed by external influences would damages of the "natural vegetation cover" occur from a thinning of forests to desertification, depending on the abiotic factors and the degree of stress (Förster 1977; Mensching 1990).

Such models anticipate anthropogenic interferences only after the introduction of agriculture, stock keeping and fire clearing in the respective areas. Prior to that, the human influence on the landscapes is believed to be of little relevance. Any effects of hunting and an anthropogenic increase of fire frequencies before the Neolithic are disregarded. Even primitive agriculture, whether it occured in Neolithic Europe or with subrecent agricultural tribes, is believed to have only a very localized influence. Stock breeding is supposed to be relevant only if it leads to the formation of "grazing-induced plant communities", to disturbances of the vegetation cover resulting in erosion or similar damages in the case of overgrazing (Ellenberg 1954).

In this contribution I intend to investigate whether vertebrate faunas untouched by man exert an influence on the vegetation cover, and how even the most primitive of mans hunting techniques changed the composition of the fauna to a degree where the vegetation was affected. In order to illustrate this process one must consider the ecological role of extant megaherbivores[**] which are of decisive importance (Paragr. 2-5) look at the composition of fossil faunas predating early man or his direct ancestors (6-8), and finally substantiate how our fore-bears were able to change the species composition and population density of the fauna they hunted to an ecologically relevant extent as early as the Tertiary/Quaternary boundary, about 2 million years ago (9).

All palaeo-sciences are of little help in the consideration of causal relationships for reasons of the theory of cognition. With few exceptions their findings are multi-causal, interpretations ambiguous. Moreover, the fossil record is far more dependent on erosion and sedimentation factors and on the chemical and hydrical environment of a potential

---

[**] **Megafauna**: vertebrates of estimated body-weight from 1,000-10,000 kg. In the Tertiary (except in the Palaeocene and Lower Eocene) on all continents. Quaternary: in cold zones of Eurasia, in America and Australia until the Upper Pleistocene, in the Old World tropics until today.

Macrofauna: vertebrates from 500-1000 kg body-weight. Not in the Palaeocene. In Australia and South America no later than the Upper Pleistocene.

Medium-sized animals: vertebrates from 50-500 kg. Not in the Palaeocene.

Small animals: vertebrates below 50 kg.

fossil deposit than it is on the abundance of fossilizable material. In soils rich in humus acid and poor in soluble minerals found in most humid forests the probability for bones to become fossilized is low. The enourmous gaps in the fossil record are further widenend by the randomness of detection and scientific evaluation of fossil material.

The testing of hypothetical, palaeo-scientific assessments by experiment is possible in the least number of cases. Rather than attempting to gain new data I shall try to combine established palaeo-scientific and actualistic findings and principles from a whole range of fields in a multidimensional network to achieve new insights into past causes and effects. Of course such an attempt cannot be successful on a regional scale or limited to a certain type of vegetation.

Modern man is debarred from observing virgin terrestrial ecosystems. Even in the famed "age of discovery" at the beginning of modern times enterprising Europeans hungry for land and resources "discovered" biota the ecosystems of which had long been disturbed by representatives of the genus *Homo* in their immigration to the respective areas (Depéret 1907; Diamond 1982; Hoernes 1911; Martin 1973, 1984; Martin & Klein 1984; Martin & Wright 1967; Remmert 1989; Ziswiler 1965). In Africa, where disturbances of the fauna are least observeable, they probably set in at the postulated change of the *Australopithecinae*, i.e. man's direct ancestors, to a more carnivorous diet during the Pliocene and Lowest Pleistocene. The Lower Pleistocene witnessed the anthropogenical increase of the fire frequency (W.Schüle 1990a). To our present knowledge both processes originated in Africa and spread all over the globe together with the different species of the genus *Homo* in the course of the Quaternary.

It is surprising to find that the direct or indirect anthropogenic effects on the vegetation cover caused by the anthropogenic faunal reduction was most momentous in those areas which are today regarded the most valuable undisturbed ecosystems: the tropical rain forests. The effects of the anthropogenic increase of the fire frequency were greatest in regions with seasonally dry climates.

Recent investigations of rain forest climate (Lettau *et al.* 1979; Weischet 1987, 1990), the role of the largely organically controlled greenhouse gases in the global energy balance (Andreae & Schimel 1989; Crutzen & Andreae 1990; Crutzen & Müller 1989; Goldberg 1982), the significance of biomass burning for the future climatic development (Andreae 1990; Goldammer 1990), global climatic catastrophes (Budyko *et al.* 1988), as well as general insights into the chemistry and physics of earth's biosphere (Berger *et al.* 1989; Dt. Bundestag 1989; Heyer 1990; Holland & Schidlowski 1982) make it obvious that climate, hydric and pedological conditions are far from being merely abiotic parameters. On the contrary: As life depends on the climate so does the climate depend on life - a view which very much reminds us of Lovelock's (1988) "Gaia hypothesis" .

It can be concluded that the disturbances of the circulation of carbon, nitrogen and water caused by the anthropogenic changes of vegetation and reduction of fauna since the Upper Pliocene as well as the changed fire frequency could have initiated loops of positive feedback in the global energy balance. This could have triggered the climatic development of the Quaternary (W.Schüle 1990a), even though we are far from understanding the mechanisms and scale of the processes involved. It could also be suspected that geologically much older climatic oscillations were caused by shifts in the biotically controlled distribution of mass and changes in the speed of fossilization of biomass.

For the benefit of a broad readership a highly specialized terminology was avoided (De Crescenzo 1983, preface). For the same reason general aspects are mentioned which specialists will in many cases find unnecessary, whereas any attempt at completeness in the listing of details would be futile.

Megaherbivores and Vegetation Structure: Today

Let me first take a summary look at extant megaherbivores and their ecological impact. Their habitat is today limited to the Old World tropics (Grzimek 1968ff; MacDonald 1984). In Africa we find the African elephant (*Loxodonta africana*) with its two subspecies: *L.a. africana* in open woods, steppes and savannas and *L.a.cyclotis* in the humid woodlands and rain forests of West Africa, the rhinoceroses *Ceratotherium simum* (wide-mouthed rhinoceros) and *Diceros bicornis* (black rhinoceros), and hippopotamus (*Hippopotamus amphibius*). Giraffe (*Giraffa camelopardalis*), eland (*Tragolaphus(Taurotragus) oryx*) in its subspecies *derbianus* and *gigas* and the savanna/steppe form of African buffalo (*Syncerus caffer caffer*) reach the "mega" border in their strongest individuals only.

In South Asia we find Indian elephants (*Elephas maximus*) and great Indian rhinoceros (*Rhinoceros unicornis*). The nearly extinct continental subspecies *Dicerorhinus sumatrensis lasiotis* of the Sumatran rhino and the recently extinct continental form of the Javanian (*R.sondaicus?subspec.*) rhinoceros, as well as the nearly disappeared dwarfed island rhinos on Sumatra, Borneo (*D.s.sumatrensis*) and Java (*R.sondaicus*) are smaller than *R.unicornis* and near the border of the mega/macro animals. The wild cattle species arnee (*Bubalus arnee*), kouprey (*Bos (Novibos?) sauveli*), gaur (*Bos (Bibos) gaurus*) and banteng (*Bos (Bibos) javanicus*) in South Asia and yak (*Bos (Poephagus) mutus*) in Central Asia are also on the rather arbitrarily drawn mega/macro border.

Ecological investigations of these species are today possible in national parks and game reserves only. All of them are endangered.

Giraffe (*Giraffa camelopardalis*)

Of all large herbivores giraffes probably least influence the species composition and structure of the vegetation cover. Without competitors, giraffes browse the branches of savanna trees which by long coevolution are adapted to the animal and are not harmed unless there is a high overpopulation of giraffes. That is and probably always has been highly unlikely. By spreading the seeds giraffes might even promote the dispersal of their feed trees. Depending on the sizes of the animals their feeding range is three to six meters above ground, the growth of young trees is not disturbed.

In the transition zone from wood to savanna the situation is different. There giraffes can do considerable harm to the trees in times of trophic stress in the savanna, yet the damages should be overcome as soon as the stress situation has ended. Only if these incidences recur may giraffes speed up a retreat of the forest.

Hippopotamus (*Hippopotamus amphibius*)

Hippopotamus does not feed on aquatic plants during the day but grazes on the shore by night (Frädrich 1967). This diurnally alternating way of life may be one of the reason why hippopotamus survived until now. It may also be an empirical (non-genetic) adaptation to human predation, analogous to European deer which prefer dusk or night browsing only where hunted.

The wide mouth of hippopotamus works like a lawn mower, cropping not only grass but also young trees. Within the range of hippopotamus populations, dense galery woods will hardly ever form, existing woods may become more open or even disappear. In Africa a certain balance developed between hippos and the river bank vegetation in the course of a long coevolution. On islands newly colonized by hippos during the Pleistocene like some Mediterranean islands (Kowalski 1986) and Madagascar (Dewar 1984) their ecological impact must have been far greater (see also 8.4).

Wide-mouthed Rhinoceros (*Ceratotherium siminum*)

The wide-mouthed rhino has a similar impact as hippopotamus. Unlike the hippos the occurence of wide-mouthed rhinoceros is not restricted to large bodies of water, its ecological impact is therefore more extended. For the lack of competing vegetation short grasses adapted to being closely grazed expand at the expense of bushes, herbs and tall gramineous plants. Owen-Smith (1983, 1987) showed how the vegetation changed in South Africa after the animals were gone, and that these changes lead to the dissappearance of several small ungulates without direct human interference.

Black Rhinoceros (*Diceros bicornis*)

Black rhinos are leaf eaters, feeding as far as possible above their heads. As African savanna trees are adapted to giraffes, so are bushes adapted to rhinos. They evolved together from the time of the immigration of Holarctic perissodactyles and artiodactyles in the Neogene and Pleistocene. If the rhinos disappear and are not substituted by other efficient leaf eaters, the bushes grow into impenetrable thickets which most medium-sized herbivores are unable to reduce (Owen-Smith 1983,1987).

Asian Rhinoceros (*Rhinoceros* and *Dicerorhinus*)

South Asian rhinos inhabit dense, humid forests and avoid open landscapes. They feed on leaves, soft bamboo, high stemmed gramines, and other soft plants. Their dentitions are not adapted to hard vegetable food or such rich in SiO_2. They hardly ever feed close to the ground. The thick skins and bodies of the South Asian rhinos enable them to trample paths and clearings into nearly every jungle. Smaller herbivores make use of these paths which are usually free of vegetation but as the clearings do not affect the crown canopy they do not admit more light to the lower zones of the humid forests for the benefit of terrestrial browsers and grazers.

The great Indian rhinoceros (*R.unicornis*) is today found only in marshy forests or bamboo woods, but its original distribution also comprised drier forests. In such woods we find the last extant(?) Sumatran rhinos in India (*D.sumatrensis lasiotis*), and the last dwarfed island rhinos on Sumatra, Borneo (*D.s. sumatrensis*) and Java (*R.sondaicus*).

Elephants (*Elephas maximus/Loxodonta africana*) and the Development of Patchwork Forest

Rhinoceros populations exert little influence on the crown canopy of forests. Populations of forest elephants (*E.maximus* and *L.a.cyclotis*) can clear forests, even hyper-humid ones, to a considerable degree (Merz 1977; Müller-Dombois 1981). Like all mega herbivores they are nearly without natural enemies. Their population density is regulated by trophic limits, epidemics, natural disasters or by emigration to zones that have for the same reasons been denuded of elephants. It is very likely that stress-induced reductions in birth rates in the case of overpopulation also play an important role in the population dynamics of extant elephants (Carrington 1958; Douglas-Hamilton 1975). These or similar mechanisms are likely to regulate the population sizes in all megaherbivore species but these mechanisms become effective only when overpopulation is imminent, i.e. the vegetation has already been damaged.

Elephants feed wherever their trunks reach: they take food off the ground or rise on their hindlegs, they break down or uproot trees, they decorticate trees with their tusks. All that they do habitually, not only when under trophic stress. The destructive effects of elephant overpopulation in the East African savannas are known all too well. Too large an elephant population may severely damage the vegetation cover, even in humid woods and rainforests. The charming picture of the "Destruction of a Forest by Elephants" (Fig.1) is not to be taken all that seriously, yet it contains a grain of thruth (Laws *et al.* 1975; McKay 1977; Merz 1977; Müller-Dombois 1981).

Fig.1. "Destruction of a Forest by Elephants" (c. 17th Century). Source: Carrington (1962)

Herbivores Following Elephants

Once the crown canopy in a forest has been cleared by elephants and more light is admitted to the lower zones, rhinos, tapirs, buffaloes, forest antelopes, deer and many smaller species find food in abundance (Fig.2). With growing species diversity demands on the vegetation become increasingly manifold, e.g. in the spatial (vertical) and qualitative (species) composition. Some of the herbivores following the elephants feed off the ground, damage saplings, and finally induce clearings. These are ideal meadows for grazers, which in turn keep the clearings open and further the expansion of short grass. Unless the herbivores belong to mega-species, carnivores keep their numbers at a level where extensive damage to the trees is prevented.

Medium and macro-sized grazers tear at plants with their lips or teeth. Elephants often tear out tufts of plants with the roots, they tear up the ground in search of food, in display behaviour (*Imponiergehabe*, Lorenz 1969b), or simply for the fun of it, or they dig at the roots of trees. Similar scars may result from the *Imponiergehabe* of horn or antler-bearing herbivores, and from pigs digging for roots and tubers. The soil which is thus loosened provides ideal conditions for tree seeds. Solitary trees or small groves develop on the clearings. Many trees densely coppice after browsing. Once the coppice is wide enough to prevent long-necked herbivores to reach the center, a young tree may grow there.

Other behavioural characteristics of herbivores also influence the development of patchwork vegetation in forests. Species inhabiting strictly defined territories graze or browse the core areas more intensively than the borders or areas overlapping other territories. Some species avoid the pasture grounds of others or are driven from them. Many ruminants and other herbivores have resting places where they do not feed and which are frequently avoided by other species. Harts and other herd animals have permanent rutting places where females and young are concentrated and where they consequently graze more intensively.

Nutrient Cycling

Due to the hot and hyper-humid climate, soils in tropical rain forests are subject to a considerable washout of nutrients. This is counterbalanced only where nutrients are imported. Plants have to rely on the inner nutrient flux of the rainforest (Hoppe 1990; Weischet 1987, 1990). In a patchwork rainforest the nutrient cycling via herbivores, dung, soils and micro organisms back into the vegetation is quick, washout of nutrients by rainfall is retarded. It seems likely that the better exploitation of light and the faster circulation of nutrients in a humid patchwork forest provoke a higher phyto production than one finds in closed rain forests.

Mammal Biomass

The biomass (Bourlière 1963) of non-arboricole herbivores in today's elephant-free tropical rain forests is a few kg/km^2. If there are still elephants in the forest the biomass reaches a few t/km^2 at best, which is probably due to the low number of elephants. In East African savannas with a complete megafauna (*Loxodonta, Hippopotamos, Diceros* and/or *Ceratotherium, Giraffa*) the mammal biomass can exceed 30 t/km^2. If the

Fig. 2. Zoogenic clearing in South Asian rain forest with "undisturbed" vertebrate fauna, semi-schematic. a: Asiatic Elephant (*Elephas maximus*), b: Great Indian Rhinoceros (*Rhinoceros unicornis*), c: Indian Tapir (*Tapirus indicus*), d: Gaur (*Bos(Bibos) gaur*), e: Water Buffalo (*Bubalis arnee*), f: Nilgai (*Bosephalus tragocamelus*), g: Blackbuck (*Antilope cervicapra*), h: Axis Deer (*Axis axis*), i: Barasingha (*Cervus (Rucervus) duvauceli*), j: Boar (*Sus scrofa vittatus*), k: Langur (*Presbytis entellus*). Relative scales approximately only. Drawing: Aenne Schwoerbel

megafauna is missing it declines to 5-10 t/km², even when the number of individuals of the surviving medium-sized and macrospecies is high (Petrides & Swank 1965). Most of them feed off or little above the ground. If the number of these species decreases and the number of individuals per species increases, they prevent the growth of young trees. Depending on the aboitic conditions, the fire regime and the available plant species, savanna, or steppe develop.

There is every reason to believe that a humid patchwork forest initiated by elephants or other megaherbivores harboured a similar, maybe even higher zoo-biomass than recent tropical savannas. The high phyto production in humid tropical patchwork forests, evenly distributed over the year, allowed a better exploiting of the phytomass by herbivores than the seasonally fluctuating phyto production of savannas.

Population Dynamics

Unfortunately one cannot verify the thesis of a hyper-humid patchwork forest intiated by megaherbivores and inhabited by a multi-specied fauna by field research, as all recent elephant populations are controlled by man. Furthermore, one must consider that not only the behaviour but also the reproduction strategies of the two extant elephant species might have been changed by the long coevolution of elephant and man (W.Schüle 1990a). If that should be the case there must necessarily be disturbances if hunting ceases and the emigration of a population surplus is prevented.

The "equilibrium" established by the reduction of elephant populations bears similiarities to the much-discussed "equilibrium of game and woods" in Central European cultural forests, which is basically an equilibrium between timber producers and hobby hunters. That remains unaltered by the fact that the hunters are a neccessary substitute for carnivores. Faunas in the temperate zones have been poor in large species since the Upper Pleistocene: All mega and macroherbivores, part of the medium-sized herbivores, and larger carnivores are missing.

Tropical and other game reserves are much too small, migrations of the larger species in particular are highly limited (Orr 1971; Sinclair & Norton-Griffith 1979), which can have devastating effects in areas with high seasonal variations in food supplies. As on oceanic islands, the animals have no chance of leaving their stressed ecosystem. In most elephant forests the number of sub-mega species of herbivores has already been reduced because some of them diassapeared in times of low elephant populatations or high kills and could not be replaced because neighboring areas had already been denuded. There had already been disturbances of the patchwork forest prior to the "overpopulation" of elephants.

A monospecific increase of herbivore density, no matter how it was initiated, always results in severe damages to the ecosystem (Thornes 1990). The classic example is overgrazing by hypsodont[***] domestic animals, which not only prevents the growth of trees but quickly results in the destruction of the vegetation cover. Yet brachyodont browsers and even pigs are also able to destroy grown trees, which is easily observed in deer and wild boar pens. The effect is similar if overgrazing by mono or oligo-specied

---

[***] Hypsodont: high-crowned molars and premolars in which abraded portions are regrown

herds of wild animals occurs. The oligo-specied grazing of American prairies by bison and pronghorn, which lasted from the Lower Holocene to the arrival of the Europeans, or the grazing of South American pampas by guanacos and ñandus is responsible for the lack of trees in these landscapes in the same degree as is the anthropogenic fire frequency, which is just as old. One must also not disregard the large numbers of rodents. All of these animals feed directly on the ground. In addition, the hoofed animals of prairies and pampa are highly hypsodont ruminants, which can chew and digest grasses with high contents of SiO_2. Until the end of the Pleistocene, large parts of both landscapes were more or less tree stocked savannas. Their Pleistocene mammalian faunas also contained many browsers. When these had disappeared and the numbers of the hypsodont grazers had increased dramatically the trees vanished. Yet the vegetation was not damaged to the same degree as with todays cattle or sheep: migrations or emmigration of population surplus relieved the stress on the vegetation.

Damages to the vegetation cover are graver the less the vegetation is adapted to the specific grazing habits of the animals. Immigrated or introduced animals will therefore cause far greater damage than overpopulation of autochtonous herbivores. This fact has probably contributed to the clearing of the Amazone forest following the Upper Pliocene faunal exchange between North and South America: The Holarctic immigrants were for the most part equipped with more efficient dentitions than their paleo-endemic biotope competitors to which the vegetation had adapted.

In a healthy, multi-specied fauna an overpopulation of sub-mega species can hardly occur. Individual numbers of the many different species are low. A shifting equilibrium is established between herbivores and carnivores. The largest extant carnivorous mammals, Siberian tiger (*Panthera (Felis)tigris altaica*) and Alaska bear (*Ursus actor middendorffi*), do not exceed 500 kg in body weight, and there were no larger carnivorous species throughout the Tertiary. Their largest prey are macroherbivores and young megaherbivores. In species with highly developed social systems, e.g. extant elephants, the offspring is watched over by all adult herdmembers. If the young are not threatened, megaherbivores ignore even large carnivores, as long as the animals' critical distance (Lorenz 1969a,b) is maintained. If this distance is not maintained the threatening pose of a megaherbivores usually scares off the carnivore, but the megaherbivores can also resort to active and effective attack. Carnivores are therefore no regulating factor in the population dynamics of megaherbivores, which results in the growth of their populations up to the trophic limit.

If for some reason a population surplus of megaherbivores cannot emigrate or be neutralized by epedemics or the like, severe damages to the vegetation are inevitable. The collapse of animal populations following the over-exploitation of food resources takes the pressure off the biotope. In humid areas the vegetation recovers faster than the fauna, woods recover if erosion or other damages are not beyond healing. If the collapse of the megaherbivore populations occured for trophic reasons, e.g. as a result of overgrazing and drought, the populations of smaller herbivores will also be reduced, regeneration of the forest favoured. The iniciated secondary forest improves the trophic situation of the area. Herbivores from neighboring areas repopulate the regrowing forest, the patchwork vegetation is reestablished. The small-scale mosaic of the patchwork forest is superimposed by large-scale patchwork systems. Conflagrations have a similar effect on the vegetation although animal populations are usually not much affected. In rain forests, large fires occur only after occasional severe droughts (Goldammer 1990) or other exceptional conditions. A disastrous, localized collapse of the ecosystem becomes part of the biosphere's overall strategy (Berggren & Vancovering 1984).

Megaherbivores and Rain-Forest Climate

Internal Water Circulation

The continual influx of moist air from the sea is the main source of precipitation in most mountain rainforests. In lowland rainforests precipitation is mostly (up to 90%) the result of the "internal water circulation" of the forests (Lettau *et al.* 1979; Myers 1989; Weischet 1990).

Steam is a highly efficient greenhouse gas. It's condensation into clouds temporarily increases the albedo above the forest but reduces the radiation of thermic energy from below the clowds. A considerable portion of the energy radiating into the system, namely 585 cal/gr H_2O, is accumulated in latent evaporation heat above the forest and set free again at the raining off of clouds (Bloom 1989). If the rain forest system covers an area of sufficient size it is stabilized by positive feedback, the zone of the internal water circulation tends to expand. An ever larger amount of atmospheric carbon is stored in plant biomass. The global decrease of climatically active CO_2 by accumulation in biomass is regionally balanced by the vapor of the internal circulation. If there are major shifts in the extension of the internal water circulation, the amount of atmospheric carbon stored in biomass and the amount of water available on the continents changes. Consequences for the global climate are to be expected.

Collapse of the Rain Forest

The system of the internal water circulation is weakened only if isolated open areas become too large. If there is a positive feedback between open spaces and the weakening of the water circulation the system collapses. It also collapses when the total area of the internal circulation becomes too small through external influences. The carbon which was stored in biomass is returned into the atmosphere.

The preservation of small areas of rain forests seems possible only where it is maintained by a steady influx of humid air, but not where the rain forest relies on its internal water circulation. For the same reasons, a human exploitation of rain forests is possible only if small interspersed areas are exploited, and if vegetation on these spaces is never cleared completely. H. Steinlin (1990) has recently developed models for the possible exploitation of rainforest resources.

Internal Water Circulation and CH_4 in Patchwork Rain Forests

In a megaherbivore-initaited tropical patchwork forest the internal water circulation should be similar to that of a rain forest with closed crown canopy as long as its extension is large enough. The larger leaf surface in the patchwork forest probably compensates for the decreased evaporation on the small clearings. The large number of herbivores in a patchwork forests may lead to a local accumulation of methane in the atmosphere. Methane is produced by anaerobic bacteria in the digestive tracts of herbivores (*Elephantidae, Perissodactyla, Artiodactyla, Rodentia, Xenarthra*), particularly in ruminants (Church 1988), in omnivores (*Ursidae, Suidae, Tayassuidae, Primates*), and in social insects as well as by soil and marsh bacteria (Clarke & Bauchop 1988; Heyer 1990 ; Langer 1984, 1985, 1988; Pearce 1989). If one assumes that the herbivore biomass in most patchwork rain forests was roughly as high as in recent African savannas, the methane concentration in the stagnant air above the forests must have been substantial.

Tertiary Rain Forests

All of these parameters probably affected the expansion of forests in the Lower Tertiary. For whichever reasons the huge dinosaurs had disappeared at the close of the Creataceous. They had doubtlessly succeeded in preventing the accumulation of large amounts of carbon in plant biomass. The amount of atmospheric carbon should therefore have been higher. We know regretfully little about digestive gases of herbivorous dinosaurs although one may assume that they produced considerable quantities of methane (writ com P.Langer 1991). Extant herbivorous reptiles can only provide clues in this respect (Vonk & Western 1984). Palaeocene mammals were very small (Carroll 1988; Müller 1989; Thenius 1980), the dentitions of the herbivores adapted to soft foods. After the disappearance of the dinosaurs, forests could grow exuberantly, the crown canopies closed like in today's rain forests. By positive feedback more and more areas were probably incorporated into the rain forests' internal water circulation, until some boundary was reached where low temperatures or high losses of moisture halted the progress.

In the Eocene, when larger mammals with more efficient dentitions and digestive systems appeared, patchwork forest developed. More efficient mammalian dentitions and digestion systems on one side and increasing resistance of the vegetation, especially of grasses rich in SiO_2, formed a loop of positive feedback resulting in a progressive development of clearings in the patchwork forests and the transformation of peripheral areas into savannas stocked with trees. The decreasing greenhouse effect of atmospheric vapour above the continents was balanced by the lower accumulation of CO_2 in plant biomass. In addition, the production of methane by mammalian herbivores and omnivores increased in the course of the Tertiary. It can be calculated only roughly either from extant animals or palaeontologically by inference from the dentitions of the animals concerned (Langer 1988; W.Schüle 1990a).

An Ecological "*Gedankenexperiment*"

Let me combine the above-mentioned premises in a thought experiment: If extant animals in the Old World tropics were left to themselves, forests in megafauna habitats would develop into patchwork forests inhabited by many species of herbivores after the recovery of forest and savanna elephant populations. At an assumed doubling of the elephant populations in 25-year intervals, the changes would have taken place in a few centuries. The Sahara desert would certainly slow down the repopulation of North Africa by mega- and other herbivores but the Nile valley is a route to the north. In rainy years the elephants would presumably migrate from the Nile Delta to the west and east along the Mediterranean shores. Forest animals can go around the folded mountains of South

Asia in the northeast, animals of open landscapes in the northwest. To elephants both routes are open.

Both species of extant elephants are highly euryoecious[****]. If all human interference was eliminated beyond the tropics as well, population pressure would lead to a migration of elephants into non-tropical regions of Eurasia, where their niche has been unoccupied since the Upper Pleistocene. Given the present climatic situation the limit of expansion for both elephant species would be somewhere along the southern slopes of the great Eurasian cordilleras. Beyond, thermic casualties among the tropical species would be too high. A genetic adaptation of the immigrating elephants to cooler climates would take much longer. It requires a reduction in ear-size, regeneration of the fur and the seasonal adaptation of calfing times. The odds are that Indian *Elephas* would probably prove superior to African *Loxodonta* if it managed to cross the dry zones between north-west India and the Caspian Sea before *Loxodonta* settled and acclimatized in the Near East, Anatolia and southern Europe. As soon as some degree of overpolution was arrived at in northwest Africa some elephants would certainly cross the Strait of Gibraltar and recolonize the Iberian Peninsula.

The rhinos, which are not as euryoecious as the elephants, would find greater, yet not insurmountable difficulties in recolonizing the warm-temperate north. The forms from the African savannas would probably be superior to those from Asia which are adapted to tropical humid forests.

The habitat of hippopotamus is likely to extend to the lower courses of the south European rivers up to the Rhône, inshore lagunas along the coasts of Southern Europe and on the Mediterranean islands would soon be inhabited. As one may see in any zoo, hippos do not need tropical water temperatures to survive. The boundary for their expansion are areas with occasionally closed snow cover and freezing water. South of this boundary hippopotamus would severely clear the vegetation along the larger bodys of open water (Turner 1975). Giraffes are not likely to be very successful in colonizing Europe, because for them treeless landscapes and wide waters are unpassable.

As mentioned above, the mental experiment requires that all human influences on the fauna be removed in and outside the tropics. Migrations and habitat expansions would affect not only tropical megaherbivores but the whole Eurasian fauna as well. The recuperating populations of lynx (*Lynx*), wolf (*Canis*), bear (*Ursus*) and smaller carnivores would decimate the herbivores from mouse to European bison (*Bison bonasus*) and elk (*Alces alces*). Feral horses and bovines would substitute extinct wild horses (*Equus spec*) and aurochs (*Bos primigenius*). Over-bred species would soon disappear but be substituted by hardier species of feral domestic horses and cattle. They would thrive in the trophic abundance supplied by former fields and pastures and enter the woods. Sheep (*Ovis*) and goats (*Capra*) would have lower chances at surviving. Beyond rugged terrain, deep snow and carnivores would endager them. In South Asia, the Near East, on the Balkan Peninsula and in North Africa feral water buffaloes (*Bubalus bubalis*) would fill their ecological niche, interbreeding with their wild cousins. In Central Asia it would be wild and feral yaks (*Bos (Poephagus) mutus*). The two species of camels (*Camelus dromedarius* and *C.ferus*) would populate steppes and semi-deserts in Eurasia and Africa, remaining onager, kulan, khur and kiang (*Equus*

[****] **Euryoecious**: having a wide range of habitat selection
Stenoecious: having a narrow range of habitat selection

hemionis subsp.), saiga (*Saiga tartarica*) and other steppe antelopes and the diverse wild sheep (*Ovis spec*) and goats (*Capra spec*) would multiply into herds in their respective biotopes.

Until the large felines like Asian or immigrating African lions (*Panthera(Felis) leo*) and Siberian tigers (*P.tigris altaica*), and their smaller relatives had re-immigrated and grown sufficient numbers, the wild and feral animals could multiply, decimated by wolfs and bears only. Allied with immigrating megaherbivores they would certainly prevent the growth of dense woods on the presently open spaces. Extant woods would be turned into patchwork forest. What is commonly called primeval forest would grow only in inaccessible spots, soggy marshes or on steep slopes. Canadian forest bison alone manage keep the boreal coniferous forest in a patchwork state which contains so much open pasture that stockbreeders throw greedy glances at the bisons' land. Beavers (*Castor fiber*) would thin out the vegetation on river banks and lake shores outside the new range of hippopotamus. Most river valleys would be a consecutive, shifting series of beaver lakes and meadows kept open by herbivores.

Summarizing the results of the *Gedankenexperiment*, one may state that if the fauna were freed fom human interference a whole mosaic of ecosystems would develop from the tropics to the warm-temperate zones. After few centuries one would find tree stocked savannas and patchwork forests in semi-arid to hyper-humid zones, and steppe or deserts in the more arid regions. Primeval forest with a closed crown canopy would grow only in few locations. All in all, what we would find in Eurasia, with the exception of cold-temperate and arctic zones, is the picture one expects in the warm phases of the Pleistocene. This picture of Pleistocene patchwork forests is supported by the palaeontological record, which shows mixed faunas rather than pure forest or steppe communities. Even the recent herbivores of the European woods could hardly survive in a so-called primeval forests. Their habitat are park landscapes.

In cold-temperate or arctic climates the megafauna would be absent for some 10^4 to 10^6 years, yet cold-resistant, partially hypsodont medium-sized and macro herbivores would produce patchwork forest there as well. Confining the deserts would take a long time. Their soils have disappeared and form very slowly in semi-arid and arid regions. The shift of zones of more plentiful vegetation into the deserts would probably slowly influence the local climate as a result of the changes in the albedo and the microclimate.

Development of the Pleistocene Eurasian Vegetation

The End-Pleistocene forestation in nearly all of Europe was made possible by the Holocene warming, but the *Gedankenexperiment* showed that its extent and structure was determined by the disappearance of the Pleistocene herds (Fig.9) of mammoth (*Mammuthus(Elephas) primigenius*), wooly rhino (*Coelodonta antiquitatis*) and musk oxen (*Ovibos moschatus*), of steppe bison (*Bison priscus*), aurochs (*Bos primigenius*), wild horse (*Equus caballus*), wild ass (*E.hydruntinus*), and giant deer (*Megaloceros giganteus*), and by the decimation of the surving species (Kahlke 1956, 1981; Kowalski 1986; Kurtén 1968). During the Upper Pleistocene the giant camel *Paracamelus* and the single-horned rhino *Elasmotherium* (Kozamkulova 1981) had disappeared from the East European and Central Asian steppes. *Elasmotherium* stood 6 feet at the withers, its extremely hypsodont dentition superior even to living African wide-mouthed rhinoceros.

If one considers that most of the extinct species were more euryoecious and migratory than the surviving ones, climatic or trophic reasons for their disappearence lose much of their credibility.

The climatic oscillations of the Pleistocene affected faunal and floral expansions, but they did not lead to an extinction of species without any substitutes. Animals were either replaced by descendants of their own species or by competing immigrants. The normal size ratio of the fauna - few megaherbivores, several macroherbivores, a number of medium-sized and many small herbivores and respective predators - remained stable throughout the Pleistocene.

If the faunas of the warmer zones had not already been denuded of their larger species these animals would have immigrated into northern Eurasia when the cold-adapted megaherbivores migrated north at the close of the last (Würm/Wisconsin) glaciation. Holocene faunas from temperate and cold Eurasia would then have contained one or two species of both elephants and rhinoceros, at least two bovides, horses, giant deer, lions and other large felines, hyenas and probably even cave bears (*Ursus spelaeus*) and saber-toothed cats (e.g. *Homotherium*). In the north musk oxen would have survived, hippos in the south, *Paracamelus* and *Elasmotherium* on the steppe. Most European forests would be made up of patchwork vegetation, most steppes would be savannas. But as these animals were missing, the remaining fauna could not prevent the closing of crown canopies on a large scale. Former savannas were gradually converted into steppe by the anthropogenic fire frequency and overgrazing by hypsodont domestic animals.

Megaherbivores and Vegetation Structure Beyond the Old World

America

When the Isthmus of Panama formed and connected the two Americas at the end of the Pliocene, about 3 million years ago, Holoarctic, "ecologically superior" immigrants supplanted a major part of the autochthonous South American fauna (Keast *et al.* 1972; Simpson 1980) in the *"Great American Biotic Interchange"* (Stehli & Webb 1985). Numerous South-American endemites became extinct.

Part of the survivors, among them elephant-size megaherbivores, migrated north, some reaching Alaska (Anderson 1984; Kurtén & Anderson 1980). There the Bering Strait prevented them from colonizing Europe during the warm phases, during the cold phases the climatic conditions of Beringia stopped them. The neotropic immigrants, giant ground sloths, giant armadillos, glyptodonts and many smaller species, were without biotope competitors in the north, where only few endemites became extinct because of the interchange.

The mingled Pleistocene faunas of North and South America (Fig. 3,4) have no rival in species diversity (Kurtén & Anderson 1980). If one disregards the supplanting of some few species by successors or Eurasian immigrants, it survived all Pleistocene climatic changes but collapsed just before its end. Pronghorns (*Antilocapra americana*), several subspecies of deer (*Odicoileus*), Atlantic seacows (*Trichechus*), and black bear (*Euarctos*) survived. Up to that time the North American forests had certainly been patchwork forests. Pleistocene prairies were presumably more savanna-like than the ones 16th-century Europeans saw, because until the end of the Pleistocene they were not grazed by huge mono-species herds of bison, and because there was no anthropogenic fire frequency. Like most extant species of large North American mammals, American bison are probably the descendents of Lower Holocene Eurasian immigrants (W.Schüle 1990a). Euryoecious like most bovines, the newcomers, adapted to being hunted, soon settled most landscapes. More open landscapes, which had begun to be overgrown by thickets after the disappearance of the Pleistocene fauna or that were kept open by fires of the first human immigrants, provided ideal conditions for the bison. They multiplied rapidly and transformed the Pleistocene savannas into treeless prairies within a few centuries. The vegetation in the semi-deserts of the south west was probably least affected. It might even have expanded because the denser vegetation at its edges was over-grazed or burned.

It is very likely that the pre-Pleistocene South American palaeo-endemic mega herbivores were similarily sucessful in turning the hyper-humid rain forests in the Amazon basin into patchwork as were the *Elephantidae* and other megaherbivores in the Old World and North America. Standing on their hind legs gigantic ground sloths like *Megatherium* or *Eremotherium* reached as high as elephants. Even tree trunks of a considerable circumference could not take their weight. On all fours they could also browse on the ground. Their dentitions were not as efficient as those of elephants but efficient enough to devastate the forests. Moreover, giant ground sloths were probably fore stomach fermenters and, like their extant relatives (Langer 1985), could profit even from low-quality food.

A multitude of smaller animals coexisted with the palaeo-endemic megaherbivores of the orders of *Xenarthra (Edentata), Pyrotheria, Toxodonta, Astrapotheria* etc) of South America (Carrol 1988; Keast *et al.* 1972; Müller 1989; Thenius 1980). Analogous to the Afro-Laurasian *Artiodactyla* and *Perissodactyla*, the *Notoungulata* and *Litopterna* filled niches up to the macroherbivores sizes until they were supplanted in the biotic interchange. The population dynamics of the smaller species were regulated by carnivorous marsupials *(Borhyaenoidea)* until placental predators immigrated. Swampy forests and gallery woods will probably have suffered under the grazing of hippo to rhino-sized *Toxodon* as those of Africa and south Europe suffered from *Hippopotamus*.

Since the Oligocene, arboreal monkeys (Primates: *Platyrrhina*) and rodents *(Caviomorpha)* were also part of the South American fauna. They had probably arrived by island hopping. Neither the "American Interchange", nor the climatic oscillations of the Pleistocene nor the End-Pleistocene extinctions affected the climatically sensitive monkeys and rodents. The biotic interchange brought a large number of holarctic immigrants to South America: Mastodonts (Gomphotheriidae: *Cuvieronius, Stegomastodon, Haplomastodon*), probably even proper elephants (*Mammuthus columbi*), tapirs (Perissodactyla: *Tapirus*), horses (Equidae: *Hippidion, Onohippidium, Equus*), peccaries (Artiodactyla: Tayassuidae: *Platygonus, Tayassu*), llamas (Camelidae: *Hemiauchenia, Protoauchenia, Lama*), deer (Cervidae: *Ozotoceras, Antifer, Morenelaphus, Epieuryceros, Odocoileus, Mazama, Hippocamelus, Pudu*) and many smaller forms. The palaeo-endemic carnivorous *Borhyaenoidea* became replaced by holarctic *Carnivora*. Throughout these changes ecological niches did not remain unoccupied. Inhabitants were simply replaced, the niches marginally restructured according to the needs of the newcomers.

Some of the Plio/Pleistocene immigrants had more efficient dentitions than the South American endemites and must therefore have damaged the vegetation far worse than the autochthonous fauna. Three million years after the appearance of the first

Fig.3. Selected extant (grey) and extinct (white) large mammals of North America from the Upper Pleistocene and Holocene, semi-schematic. Extinctions: End-Pleistocene. Holarctic forms: a: *Arctodus*, b: *Canis*, c: *Rangifer*, d: *Ovibos*, e: *Cervalces*, f: *Odicoileus*, g: *Hydro(da)malis = Rhytia* (extant: *Trichechus*), h: *Bison*, i: *Castoroides* (extant: *Castor*), j: *Smilodon*, k: *Mammuthus*, l: *Gomphotherium (=Mammut)*, m: *Camelops*, n: *Equus*, o: *Breameryx* (extant: *Antilocapra*), p: *Platygonus* (extant: *Tayassu*), q: *Tapirus*. Plio-Pleistocene immigrants from South America: r: *Paramylodon*, s: *Chlamydotherium*, t: *Neochoerus* (extant: *Hydrochoerus*), u: *Ateles*. Not presented: extinct *Myrmecophaga* (extant in SA), *Glyptotherium*, *Panthera leo atrox*, *Panthera onca* (extant in SA), *Felis puma* (extant), *Tremarctos* (extant in SA), *Acinonyx* (extant in Asia and Africa), *Euarctos* (extant) *Sangamona*, *Oreamnus* (extant), *Geochelone*, etc. End Pleistocene/Lower Holocene hunting-adapted immigrants from Asia: *Alces, Cercus, Ovis, Castor* and *Ursus, Bison bison?*, possibly *Rangifer, Oreamnus* and *Ovibos*. Relative scales aprox. only. Drawing: Wolfgang Nestler, based on Thenius (1980), Kurtén & Anderson (1980), Anderson (1984)

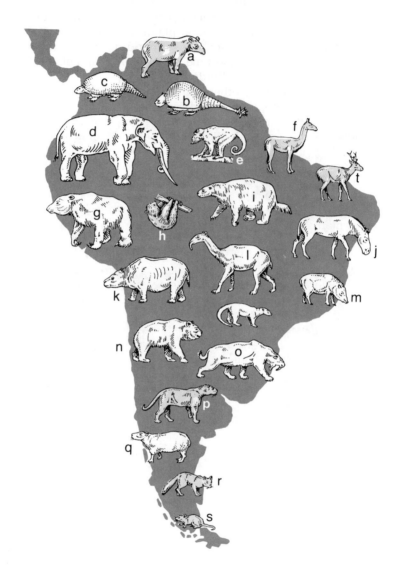

Fig.4. Selected extant (grey) and extinct (white) large mammals of South America from the Upper Pleistocene and Holocene, semi-schematic. Extinctions: End-Pleistocene. Looking left: palaeo-endemits, looking right: Plio/Pleistocene immigrants. a: *Tapirus* (several species extinct), b: *Glyptodon*, c: *Doedicurus* (several related genera), d: *Cuvieronis*, *Stegomastodon* and *Haplomastodon, Mammuthus?*, e: *Alouatta* (many related genera, most still extant), f: *Lama*, g & i: *Megatherium* and *Mylodon* (several related genera), h: *Choloepus* and *Bradypus* (no fossil record!), j: *Equus(Amerhippus), Hippidion* and *Onohippidium*, k: *Toxodon*, l: *Macrauchenia*, m: *Platygonus* (smaller *Tayassu* extant), n: *Arctodus* (related *Temarctos* extant in SA, extinct in NA), o: *Smilodon*, p: *Panthera*, q: *Neochoerus* (extant: *Hydrochoerus*), r: *Dusicyon*, r: *Marmosa*. Relative scales aprox. only. Drawing: W. Nestler, based on Thenius (1980) and Anderson (1984)

immigrants the South American vegetation is still more sensitive to grazing than in the Holarctic, rainforest vegetation in the Amazon is more easily destroyed than in the Old World tropics (oral com. T.May). Three million years have obviously not been enough for a genetic adaptation of the South American plants to the trophic habits of the Plio/Pleistocene immigrants. This explains the superiority of plants introduced with palae-arctic domestic animals from the time of the European colonization in the 16th century AD (Crosby 1986; Groves & Burdon 1986).

When the megafauna and most other game species disappeared at the end of the Pleistocene the crown canopy of the humid forests of South America closed and took its present shape. From the time of its separation from Gondwana, South America had always been close to the equator. Millions of years of undisturbed evolution of a patchwork forest rich in ecological niches explains the species diversity and the complicated network of interdependencies (Almeda & Pringle 1988; Riede 1990) in Amazonia much better than the idea of Pleistocene refugia.

The closing of the crown canopy presumably also resulted in the loss of plant and invertebrate species. It was a disadvatage at least for those adapted to edge-of-the-wood biotopes or plants whose seeds were spread by megaherbivores (Janzen & Martin 1982). The same applies to all other forms of vegetations affected by the wave of mammal extinctions at the end of the Pleistocene.

During the cold phases of the Pleistocene the extension of the rain forest seems to have been smaller (Flohn 1985). The lower temperatures reduced oceanic evaporation and atmospheric humidity. Yet the disturbance of the internal water circulation of the basin rain forests seem a more important factor. In the center of the basin, where less moisture-dependent tree species might not immigrate fast enough, patchwork rainforest might collapse and turn into steppe. Some portion of the species diveritsy of the Amazon basin might also be attributed to that.

Overkill

The cause for End-Pleistocene mass extinctions in both the Americas was the immigration of man (Martin & Klein 1984; Martin & Wright 1967). Recent investigations show that all dates for a human presence in America predating 11,500 BP, i.e. the seperation of the North American iceshields, are doubtful (Greenberg *et al.* 1986). The species that disappeared were medium-sized to gigantic, euryoecious, migratory and easy to hunt. Surviving species are medium-sized at best, most of them stenoecious, many nocturnal, partially non-migratory, live in unaccessible places (swamps, tree-tops, mountains) or can at least survive there. Many of them, like monkeys (*Platyrrhini*), treesloths (*Choloepus, Bradypus*), armadillos (*Dasipus*) and anteater (*Myrmecophaga*), but also tapir (*Tapirus*), guanaco and vicuña (*Lama*), musk ox (*Ovibos*), reindeer (*Rangifer*) and pronghorn (*Antilocapra*) are highly sensitive climatically, most of their extinct relations certainly were not. In no way can these be superior criteria in natural selection (W. Schüle 1990a). Ethnographical parallels drawn from the ecologies of recent hunter-gatherers (Webster & Webster 1984) are not conclusive because their "ecological hunting strategies" are the result of complex sets of taboos and ethical regulations aimed at not overexploiting the resources of poor environments as well as keeping human populations low. Their foundations have probably been laid down as early as the Lower Pleistocene (W.Schüle 1990a,b) but may collapse any time at the sight of overabundance. That appears to have happened when the first hunters from the

Beringian tundra invaded the zone south of the North American ice-shield at the end of the last (Wisconsin) glaciation and found a land of milk and honey. Economical resource-management is certainly not a trait anchored in the genes of *Homo s.sapiens* or his ancestors.

Horribile dictu: The closed crown canopy of the Amazon is of indirectly anthropogenic origin. It developed when invading humans exterminated the paleo- and neoendemic megafauna as well as the greater part of all other mammals over 50 kg body weight. In the Americas this happened at the end of the Pleistocene, elsewhere earlier (see below). Yet at the same time the accumulation of carbon in rain forest biomass and the reduction of the herbivores' methane production prevented a heating of the atmosphere through a build-up CO_2 released by the dramatically increasing number of anthropogenic fires. "Civilized humans" of the 20th century are just now working at cut that sheet-anchor by destroying the world's rain forests.

Australia

In Australia the break-down of the paleo-endemic marsupialian fauna (Fig.5) followed a similar pattern. To our present knowledge it took place about 50,000 years ago during the last glaciation, not at its termination like in America. All animals larger than a red kangaroo (*Macropus (Megaleia) rufus*) suddenly dissapeared (Martin & Klein 1984; Martin & Wright 1967). The largest marsupials were approximately the size of a medium rhinoceros. The largest Pleistocene ratite *Genyornis* was about as heavy as extant emus (*Dromaius*) and casuaries (*Casuarius*). Giant tortoises of the genus *Meiolania*, and carnivorous *Megalania prisca*, a kind of over-dimensioned Kommodo monitor weighing 2 t disappeared as well. They probably starved, sharing the fate of *Thylacoleo carnifex*, the marsupial "lion", when their prey was no more.

The oldest reliable dates for a human presence are of approximately the same age (Flood 1990). A little later the soot content of Australian lake sediments increases dramatically and continues at that level, pollen spectra show a transition from pyrosensitive *Araucaria* to pyrotolerant *Eucalyptus* communities. A identical increase in soot particles is documented in Panama at the end of the Pleistocene (Piperno *et al.* 1990). The cause of these contemporaneous changes is hunting man and an anthropogenic increase of the fire frequency (W.Schüle 1990b).

One may assume that the Australian marsupials had a similar influence on the forests as the placental herbivores in the rest of the world, i.e. that there had been patchwork forests. When the fauna collapsed, the crown canopies in humid forests became denser, with all the results mentioned earlier. In less humid climates quantities of combustible material accumulated because of the lacking browsers and grazers, which resulted in the increase of the intensity of occasional fires. As a countermeasure Pleistocene Aborigines seem to have developed a sophisticated fire management at an early stage, which was practised until recently (Jones 1975). Pyrotolerant vegetation from the semi-arid zones of Central and West Australia expanded at the expense of species of lower pyrotolerance. The anthropogenic fire frequency kept forests clear of brush, favoured grazing kangaroos and prevented the accumulation of fire potential. Fire intensities were kept low. With the immigration of Europeans bushfires became disastrous. The Aborigines pyro-ecological knowledge was almost forgotten. A modern, scientific fire ecology is labouriously developing new forms of fire management (Goldammer 1990; Goldammer & Jenkins 1990).

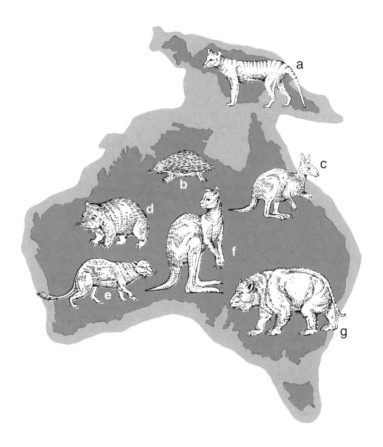

Fig.5. Selected extinct large marsupials and monotremes of Australia (Sahul) from the Upper Pleistocene, semi-schematic. Extinctions: Last glaciation. a: *Thylacinus* (extant on Tasmania?), b: *Tachyglossus*, c: *Protemnon*, d: *Phascolonus*, e: *Thylacoleo*, f: *Procoptodon*, g: *Diprotodon*. Relative scales aprox. only. Drawing: W. Nestler, based on Thenius (1980) and Anderson (1984)

Off-Shore Islands

It is difficult to estimate what Pleistocene woods on off-shore islands looked like. One can only speculate on the influence animals might have had on island vegetations (W.Schüle 1990a), on the structure and species composition of the vegetation on New Zealand and Madagascar on which ratites of all sizes grazed (Fig. 6,7). On over-populated ostrich or poultry farms the vegetation is soon destroyed. The birds' beaks and digestive systems handle hard food as well as soft, their scratching does the rest.

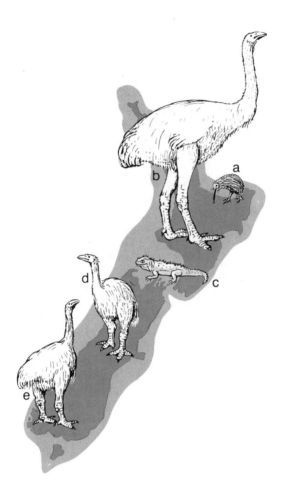

Fig.6. Selected extinct (white) and extant (grey) ratites and reptiles of New Zealand from the Upper Pleistocene and Holocene, semi-schcematic. Extinctions: First millenium AD. a: *Apteryx*, b: *Dinornis*, c: *Sphenodon*, d: *Emeus*, e: *Euryapteryx*. Ca. 30 species of ratites and flying birds extinct. Relative sizes aprox. only. Drawing: W. Nestler, based on Müller (1985) and Martin & Klein (1984)

In the complete absence of carnivores (New Zealand) or the lack of large ones (Madagascar), the population dynamics of larger island vertebrates was probably determined by trophic factors as in mainland megaherbivores. Especially the numerous ratites in New Zealand had developed species for every vegetational zone from the ground to 3-4 m above it (Burrows 1980). The result was probably also more or less dense patchwork forest.

Birds also produce considerable quantities of methane (Vonck & Western 1984). The ratites, some of them as heavy as oxen, will have added their share to the methane content of the atmosphere.

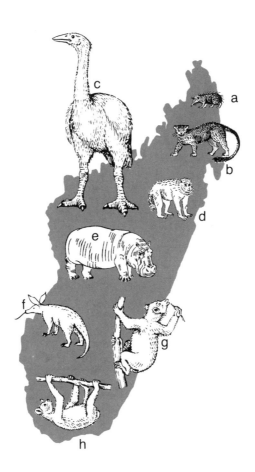

Fig.7. Selected extinct (white) and extant (grey) ratites and mammals of Madagascar, semi-schematic. Extinctions: First millenium AD. a: *Tenrec* (extinct species larger), b: *Cryptoprocta* (extinct species larger), c: *Muellerornis* and *Aegyornis*, d: *Archaeolemur*, e: *Hippopotamus* (dwarfed), f: *Plesiorycteropus* (larger than extant African *Orycteropus afer*), g: *Megalapis*, h: *Palaeopropithecus*. Not presented: *Archaeoindris*, a lemur the size of a male gorilla, largest extant lemurs the size of a fox. Relative sizes aprox. only. Drawing: W. Nestler, after Thenius (1980) and Fleagle (1989)

Megaherbivores in the strict sense neither do nor did exist on off-shore islands. If mega or other herbivores like hippos or elephants colonized islands they apparently dwarfed within geologically short timespans (Kowalski 1986). In not a single case of the numerous colonizations in the Mediterranean, on Sulawesi-Celebes, the Philippines and the "Wallacean Islands" between the Sunda and Sahul shelfs (Wallace 1911) are there fossils of the first generations of colonists. As predators did not exist and trophic situations were good, mass-multiplications were inevitable. The consequences for the ecosystems were the more drastic the less the endemic vegetation was adapted to browsing. The general tendency of such colonists towards dwarfing is probably a result of over-population and the destruction of the vegetation. A balance between dwarfing herbivores and vegetation could have been established only after many generations. The first humans certainly did not find forests with closed crown canopies on islands settled by herbivores. Within a short time the humans destroyed the whole vertebrate fauna except for very small, nocturnal or arboricole animals. After many generations in a world without predators the island faunas had lost the genetically fixed tendencies for fleeing enemies, as one may observe e.g. on the Galapagos Islands.

Pleistocene colonies of hippopotamus (*H.lemerlei*) on Madagascar should have had a similar effect on the vegetation as their extant counterparts in Africa. On Madagaskar, which was isolated from Africa since the oldest Tertiary, the vegetation was not adapted to such treatment. Within a short time the shores no longer supplied enough food for the dwarfing hippos. Their extremities exhibit distinct signs that the hippos wandered on hard ground in search of food. They became competitors of palaeoendemic ratites (*Mullerornis, Aepyornis*), gorilla-sized lemurs (*Archaeoindris fontoynonti*) and giant tortoises (*Geochelone*). One must assume that major parts of Madagascan forests were cleared by immigrated hippopotamus in the Pleistocene.

When man settled both Madagascar and New Zealand in the first millenium AD, animals larger than a fox disappeared (Martin & Klein 1984; Martin & Wright 1967). New Zealands first human settlers were Polynesians who did not bring domestic animals and whose domestic plants were from the tropics. Had it not been for the unwary moas, they would soon have run into difficulties. Yet the moas did not last forever. The crown canopy of the forests closed. On Madagaskar, the Malayan and African settlers brought zebus (*Bos taurus zebu*), goats (*Capra hircus*) and pigs (*Sus scrofa*), part of which turned feral. The anthropogenically increased fire frequency was added to that (Humbert 1927). It is unknown when the Madagascan subspecies of the African bush pig (*Potamochoerus porcus lavatus*) arrived on the island. It might have been introduced by Africans, who then kept its populations low by hunting.

Elephants (*Archidiscodon?, Palaeoloxodon*) and hippopotamus (*H.antiquus*), which colonized most of the Mediterranean islands and soon developed dwarfed forms, would have spared the islands' vegetation only in inaccessible places. The Balearic Islands were inhabited by *Myotragus balearicus*, a dwarfed, goat-like bovid of uncertain systematic position which had developed a nearly rodent-like dentition in the end. It had probably colonized the islands during the "Great Messinian Salinity Event" (Hsü 1983). Its short sturdy legs and the frontal positioning of its eyes show *Myotragus* to have been a good climber like domestic Moroccan dwarf goats. It seems unlikely that *Myotragus*, not having any predators, treated the vegetation more gently than did the dwarf elephants and hippos on the other Mediterranean islands.

Megaherbivores, Early Man, and Forest Structure in Africa and Eurasia

Only in Africa (Fig.8) and Eurasia (Fig.9) did megafauna and *Hominidae* coexist for a long time. In Africa partially or predominantly terrestrial *Hominoidea* (Fleagle 1988; Tobias 1985) had developed in the course of the Miocene. Out of these semi-terrestrial *Hominoidea* terrestrial *Hominidae* developed in the Pliocene. Their oldest known form is

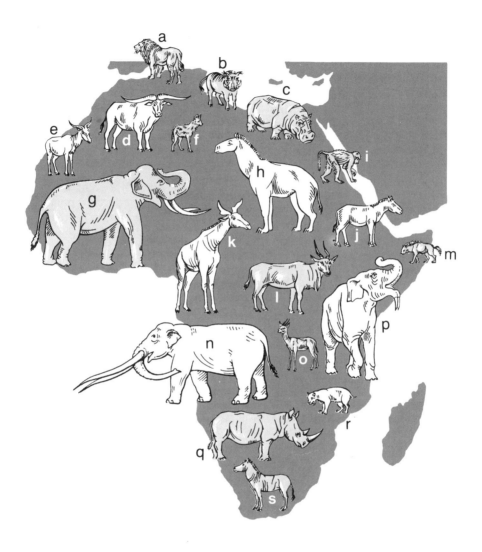

Fig.8. Selected extinct (white) and extant (grey) large mammals of Africa, semi-schcematic. Extinctions: Upper Plio/Lower Pleistocene. a: *Panthera*, b: *Phacochoerus* (extinct genera larger), c: *Hippopotamus* (related Plio/Pleistocene genera extinct), d: *Peloceras*, e: *Homoioceras*, f: *Lycaon*, g: *Loxodonta*, h: *Ancylotherium*, i: *Dinopithecus, Gorgopithecus, Theropithecus* (up to the size of a male gorilla, surviving *Cercopithecoidea* much smaller) j: *Stylohipparion* (substituted by *Equus* during Lower Pleistocene), k: *Siva(Libyo)therium*, l: *Tragolaphus (Taurotragus)*, m: *Hyaena* (extinct genera and species much larger), n: *Gomphotherium (Anancus)*, o: *Gazella*, p: *D(e)inotherium*, q: *Ceratotherium*, r: *Megantheron, Machairodus* and *Homotherium*, s: *Equus*. Relative scales aprox. only. Drawing W. Nestler, based on Thenius (1980), Martin (1984), Maglio & Cooke (1978)

Fig.9. Selected extinct (white) and extant (grey) mammals of Eurasia. Extinctions:
South Asia: Lower Pleistocene, further north successively to Holocene. a: *Rangifer*, b: *Ovibos* (extant in North America), c: *Coelodonta*, d: *Mammuthus*, e: *Alces* (related larger species extinct), f: *Castor* (larger *Trogontherium* extinct during Riß/Würm interglacial), g: *Hemitragus*, h: *Cervus*, i: *Canis*, j: *Equus* (surviving into Holocene in Eurasia, extant in Mongolia?), k: *Saiga*, l: *Macaca* (extinct during Riß/Würm interglacial, surving in Africa and tropical Asia), m: *Crocuta* (surviving in Africa), n: *Ursus* (larger *U.spelaeus* extinct), o: *Bison* (larger *B.priscus* extinct), p: *Elasmotherium*, q: *Mega(lo)cerus*, r: *Lepus*, s: *Paracamelus* (smaller *Camelus* extant in ?Mongolia) t: *Capra*, u: *Sus*, v: *Homotherium*, w: *Elephas (Stegodon* extinct*), x:* *Ailuropoda*, y: *Sivatherium* (extinct Middle Pleistocene), z: *Panthera* (extant: *P.tigris altaica* in the south), aa: *Bos primigenius* (surviving domesticated and related species in Central and South Asia), bb: *Hexaprotodon* (extinct without substitute in Middle Pleistocene), cc: *Bubalus*, dd: *Tapirus*, ee: *Pongo*. Relative scales aprox. only. Drawing W. Nestler, based on Thenius (1980), Kurtén (1968), Kowalski (1986)

Australopithecus afarensis ("Lucy"), whose age is estimated at 3.8 million years (Johanson & Edey 1980), i.e. Upper Pliocene. More important than their still-disputed age is that they were bipedal, although their brain capacity was approximatly that of extant chimpanzees. The only plausible explanation for that is that they needed their fore-feet for the continuous transport of objects even while moving (W.Schüle 1990a,b). There are only two kinds of objects which must continuously be carried: children and weapons. If *A.afarensis* had still been fur-clad the children would have clung to their mothers fur. If they were furless there must have been a reason for that.

For small, warm-blooded animals (Lucy's weight was below 50 kg) hairlessness is useless, even dangerous because of the loss of body heat during the cool nights in the savannas. If, on the other hand, it is combined with perspiratory glands it permits continuous fast locomotion, especially in warm arid or semi-arid climates. *Homo* posses such an unique cooling system. Hunting as a major subsistence basis seems to be the most plausible explanation for the development of this combination of bipedalism, furlessness, endurance and perspiratory glands. The system is useful only as a whole, its single components alone are not of any special value. Provided that suitable weapons existed, it enabled the defenseless Upper Pliocene and Lower Pleistocene hominids to hunt animals of all sizes in the dry heat of a savanna day, when most large carnivores rested in the shadows.

Small animals can be killed with clubs. For larger prey clubs are not of any use, but thrusting-spears are. Their concept does not require all that much intelligence, and they are easily manufactured from any tolerably straight staff of hardwood. Medium-sized and macroherbivores are hunted by predators and therefore posses genetically fixed patterns of behaviour (Lorenz 1969a,b) for fleeing enemies. Animals without enemies lose these patterns, and in the course of time they also lose the genetic information on these *patterns (see 8.4 above). Once the patterns are lost the reactions cannot be reacquired. Megaherbivores do not have predators. They react to carnivores only if their young are threatened. Biped primates neither look, smell nor behave like carnivores, so most Plio/Pleistocene megaherbivores probably ignored them. To kill megaherbivores, early *Hominidae* simply had to run a sharpened wooden staff into the animals bellies and follow until their prey collapsed. That was far less dangerous than hunting medium-sized animals with their genetic patterns for self-defense intact. It was less energy consuming and presented maximum profit.

Wherever man or his direct ancestors coexisted with megafauna for some time there are indubitable signs that they fed from the animals carcasses. Scavenging which is usually cited as an explanation (Blumenschine 1987) seems unlikely for physiological and ethological reasons: lethal ptomaine develops quickly in the tropics. The low reproduction rates of the *Hominoidea* could not compensate such losses. Furthermore, extant chimpanzees and baboons which frequently hunt small animals never touch carrion. A dislike of the smell of carrion seems to be genetically fixed in humans, apes and monkies. The hunting of small animals by primates may have begun as early as in the Miocene (Boesch 1990).

Megaherbivores have low reproduction rates and long pre-adult phases. Mathematical models show that the appearance of a new predator often leads to the quick extinction of a species (Mosiman & Martin 1975; A.Schüle 1990, 1991). In Africa, which to our present knowledge seems to be the cradle of the hominids, a number of megaherbivores became extinct without obvious reasons in the Plio/Pleistocene (Maglio & Cook 1978; Martin 1984). Only the direct ancestors of extant megaherbivores survived. They had somehow managed to adapt to the new predator. During the Lower Pleistocene there assumably was a kind of *bottleneck* in megaherbivore biomass in the biotopes of origin of the hominids, e.g. savannas and open forests, until the surviving species had recovered and occupied the niches of the extinct species.

To find more unwary megaherbivores the hominids advanced into landscapes unappropriate for them. These were landscapes without open water, and hyperhumid woods for which their cooling system was unsuited. All forest forms of African megaherbivores (e.g. *Dinotherium, Anancus, Ancylotherium*) dissapear within the Lower

Pleistocene. From what is stated above one may easily imagine the results of this for the stucture of the forests and the population densities of other herbivores. Not before hunting-adapted animals, including elephants, from the savannas immigrated into the dense forests in the course of the Pleistocene did some degree of patchwork vegetation reappear. Predation by man kept their populations at levels where they could not completely reestablish the former state, the trophic situation for secondary ungulates improved only slightly. When the populations of forest elephants were further decimated by ivory merchants and trophy hunters the crown canopy closed anew.

The hominid's expansion into treeless landscapes was hindered by the lack of drinking water, and the absence of sleeping trees to protect them from carnivores by night. The use of calabasses solved the first problem, the capacity to preserve and transport fire solved the second one. This had probably been achieved by the Lower Pleistocene (W. Schüle 1990a).

In posession of spear and fire *Homo erectus* reached Java in the upper Lower Pleistocene or lower Middle Pleistocene, exterminating most of the South Asian megafauna (Fig.9) and introducing the anthropogenic fire regime. Man's conquest of cooler climates was more difficult. From the Middle to the Upper Pleistocene the hominids (*H.erectus, H.sapiens praesapiens, H.s.neanderthalensis*) concentrated along a climatically limited line throughout Eurasia. There they lived under unfavourable climatic yet favourable trophic conditions. The population surplus and migrating herds from the zones too cold for *Homo* supplied the hunters with game from beyond the Eutrophic Line. South of this line conditions were poor for human hunters and large carnivores: game biomass was kept low by the human hunters. This resulted in the thickening of humid forests and all other repercussions. The anthropogenic fire regime turned semi-arid woodlands and forests into savanna and steppe, pyro-tolerant plants expanded. The carbon flux was influenced to a high degree. The more efficient *Homo* became at hunting the more the game was decimated. The fewer game there was and the more shy it behaved, the worse man's living conditions became.

Only when sewn clothing, tents etc. improved the thermo insulation of the human hunters towards the end of the last interglacial (Riss-Würm) and during the last glaciation (Würm/Wisconsin) the colonization of cold-temperate and cold zones was made possible. The mega and macrofauna (*Mammuthus, Coelodonta, Bison priscus* and *Megalocerus* in tundra, boreal forest and cold savanna, the giant rhinoceros *Elasmotherium* and giant camel *Paracamelus* in eastern steppe and semi-desert, musk-ox *Ovibos moschatus* in the Eurasian tundra) became extinct along with their predators. Relics of aurochs (*Bos primigenius*) survived into the Holocene, tiny populations of wild horses and of the relatively small European forest bison *(B.bonasus)* until today. In the absence of large herds of herbivores the Holocene warming transformed vast parts of Europe and temperate Asia into "primeval forest" unless counteracted by anthropogenic fires.

Agriculture and domestication spread from their probable place of origin in the Near East all over of Eurasia and Africa, starting in the earliest Holocene. By fire clearing and other intentional or unintended fires, clearings developed in the forests. Even in the humid Atlantic climate of Central and Western Europe forest pasturing of domestic herds resulted in the thinning, partly even in a destruction of woods. In less humid regions savanna transformed into steppe, steppe in part into semi-deserts or badlands for the same reason. Urbanization and energy intensive technologies (ceramics, metallurgy) dramatically increased the demand for timber, fuelwood and charcoal.

Sumerians and Egyptians, Greeks and Romans had to import timber from far away. Minery and charcoal burning devasted even nearly inaccessible montains, the goats of the miners did the rest. The forests retreated further.

Wherever the crown canopies of the forests were reopened by human activities, trophic conditions improved for both wild and domestic grazers, unadapted trees disappeared. In humid zones, the lack of wild grazers leads to the accumulation of fire potential. Fires following droughts reached high intensities which severely damaged the vegetation. Trees which grow well on fire clearings like *Pinus* or *Eucalyptus* species were favoured. Most Holocene pollen spectra are probably better indicators for the effects of the disappearing fauna, of an anthropogenic fire regime, of the exploitation by domestic animals, and of the increasing demand for fuel and timber than they are for the climatic development (Betancourt & Van Devender 1981).

Quintessence

Primeval forest with a closed crown canopy, low phytoproduction in the lower vegetation zones and resulting poverty in numbers and species of terrestrial herbivores is not the natural structure of forests, but rather patchwork forest, intitiated by megaherbivores and containing dense populations of many smaller herbivores.

World-wide and nearly independent of the amount of precipitations the formation of extended closed crown canopies was made possible only after man had exterminated the megafauna and decimated other vertebrates. This happened successively from the Plio/Pleistocene (in Africa) to the Holocene (on large off-shore islands). Only in Africa and South Asia was this process in part reversed by surviving megaherbivores which immigrated into the dense humid forests in the course of the Quaternary. The basic requirement for that was the "ecological hunting" practised by African and Asian tribes and the strict protection of the fauna proscribed by advanced Hindoo and Buddhist civilizations. Our modern technological civilization has so far been incapable of developing equivalent ethics.

The anthropogenic increase in the fire frequency, which has been spreading all over the world with the genus *Homo* since the Lower Pleistocene, has been affecting humid woods only after the modern destruction of rain forests set in, but has since assumed alarming proportions. Yet it has had considerable ecological effects in coniferous and all seasonally or continuously dry forests and savannas from the beginning of the use of fire by humans. By careful fire management these were kept at levels the biosphere could just tolerate. As with hunting, the fire-ecological ethics of the so-called "primitives" have proven far superior to those of modern "civilizations".

Anthropogenic interference with the distribution of mass in the biosphere (by reduction of the fauna and an increased fire frequency) could have sufficed to initiate loops of positive feedback which governed the climatic development of the Pleistocene. We are far from understanding these processes in detail, or from even realizing all participating parameters.

74 W. Schüle

Acknowledgements

This research has been funded by the Volkswagen Foundation through a research program on culutural ecology. I would like to thank Sandra Pichler for critical comments on this paper and for its translation.

References

Almeda F & CM Pringle eds (1988) Tropical Rainforests : Diversity and Conservation. San Francisco: Calif Acad Press

Anderson E (1984) Who's Who in the Pleistocene: A Mammalian Bestiary. In: PS Martin & R Klein (eds), Quaternary Extincitons. Tucson: Univ Arizona Press, 40-89

Andreae MO (1990) Biomass burning : Its history, use and distribution and its impact on environmental quality and global climate. Paper pres at Chapman Conference on Global Biomass Burning: Athmospheric, Climatic and Biosperic Implications. Willamsburg, Virginia. Unpublished

Andreae MO & DS Schimel (1989) Exchange of trace Gases between Terrestrial Ecosystems and the Atmosphere. Life Sci Res Rep 47

Berger A, S Schneider & JC Duplessey eds (1989) Climate and Geo-Sciences. A Challenge for Science and Society in the 21st Century. Dordrecht-Boston-London: Kluwer

Betancourt JL & TR Van Devender (1981) Holocene Vegetation in Chaco Canyon, New Mexico. Science 214, 656-658

Berggren WA & JA Vancovering eds (1984) Catastrophes and Earth History, the New Uniformitarians. New York: Princeton Univ Press

Bloom AL (1989) Die Oberfläche der Erde. Geowissen Kompakt 1. Stuttgart: Enke

Blumenschine RJ (1987) Characteristics of an Early Hominid Scavenging Niche. Curr Anthropol 28, 383-407

Boesch C (1990) First hunters of the forest. New Scientist 19, 38-41.

Bourliere F (1963) Observations on the ecology of some large African mammals. In: FC Howel & F Bourlière (eds), African ecology and human evolution. Chicago: Aldine, 43-54

Budyko MI, GS Golitsyn & YA Izrael (1988) Global Climatic Catastrophes. Berlin-Heidelberg-New York: Springer

Burrows CJ (1980) Diet of New Zealand Dinornithiformes. Naturwiss 67, 151-53

Carrington R (1958) Elephants. Short account of their natural history, evolution and influence on mankind. London: Chatto & Windus

Carroll RL (1988) Vertebrate Paleontology and Evolution. New York: Freeman

Church DC ed (1988) The ruminant animal. Digestive physiology and nutrition. Englewood Cliffs: Prentice Hall

Clarke RTJ & T Bauchop eds (1988) Microbial ecology of the gut. London: Acad Press

Clements FE (1916) Plant succession. An analysis of the development of vegetation. Carnegie Inst Washington Publ 242

Clements FE (1936) Nature and structure of the climax. J Ecology 24, 252-284

Crosby AW (1986) Ecological Imperialism. The Biological Expansion of Europe. Camebridge: Univ Press

Crutzen PJ & MO Andreae (1990) Biomass Burning in the Tropics: Impact on Atmosperic Chemistry and Biogeographical Cycles. Science 250, 1669-1678

Crutzen PJ & MM Müller Hrsg (1989). Das Ende des blauen Planeten? München: Beck

De Crescenzo L (1983) Storia della Filosofia Greca I, Presocratici. Milano: Mondadoci

Depéret C (1907) Les transformations du monde animal. Paris

Dt Bundestag Hrsg (1989) Schutz der Erdatmosphäre. Eine internationale Herausforderung. Zwischenber Enquete-Komm 11. Dt Bundestag, Vorsorge zum Schutz der Erdatmosphäre. Bonn: Univ Buchdruckerei

Dewar RE (1984) Extinctions in Madagascar: The Loss of the Subfossil Fauna. In: PS Martin & R Klein (eds), Quaternary Extinctions. Tucson: Univ Arizona Press, 574-593

Diamond JM (1982) Man the exterminator. Nature 298, 787-789

Douglas-Hamilton I & O Douglas-Hamilton (1975) Among the Elephants. London: Collins & Harvell

Ellenberg H (1954) Steppenheide und Waldweide, ein vegetationskundlicher Beitrag zur Siedlungs- und Landschaftsgeschichte. Erdkunde 8, 188-194

Ellenberg H (1986) Vegetation Mitteleuropas und der Alpen in ökologischer Sicht. Stuttgart: Ulmer

Fleagle JG (1988) Primate Adaptation & Evolution. San Diego: Acad Press

Flohn H (1985) Das Problem der Klimaänderungen in Vergangengheit und Zukunft. Darmstadt: Wiss Buchgesell

Flood J (1990) The Riches of Ancient Australia. A Journey into Prehistory. St Lucia: Univ Queensland Press.

Förster M (1977) Die Beeinflussung der Vegetationsstrukturen durch Wildbestände, dargestellt an Beispielen aus dem Staatlichen Forstamt Saupark (Niedersachsen). In: R Tüxen (ed), Anthropogene Vegetation. Den Haag: Mouton, 541-551

Frädrich H (1967) Das Verhalten der Schweine (Suidae, Tayassuidae) und Flußpferde (Hippopotamidae). In: W. Kükenthal, Handbuch der Zoologie 8, 10(26), 1-44

Goldammer JG ed (1990) Fire in the Tropical Biota. Ecosystem Processes and Global Changes. Ecol Stud 84

Goldammer JG & MJ Jenkins ed (1990) Fire in Ecosystem Dynamics. Proc 3rd Int'l Symp on Fire Ecology, Freiburg/Brsg, May 1989. The Hague: Academic

Goldberg ED ed (1982) Atmosperic Chemistry. Dahlem Workshop on Atmospheric Chemistry, Berlin 1982. Physic & Chemic Sci Res Reports. Berlin-Heidelberg-New York: Springer

Greenberg JH, CG Turner & SL Zgura (1986) The settlement of the Americas: a comparison of the linguistic, dental and genetic evidence. Curr Anthropol 27, 477-97

Groves RH & JJ Burdon (1986) Ecology of Biological Invasions. Cambridge: Univ Press

Grzimek B ed (1968-72). Grzimeks Tierleben. Enzyklopädie des Tierreichs X-XIII. Zürich: Kindler

Heyer J (1990) Der Kreislauf des Methans. Mikrobiologie/Ökologie/Nutzung. Berlin: Akademie

Hoernes GR (1911) Das Aussterben der Arten und Gattungen sowie der größeren Gruppen des Tier- und Pflanzenreiches. Festschr k.k. Franzens-Universität Graz Studienjahr 1910/11 aus Anlaß d Wiederkehr des Jahrestages ihrer Vervollständigung. Graz

Holland HD & M Schidlowski eds (1982) Mineral Deposits and the Evolution of the Biosphere. Berlin-Heidelberg-New York: Springer

Hoppe A ed (1990) Amazonien, Versuch einer interdisziplinären Annäherung. Ber Naturfor Ges Freiburg 80

Hsü KJ (1983) The Mediterranean was a Desert. A Voyage of the Glomar Challenger. Princeton: Univ Press

Janzen DH & PS Martin (1982) Neotropical Anachronisms: The Fruit the Gomphotheres Ate. Science 215, 19-27

Johanson D & M Edey (1980) Lucy: the beginning of mankind. New York: Simon & Schuster

Jones R (1975) The Neolithic, Paleolithic and the hunting gardeners: man and land in the antipodes. In: RP Suggate & MM Cresswell (eds), Quaternary Studies. Selected Papers IX INQUA Congr, Christchurch, NZ 1973. Roy Soc NZ Bull 13, 21-34

Kahlke HD (1956) Großsäugetiere im Eiszeitalter. Leipzig: Aulis

Kahlke HD (1981) Das Eiszeitalter. Leipzig: Aulis

Keast A, FC Erk & B Glas eds (1972) Evolution, Mammals and Southern Continents. Albany: State Univ Press

Kowalski K (1986) Die Tierwelt des Eiszeitalters. Erträge der Forschung 239. Darmstadt: Wiss Buchges
Kozamkulova BS (1981) Elasmotherium sibiricum und sein Verbreitungsgebiet auf dem Territorium der UdSSR Quartärpaläont 4.

Kurtén B (1968) Pleistocene mammals of Europe. London: Weidenfeld

Kurtén B & E Anderson 1980. Pleistocene Mammals of North America. New York: Columbia Univ Press

Langer P (1984) Comparative Anatomy of the stomach in mammalian herbivores. Quaterly J Exper Physiol 69, 615-625

Langer P (1985) Enddarm und Vormagenverdauung bei herbivoren Säugetieren des tropischen Regenwaldes. Verh Dtsch Zool Ges 78, 252

Langer P (1988) The mammalian herbivore stomach. Comparative anatomy, function and evolution. Stuttgart-New York: Fischer

Laws RW, ISC Parker & P Johnstone (1975) Elephants and their habitats: the ecology of elephants in north Bunyoro, Uganda. Oxford: Univ Press

Lettau H, K Lettau & LCB Molion (1979) Amazonia's hydrologic cycle and the role of atmospheric recycling in assessing deforestation effects. Monthly Weather Rev 107, 227-237

Lorenz K (1969a) Innate Bases of Learning. Cambridge: Harvard Univ Press

Lorenz K (1969b) Über tierisches und menschliches Verhalten I-III. München: Piper

Lovelock JE (1988) The Ages of Gaia. A Biography of our living Earth. Oxford: Univ Press

MacDonald D (1984) The Encyclopedia of Mammals I-II. London: Allen & Unwin

Maglio VJ & HBS Cooke (1978) Evolution of African Mammals. Cambridge: Harvard Univ Press

Martin PS (1973) The discovery of America. Science 179, 969-974

Martin PS (1984) Prehistoric overkill: the global model. In: PS Martin & R Klein (eds), Quaternary Extinctions. Tucson: Univ Arizona Press, 354-403

Martin PS & R Klein eds (1984) Quaternary Extinctions. Tuscon: Univ Arizona Press

Martin PS & HE Wright eds (1967) Pleistocene Extinctions. New Haven: Yale Univ Press

McKay GM (1977) Behaviour and ecology of the Asiatic Elephant in southeastern Ceylon. Smithsonian Contrib Zool 125

Mensching HG (1990) Desertifikation, ein weltweites Problem der ökologischen Verwüstung in den Trockengebieten der Erde. Darmstadt: Wiss Buchges

Merz G (1977) Untersuchungen über die Ernährungsbiologie und Habitatpräferenzen des Afrikanischen Waldelephanten Loxodonta africana cyclotis. Heidelberg: Matschie

Mosiman JE & PS Martin (1975) Simulating overkill by Paleoindians. Amer Scientist 63, 304-313

Müller AH (1989) Lehrbuch der Paläozoologie III: Vertebraten. Jena: Fischer

Müller-Dombois D (1981) Crown distortion and elephant distribution in the woody vegetation of Ruhunu National Park, Ceylon. Ecology 53, 208-26

Myers N (1989) Tropical Deforestation and Climatic Change. In: A Berger, S Schneider & JC Duplessy (eds), Climate and Geo-Sciences. Dordrecht-Boston-London: Kluwer, 341-53

Orr RT (1971) Das große Buch der Tierwanderungen, Motive-Orientierung-Verhalten. Düsseldorf: Diederichs

Owen-Smith N (1983) Management of large mammals in African conservation areas. Pretoria

Owen-Smith N (1987) Pleistocene extinctions: the pivotal role of megaherbivores. Paleobiol 13, 351-62

Pearce F (1989) Methane: the hidden greenhouse gas. New Sci 6, 37-41

Petrides GA & WG Swank (1965) Population densities and range-carrying capacity of large mammals in Queen Elisabeth National Park, Uganda. Zool Afric 1, 209-226

Piperno RD, MB Bush & PA Colinvaux (1990) Paleoenvironments and Human Occupation in Late-Glacial Panama. Quat Res 33, 108-116

Remmert H (1985) Was geschieht im Klimax-Stadium? Naturwiss 72, 505-12

Remmert H (1989) Ökologie. Berlin-Heidelberg: Springer

Riede K (1990) Die amazonischen Regenwälder als Labor der Evolution. In: A Hoppe (ed), Amazonien. Ber Naturfor Ges Freiburg 80, 93-118

Schüle A (1990) Simulation of population dynamics as a means of palaeoecological research. In: DL Bruton & DAT Harper (eds), Microcomputers in Paleontology. Contrib Palaeoontol Mus Univ Oslo 370, 82-105

Schüle A (1991) A finite-element model to simulate the spacial distribution of populations of large mammals. This volume

Schüle W (1990a) Landscapes and Climate in Prehistory: (ed), Fire in the Tropical Biota. Ecol Stud 84, 273-318

Schüle W (1990b) Human evolution, animal b Quaternary extinctions: A paleo-ecology of hunting. Homo 41, 229-250.

Simpson GE (1980) Splendid Isolation. The Curious History of South American Mammals. New Haven: Yale Univ Press

Sinclair ARE & M Norton-Griffith eds (1979) Serengeti: Dynamics of an ecosystem. Chicago; Univ Chicago Press

Stehli FG & SD Webb eds (1985) The Great American Biotic Interchange. New York: Plenum

Steinlin H (1990) Andere Möglichkeiten als die Holzproduktion zur Nutzung tropischer Wald-Ökosysteme. In: A Hoppe (ed), Amazonien. Ber Naturfor Ges Freiburg 80, 169-192

Thenius E (1980) Grundzüge der Faunen- und Verbreitungsgeschichte der Säugetiere. Eine historische Tiergeographie. Stuttgart: Fischer

Thornes JB ed (1990) Vegetation and Erosion. Processes and Environments. Chichester-New York: Wiley

Tobias PV ed (1985) Hominid Evolution, Past, Present and Future. New York: Liss

Turner CH (1975) Der Einfluß großer Mammalia auf die interglaziale Vegetation. Quartärpaläont 1, 13-19

Tüxen R ed (1961) Anthropgene Vegetation. Den Haag: Mouton

Vonk HJ & JRH Western (1984) Comparative biochemestry and physiology of enzymatic digestion. London: Acad Press

Wallace AR (1911) The World of Life. New York: Moffot

Walter H (1984) Vegetation und Klimazonen. UTB 14. Stuttgart: Ulmer

Walter H & SW Breckle (1983) Ökologie der Erde I-III. UTB Große Reihe. Stuttgart: Ulmer

Webster D & G (1984) Optimal Hunting and Pleistocene Extinctions. Hum Ecol 12, 275-89

Weischet W (1987) Las conditiones climáticas en Amazonia. Tübinger Geogr Stud 94, 17-29

Weischet W (1990) Das Klima Amazoniens und seine geoökologischen Konsequenzen. In: A Hoppe (ed), Amazonien. Ber Naturfor Ges Freiburg 80, 59-92

Ziswiler V (1965) Bedrohte und aussterbende Tiere. Eine Biologie des Aussterbens und des Überlebens. Berlin: Springer

Tropical Forests in Transition
J. G. Goldammer (ed.)
© 1992 Birkhäuser Verlag Basel/Switzerland

Succession After Disturbance of Lowland Mixed Dipterocarp Forest by Shifting Agriculture in East Kalimantan, Indonesia

Soedarsono Riswan and Rochadi Abdulhadi[*]

Abstract

A series of successional developments of lowland tropical forest in East Kalimantan after slash-and-burn for agriculture was assessed. These agricultural activities resulted in decreasing number of species, percentage of cover, frequency of seedling and sproutings. It is suggested that the initial seedlings play a major role in vegetation recovery of a tropical forest. The species composition changes along the successional gradients (i.e., reducing the proportion of pioneers vs increasing the primary forest species). Repeated burning for agriculture however, would change the forest community into *Imperata* grassland.

Introduction

The tropical rain forests of Kalimantan are well known as a center of biological diversity of Indonesia. The extent of this forest is rapidly decreasing because of forest exploitation

---

[*] Herbarium Bogoriense, Research and Development Center for Biology, LIPI, Jalan Raya Juanda 22-24, Bogor 16122, Indonesia

activities such as commercial logging, conversion for development projects, shifting cultivation and forest fires. This development has attracted world wide concern, especially in the past five years, to preserve and conserve the rich biological diversity of the area.

Possible solutions to this problem will involve a better understanding of how tropical rain forests function. This will be a prerequisite for developing improved schemes of sustainable management and utilization of the natural resources.

Few studies have attempted to investigate the succession within a depleted forest in detail. The successional development of vegetation of a mixed dipterocarp forest following disturbances after slash and burn agriculture is assessed in this paper.

Study Area

The study area is located at Lempake, about 12 km northeast of Samarinda, the capital city of the East Province Kalimantan of Indonesia (Fig. 1). This site covers a mixed dipterocarp forest, a 35-year old forest after abandonment of pepper plantation, young secondary vegetation and sites treated by slash-and-burn agriculture.

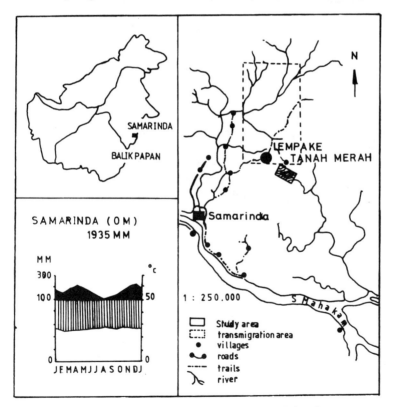

Fig.1. Maps of the study area at Lempake, East Kalimantan, Indonesia

The area consists of sedimentary rocks formed during the Upper Miocene period (Anonymus 1965). Topography is undulating to somewhat hilly, with an altitude range of 40 - 80 m. The soil belongs to the red-yellow podzolic group (Hardjono 1967), roughly equivalent to ultisols. Climate is humid, with the average rainfall of 1964 mm per year. Monthly rainfall ranges from 110 mm in August to 240 mm in December. The dry season occurs from July to September (Anonymus 1982; Berlage 1949). The average of temperature ranges from 26.5^0 C in January to 28^0 in July (Berlage 1949).

Mixed Dipterocarp Forest at Lempake

The primary Mixed Dipterocarp Forest in the study site has been described by Riswan (1982, 1987). It is assumed that these primary forest characteristics also refer to the located sites nearby that are disturbed by the slash-and-burn agriculture and which grow on the similar soils, topography and climates. The description of this forest is summarized below.

This forest is rich in species. A total of 209 species of trees (DBH greater than 10 cm) was recorded within the 1.6 ha plot, with the density of 445 trees/ha and the total basal area of 33.74 m^2/ha. Tree diameters ranged from 10 to 223 cm. Three canopy strata were recognized. The first stratum, with the height of 25-45 m were mostly dominated by *Eusideroxylon zwageri, Baccaurea macrocarpa* and *Dillenia eximia*. The second stratum (15-25 m) and third stratum (5-15m) were composed of young trees (regeneration) of the first stratum and the understory species. The emergent trees, mostly composed of dipterocarp species including *Dryobalanops beccarii, Shorea polyandra, S. ovalis, S. koordersii, S. parvifolia, Dipterocarpus cornutus* and other species i.e.*Intsia palembanica*, reach up 60 m.

A dipterocarp family was the most prevalent, with the comparison of Dipterocarp and non-Dipterocarp species of 1 : 16 for the tree species and 2 : 3 for the basal area. A total of 12 dipterocarp species was recorded with the total basal area of 13.18 m^2/ha (39.06%) and the density 27 trees/ha (6.04%). The most common species were *Shorea johorensis, S. parvifolia, S. polyandra* and *Hopea rudiformis*. However, regarding the species level, Bornean iron wood (*Eusideroxylon zwageri*) was the most prevalent with the basal area 5.83 m^2/ha (12.28%).

Succession Following Experimental Slash-and-Burn

The recovery process following clearing and burning was experimentally studied. Six weeks following clearing and burning, 38 and 16 species of seedlings and resproutings respectively were recorded within 100 plots of 1 x 1 m. This number was smaller than in the experimental plot described by Riswan & Kartawinata (1989), i.e. 42 and 60 species of seedlings and resprouting respectively.

The number of tree seedling species in burnt and unburnt plots was similar, i.e., 28 and 29 species respectively. However, the number of individuals was much smaller in the burnt plot (464/100 m^2) than in the unburnt plots (4529/100 m^2), with the ratio 1 : 9. This suggests that burning might have killed many of viable seeds on the forest floor and soil surfaces (Riswan 1982; Abdulhadi 1989; Brinkman & Vierera 1985) as well as tree stumps and roots (Kartawinata et al. 1980). Thus seedlings in the burnt site are likely recruited from a continuous seed rain which came from adjacent secondary and primary forests.

Succession Following Abandonment of Slash-and-Burn Agriculture

After a fallow period of six months following the first hill rice cultivation, secondary species grew well and began to form young secondary forest. Structurally, it was similar to those with the same age although floristically different. This community vertically consists of two strata, i.e. ground cover and sapling stratum respectively. There are no trees occuring in this stage.

Undergrowth species consist of seedlings and herbs with the height of 5 - 200 cm (with the highest herb *Blumea balsamifera*). The average of sapling height was 300 cm, but several species such as *Callicarpa pedicellata, Trema orientalis,* and *Macaranga* spp. reach up to 650 cm. As woody pioneers these saplings grew rapidly with an average of 82 cm in height and 0.5 cm in diameter per year, considerably faster than the rate of growth in an undisturbed forest.

The most abundant and locally often dominant species were *Macaranga gigantea, M. triloba, M. pruinosa, Mallotus paniculatus, Callicarpa pedicellata* and *Trema orientalis*. The floristic composition and the abundance of species attributed to the intensity of fire which affects the soil seed stores and the distance and availability of seed sources (Kostermans 1960; Kellman 1973; Riswan 1982; Abdulhadi 1989).

When there are no further disturbances, sapling of secondary tree species such as *Callicarpa pedicellata, Macaranga gigantea, M. triloba, Mallotus affinis* and *Trema orientalis* will become prevalent in the following stages. With further development of shading herbs and shrubs such as *Blumea balsamifera* and *Melastoma malabathricum* disappear.

Similar successional developments were described in a study earlier this century in which Jochem (1928) observed a ca. 8 years fallow on tobacco land at Deli, Sumatera, Indonesia. He recognized three stages during this fallow, i.e., (1) herbaceous stage, a community dominated by short-lived herbs and mixed with tree seedlings; (2) *Trema-Blumea* stage, a community were the main small tree species are associated with *Blumea balsamifera*; and (3) the tree stage, a typical secondary growth or "belukar", which is dominated by one or the mixture of the following species *Trema* spp., *Macaranga tanarius, M. denticulata, Callicarpa tomentosa, Mellochia umbellata*.

In further development, these secondary trees were being gradually replaced by primary trees. In the 35-year old regrowth after several years of pepper plantation, the site was still dominated by secondary trees such as *Macaranga gigantea, M. pruinosa,*

M. bancana, Artocarpus tamaran and other late secondary trees. However, about 60% of the species were primary species. Most saplings and seedlings were also primary tree species .

Riswan et al. (1985) estimated how long it takes the number of primary species in this successional process to become stabilized or to reach an equilibrium by calculating the rate of influx of these species. They concluded that the time required for successful reestablishment of this mixed dipterocarp forest would be between 150 and 500 years (Fig. 2). A similar estimation has been noted by Knight (1975) in Baro Colorado Island, and by Abdulhadi (1989) in a successional sequence of a subtropical rain forest after clearing and burning for pasture in southeast Queensland.

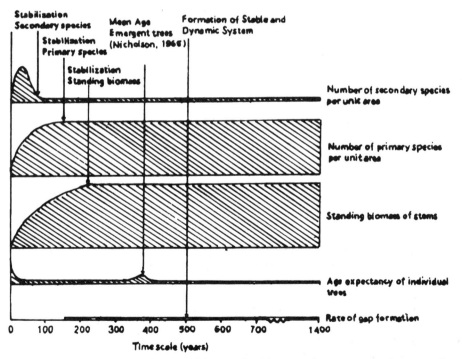

Fig.2. Proposed changes in species composition, standing biomass and age expectancy for tree species associated with the re-establishment and gap formation of lowland mixed dipterocarp forest, based upon data from Samarinda, East Kalimantan, Indonesia (adopted from Riswan *et al.* [1985])

Assessment of Repeated Slash-and-Burn

Repeated burning for cultivation resulted in drastic floristic changes. In 25 permanent plots of 10 x 10 m, Abdulhadi *et al.* (1990) recorded 221 species in the first fallow following forest clearing, burning and cultivation in 1978 (Tab. 1). This number was reduced to 36 species after the fourth cultivation in 1981.

The most striking feature was the change in number and composition of tree species. In the first fallow in 1978, 113 primary tree species were recorded (both seedlings and resprouting from the remaining stumps). They embraced five dipterocarp species, *Dipterocarpus oblongifolius, Shorea leprosula, S. parvifolia, S. ovalis* and *Shorea* sp. and 108 other species including *Aglaia borneensis, Artocarpus heterophyllus, Crudia reticulata, Dacryodes rostrata, Dehaasia incrassata, Durio acutifolius, Eusideroxylon zwageri, Koordersiodendron pinnatum, Lithocarpus* spp., *Polyalthia glauca* and *Sindora sumatrana*. Most species disappeared in the following three years record and *Artocarpus heterophyllus* and *Cleistanthus myrianthus* also disappeared.

Tab. 1. Number (A) and proportion (B: total percentage [%]) of species during the fallow period of the shifting agriculture in Lempake, Samarinda

| Life Forms | Year of Observation | | | | | |
| | 1978 | | 1979 | | 1981 | |
	A	B	A	B	A	B
Primary Trees	113	(51.1)	13	(25.0)	5	(13.9)
Secondary Trees	24	(10.9)	12	(23.0)	10	(27.7)
Shrubs	20	(9.0)	12	(23.0)	7	(19.0)
Herbs	33	(14.4)	8	(15.4)	9	(25.0)
Grasses	7	(3.1)	4	(7.7)	3	(8.4)
Vines	24	(10.9)	3	(5.7)	2	(5.5)
Total	221	(100)	52	(100)	36	(100)

The decline in number of species was accompanied by the changes in the floristic composition. The proportion of trees declined after repeated burning (i.e. 51.1% in 1978 and 13.9% in 1981). However, the secondary trees as well as the pioneer trees tended to increase.

The dominant species also changed (Fig. 3). In the beginning of fallow period, the secondary vegetation was dominated by *Paspalum conjugatum, Trema cannabina, Macaranga pruinosa* and *Trema orientalis*, and accompanied by many other pioneers and primary species as well. These species were recruited from the soil seed bank, seed rain and vegetative resprouts. Repeated burning reduced the ability of resprouting (Kartawinata *et al.* 1980), and killed the viable soil seed stores (Riswan 1982; Abdulhadi 1990; Brinkman & Vierera 1985).

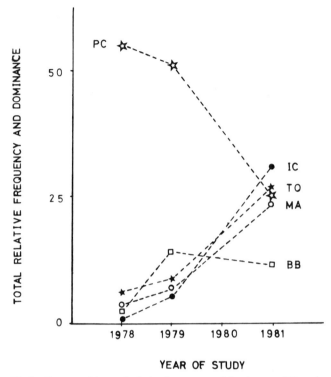

Fig.3. Changes of the total relative frequency and dominance of *Paspalum conjugatum* (PC), *Imperata cylindrica* (IC), *Trema orientalis* (TC), *Melastoma affine* (MA) and *Blumea balsamifera* during three years studies

Thus, the species regenerating after repeated burning are either brought into the site by dispersed seeds or by coppicing from suckers that are buried in deep soil. As Figure 3 indicates, agressive grasses such as *Imperata cylindrica*, *Melastoma affine* and *Trema orientalis* took over the *Paspalum conjugatum* dominancy. Even in the following year the block was covered by *Imperata cylindrica* and *Melastoma affine* which sparsely occured.

Conclusions

It is concluded that the impact of slash and burn practices in the mixed dipterocarp forest showed a sharp decline of species diversity of forest vegetation, in particular of tree species, seedlings and resprouts. The new composition of species may depend on kind of disturbance (i.e. repeated of slash and burn will lead to *Imperata cylindrica* grassland), survival of seed-bank on the forest floor and the immigrant species (seed rain) which arrive after the fire or burn.

References

Abdulhadi, R (1989) Subtropical rain forest seed dynamics. Ph.D. Thesis, Univ. of Queensland, Australia

Abdulhadi, R (1990) Effects of heating and burning on seed bank germination. Ekologi Indonesia 1: 57-62

Abdulhadi R, Kartawinata K, Suhardjono YR (1990) Perubahan flora akibat perladangan aktif di bekas kawasan hutan tropika lahan pamah, Lempake, Samarinda. Proc. Regional Seminar on Conservation for development of tropical rain forest in Kalimantan, pp 129-145

Anonymus (1965) Peta Geologi Indonesia. Direktorat Geologi, Bandung

Anonymus (1982) Rainfall records, East Kalimantan. Report, analysis summaries and histograms. Transmigration Area Development Project, Samarinda, Kalimantan Timur

Berlage HP Jr (1949) Regenval in Indonesia. Verhandelingen No.37 Koninklijk Magnetish en Meterologisch Observatorium te Batavia

Brinkman WLF, Vieira AN (1971) The effect of burning on germination of seeds at different soil depths of various tropical tree species. Turrialba 21: 77-82

Hardjono (1967) Uraian Satuan Peta Tanah Eksplorasi Kalimantan Timur bagian Selatan. Lembaga Penelitian Tanah, Bogor

Jochem SCJ (1928) De begruing der tabaks landen in Deli enhare betekeuis voor de tabaks cultuur. Med Deli Proefsta No. 59

Kartawinata K, Riswan S, Soedjito H (1980) The floristic changes after disturbances in lowland dipterocarp forest in east Kalimantan, Indonesia. In: Tropical Ecology and Development (JI Furtado ed.) pp 47-54. Int Soc Tropical Ecology

Kellman MC (1973) Secondary plant succession in tropical montane Mindano. Research School of Pacific Studies, Department of Biogeography and Geomorphology blications BG. 2 (1970), Australian National University

Knight DH (1975) A phytosociological analysis of species rich tropical rain forest on Barro Colorado Island, Panama Ecol Monogr 45: 259-284

Kostermans AJGH (1960) The influence of man on the vegetation of the humid tropics. Symposium on the Impact of Man on Humid Tropics Vegetation, Goroka, Territory of Papua New Guinea, September 1960, pp 332-338

Riswan S (1982) Ecological studies in primary, secondary and experimentally cleared mixed dipterocarp forest and kerangas forest in East Kalimantan, Indonesia. Ph. D.Thesis. University of Aberdeen, Scotland, UK

Riswan S (1987) Structure and floristic composition of mixed dipterocarp forest at Lempake, East Kalimantan. In: Proceeding of the Third International Round Table Conference on Dipterocarps (AJGH Kostermans, ed), pp. 435-457, Unesco, Jakarta

Riswan S, Kentworthy JB, Kartawinata K (1985) The estimation of temporal process in tropical rain forest: a study of primary mixed dipterocarp forest in Indonesia. J Trop Ecol 1: 171-182

Riswan S, Kartawinata K (1989) Regeneration after disturbance in a lowland mixed dipterocarp forest in East Kalimantan, Indonesia. Ekologi Indonesia 1: 9-28

Whitmore TC (1983) Secondary succession from seed in tropical rain forests. Forestry Abstracts 44: 767-779

Tropical Forests in Transition
J. G. Goldammer (ed.)
© 1992 Birkhäuser Verlag Basel/Switzerland

Degradation of a Forest in the Shimba Hills National Reserve, Kenya, as Initiated by Man and Maintained by Wildlife

Robert Schmidt[*]

Abstract

An evergreen seasonal lowland forest in Kenya was chosen as an example to demonstrate the effects of forest use in the Holocene. Heavily disturbed and little influenced sites within this forest were compared in regard to structure and floristics. The *Lagynias pallidiflora* community and its seral stages of natural gap dynamics were described as the zonal vegetation type which was little influenced in the past. The *Leptonychia usambarensis* community and its seral stages were considered to be a consequence of logging activities. Phytosociological analysis indicated the general possibility of a regeneration of the disturbed sites, i.e. a transition from the *Leptonychia usambarensis* to the *Lagynias pallidiflora* community. However, at present, the strain on the vegetation caused by a large population of elephants impedes succession in the open forest sites. The *Leptonychia usambarensis* community is thus considered to be at a proclimax stage.

Introduction

In equatorial Africa, large areas of tropical rain forest have been exploited or converted into agricultural land. On the Kenyan coast - an area largely covered by rain forest during and after the Pleistocene - less than five percent of the original forest remains.

---

[*] Department of Botany, University of Bayreuth, P.O. Box 101251, D-8580 Bayreuth, Germany

These East African coastal forests are considered to be the last refuges of an ancient forest mass that covered most of Central Africa between the Atlantic and the Indian Ocean (Faden 1974; Grubb 1982; Livingstone 1982).

In addition to post-glacial climatic changes, a long history of anthropogenic activity resulted in the patchy structure of small fragile forests which is encountered today (Lind & Morrison 1974; Kuyper 1982).

At present, the remnants of coastal forests in Kenya are shielded by various protective regimes ranging from the local sanctity observed by the local inhabitants to nature reserves under the guardianship of central government. Nevertheless, the demand for forest products and the need for land still exerts pressure even on protected forest areas.

This study investigated the consequences of anthropogenic and zoogenic impact on a Kenyan coastal forest of high diversity. Within this forest system, mostly undisturbed parts contrast sharply with areas that were subjected to logging activities and subsequent damage by large herbivores. This study will attempt to explain today's vegetation cover in terms of historical anthropogenic impact on the land. The consequences of past human influence on the area are extrapolated from recent forest dynamics which were studied with phytosociological methods.

The Study Area

The study was carried out in Longomagandi Forest, a forest about 22 ha in size in the Shimba Hills National Reserve (Fig. 1). The whole park encompasses 220 km² of grassland, deciduous forest, riverine forest and tropical evergreen seasonal lowland forest. The Shimba Hills are part of a coastal plateau which rises up to an altitude of 450 m at a distance of 15 km from the Indian Ocean. The top of the plateau is flat to undulating. In location of the Shimba Hills and Longomagandi Forest some parts are deeply incised by permanent or semi-permanent rivers. On the eastern and western sides, the plateau is bordered by steep escarpments as a result of late-Tertiary faulting.

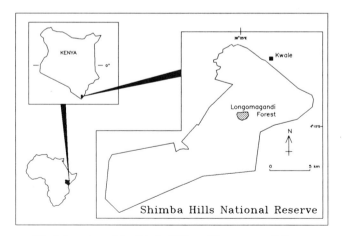

Fig.1. Location of the Shimba Hills and Longomagandi Forest

The Shimba Hills plateau is entirely made up of sediments. The Triassic Shimba grits and Mazeras sandstones, which underlie most of the area of the park yield coarse-grained deeply weathered ferralitic soils, mainly ferralic Acrisols. During the Pliocene, a cover of medium-grained Magarini sands was deposited on top of the Shimba grits in the central part of the park. The soils derived from Magarini sands, mostly Ferralsols, have a slightly higher cation exchange capacity (CEC) and base saturation, and a larger water storage capacity than those on Shimba grits. Longomagandi Forest is entirely underlain by Magarini sands.

The area's climate is governed by the tradewinds. The annual mean rainfall of about 1200 mm is mainly confined to the 'long rains' between April and July and the 'short rains' between October and December. Two months (January and February) are considered arid. In addition to the rainfall, a considerable amount of precipitation occurs in the form of fog and dewfall. The mean annual temperature between July 1988 and June 1989 was 23.7°C. The average daily temperature span was 6.9°C.

The Shimba Hills plateau, although being potential forest land (Schultka 1974a), today consists of a mosaic of pure or wooded grassland and forest. Corresponding to the geological underground, two major types of evergreen forests occur on the flat parts of the plateau (Schmidt in prep.). The forests on Shimba grits and Mazeras sandstones bear a monodominant Paramacrolobium forest whose occurrence was previously attributed to the removal of original tree species (Kenya Soil Survey 1978). The highly diverse forest stocking on Magarini sands was classified as *Sterculia - Chlorophora*[**]*-Memecylon* lowland rain forest (Moomaw 1959), *Chlorophoro - Strychnetalia* (Knapp 1965), *Chlorophora excelsa - Antiaris toxicaria* forest (Kenya Soil Survey 1978) or *Chlorophora - Lovoa* high forest stage (Schultka 1974b). As a result of careful phytosociological analysis, it will be termed *Olyra - Rawsonia* community group in this paper. This forest type is restricted to the central part of the park and typically is represented by Longomagandi Forest.

Today, the area of the National Reserve is densely populated by wildlife. Among the larger herbivores are elephant, buffalo and sable antelope. In addition to these, a few giraffes have already been and zebras will be introduced in the near future.

History of Anthropogenic Disturbance

The East African coast was colonized very early and was thence intensively cultivated. The oldest traces of human impact are lumps of charcoal originating from about 260 A.D. (Soper 1967). The corresponding pottery is considered to be the earliest so far encountered at an Early Iron Age site in East Africa. Grinding stones, iron weapons, iron slags, clay tuyere and lumps of burnt clay show evidence of human settlements in the Shimba Hills. These tools originate from small groups of bushmanoid hunters and herdspeople and a few Bantu-speaking people who practiced small-scale slash-and-burn agriculture in the area. The activities of these early settlers must be regarded as the first stage of nibbling at the closed forest cover.

The second stage commenced in the 15th century when today's resident population, the Mijikenda, invaded the area (Prins 1972; Morton 1973). The Mijikenda had to

[**] *Chlorophora excelsa* is the former name of *Milicia excelsa* (Welw.) C.C. Berg

conceal themselves on hilltops inside the dense forests to avoid the attacks of raiding Galla-warriors. Most of today's remaining forests are former fortified villages, so-called 'kayas' (Spear 1978). Two clans of Mijikenda-settlers had their homesteads in Longomagandi Forest, the best conserved part of the highly diverse forests of the *Olyra - Rawsonia* community group in the Shimba Hills. The Mijikenda influenced the forest in two ways: they cleared land for agricultural purposes and they cut selected trees for domestic use. The necessity to keep their villages out of sight, however, forced the Mijikenda to preserve at least the outer parts of the forest in their original condition (Robertson 1987, unpublished). It is very probable that the Mijikenda replanted trees within the forest.

The next stage of anthropogenic influence on the coastal forests started with colonial times. From the beginning of the century, the colonial Forest Department intended to convert the "virgin jungle" into profitable forest plantations. In 1903, the Shimba Hills forests were first demarcated and the Mijikenda chased from their kayas. Large caoutchouc plantations (*Hevea brasiliensis*) were started without success. Trials with various species of *Eucalyptus, Casuarina* and *Araucaria* followed but suffered a similar fate (Wildlife Planning Unit 1983). A major attempt was made to grow a valuable timber species from the neighbouring forest: over 400 ha of grassland were planted with mvule (Milicia excelsa) but due to the poor soil and an impervious lateritic layer, the saplings died (Glover 1968). Pinus caribaea was the only species that was succesfully planted in the Shimba Hills. However, even those plantations are not very vigorous.

In addition to clearing forest for plantations, the Forest Department harvested selected tree species from within the forest. In 1956, the forests were gazetted. After Kenya's independence in 1963, the District Forest Department awarded licenses for private sawmillers to exploit the forests without any control. Table 1 gives a list of the most valuable timber species of the forests in the central part of the park.

In 1968, the Shimba Hills National Reserve was established. In addition to the Forest Department's activities, the Wildlife Department started to manage the area with the intention of attracting tourists to the park. The major impact of the Wildlife Department on the forests was a relatively uncontrolled burning scheme of grass- and bushland. Parts of the park were burnt twice a year the fires being stopped only by the forest fringes.

Up to 1987, the Forest Department continued to grant logging licenses. From 1988, felling was prohibited but it was still legal to remove lying trunks. Since 1990, the sawmill companies have been forbidden from entering the park.

Tab.1. Important timber species of Longomagandi Forest

Vernacular name	Scientific name	Family
mvule	*Milicia excelsa* (Welw.) C.C. Berg = *Chlorophora excelsa*	Moraceae
mleha	*Newtonia paucijuga* (Harms) Brenan	Mimosaceae
msandarusi	*Hymenaea verrucosa* Gaertn.	Caesalpiniaceae
mng'ambo	*Manilkara sansibarensis* (Engl.) Dubard	Sapotaceae
nguoguo	*Antiaris toxicaia* (Pers.) Lesch.	Moraceae
mnwa madzi	*Trichilia emetica* Vahl	Meliaceae
mpalawanda	*Fernandoa magnifica* Seem.	Bignoniaceae

Description of the Problem and Methods

In Longomagandi Forest, there is both an obvious structural and a floristic difference between the relatively undisturbed parts and areas formerly subjected to logging activities. The open canopy in the disturbed forest parts attracts larger numbers of elephants as compared to the undisturbed sites. The different forest structure also triggers a different behaviour in the large herbivores. In the open forest, the elephants do not keep to fixed tracks. Hence, the impact of elephants on the logged-over parts of Longomagandi is much larger than in the closed-canopy parts. The following major questions arise from these observations:

(1)   How did the floristic difference between the closed-canopy and the open forest sites evolve?

(2)   Can structural differences be overcome under the present conditions when succession goes on?

(3)   Are nomad species invading disturbed forest parts competitive when regeneration takes place?

(4)   Did soil conditions change as a result of forest disturbance?

The methodology to answer these questions was centered on a phytosociological as well as on an ecological approach.

The plant communities were described using the relevé method introduced by Braun-Blanquet (Braun-Blanquet 1964; Mueller-Dombois & Ellenberg 1974). The relevé size was 200 m^2 and within each relevé up to four strata were recorded separately (plants with more than 15 m in height; plants between 5 and 15 m, plants between 1 and 5 m and plants below 1 m in height). This approach allowed a detailed analysis of the regeneration ability of the arboreal species.

The vegetation analysis intended to identify differential species to characterize the respective vegetation units. The numerical analysis was carried out using Twinspan (Hill 1979) and Wildi (Wildi & Orloci 1983) computer programs.

The basic vegetation unit was termed 'community'. Syntaxonomically defined terms such as 'association' were avoided as the hierarchical position of the vegetation units is not yet clear. The term 'stage' has been adopted to describe floristical differences within a community which can be traced back to obvious historical influences.

In addition to the floristic analysis, profile diagrams of the important stages (horizontal and vertical projection) were prepared.

Soil analysis was performed comparing 9 soil profiles under different plant communities or successional stages. As far as soil depth permitted, pits were made 180 cm deep. The soil profile description was accomplished following the guidelines of the FAO (1977) and the soils were classified using the terminology adopted by the Kenya Soil Survey (1978) and the revised FAO-nomenclature (FAO-UNESCO 1988). Physical and chemical analyses were carried out by the National Agricultural Laboratories (NAL) of the Kenya Agricultural Research Institute (KARI), Nairobi.

Results

A. Vegetation Analysis

Although several community groups can be distinguished within the East African tropical evergreen seasonal lowland forest formation, the *Olyra - Rawsonia* community group is the only one represented in Longomagandi Forest. This community group comprises two communities, the *Lagynias pallidiflora* community and the *Leptonychia usambarensis* community. Both communities were encountered in several regeneration stages. Figure 2 presents a simplified schema of the vegetation units established. A frequency table with the most important species occuring in Longomagandi Forest is given in Tab. 2 in the Appendix.

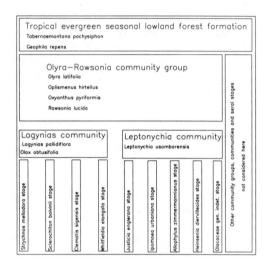

Fig.2. Simplified schema of the vegetation units occuring in Longomagandi Forest and their differential species

The highly diverse forest type encountered in Longomagandi Forest generally has a closed canopy and at least three distinct strata of vascular plants. The tallest trees sometimes reach 40 m in height although true emergents are rare. The uppermost stratum (stratum 1) generally forms an uneven canopy between 25 and 35 m. The discontinuity of the canopy is attributed to different types of disturbance rather than to different maximum heights of the mature trees. The forest consists mainly of evergreen trees, however, individual trees of the upper canopy may seasonally shed their leaves and remain leafless for a few weeks. The formation is termed tropical evergreen seasonal lowland forest according to the tentative physiognomic-ecological classification of plant formations of the earth [revised from Ellenberg & Mueller-Dombois (1967) and reappraised in the Unesco international classification and mapping of vegetation (1973)].

The trees are sometimes buttressed and the stems frequently fluted. The bark is often thin. Cauliflory and ramiflory is found in a number of species and is especially frequent among lianas. The large trees more often have a rough than a smooth bark.

In general, the leaves are sclerophyllous, have entire margins and belong to the mesophyll size class. Compound leaves are abundant. Bud protection by scales is very rare. Leaf shedding is a frequent feature of the species of all strata. Heavy lianas are common. Vascular epiphytes are present though not common and they only consist of a few species. Mosses and lichens are rare.

The closed-canopy evergreen seasonal lowland forest is phytosociologically well characterized by two species, namely *Tabernaemontana pachysiphon* (Apocynaceae) and *Geophila repens* (Rubiaceae).

Among the frequent companions of this formation are large trees such as *Ellipanthus hemandradenioides* (Connaraceae), *Antiaris toxicaria* (Moraceae), *Fernandoa magnifica* (Bignoniaceae), *Malacantha alnifolia* (Sapotaceae), *Odyendea zimmermannii* (Simaroubaceae), *Trichilia emetica* (Meliaceae), *Zanha golungensis* (Sapindaceae), *Newtonia paucijuga* (Mimosaceae) and *Bombax rhodognaphalon* (Bombacaceae). Trees which hardly or never exceed 15 m in the evergreen seasonal lowland forest are *Diospyros greenwayi* and *Diospyros kabuyeana* (Ebenaceae), *Haplocoelopsis africana* (Sapindaceae), *Pavetta tarennoides* and *Tarenna drumondii* (Rubiaceae), *Rauvolfia mombasiana* (Apocynaceae), *Alchornea laxiflora* (Euphorbiaceae), *Pseudobersama mossambicensis* (Meliaceae) and *Rinorea arborea* (Violaceae). Conspicuous climbers within the formation are *Agelaea setulosa* and *Connarus longistipitatus* (Connaraceae), *Dioscorea sansibarensis* (Dioscoreaceae), *Dioscoreophyllum volkensii*, *Tiliacora funifera* and *Triclisia sacleuxii* (both Menispermaceae), *Caesalpinia volkensii* (Caesalpiniaceae) and *Tetracera litoralis* (Dilleniaceae). Shrubs as companions of the understorey are *Kraussia speciosa* and *Psychotria leucopoda* (both Rubiaceae), *Memecylon verruculosum*, *Memecylon amaniense* and *Memecylon mouririifolium* (Melastomataceae), *Erytrococca usambarica* (Euphorbiaceae) and *Teclea amaniensis* (Rutaceae). Herbs that are frequently found in the evergreen seasonal lowland forest are *Gonatopus boivinii* (Araceae), *Psilotrichum majus* and *Psilotrichum scleranthemum* (Amaranthaceae) and *Lankesteria alba* (Acanthaceae).

The *Olyra - Rawsonia* community group represents the evergreen seasonal forest formation in Longomagandi Forest.

Stratum 1 is normally very diverse but in isolated spots a single tree species may gain dominance in an area of approximately one hectare (see for example Fig. 3, *Ellipanthus hemandradenioides*).

The species characterizing the *Olyra - Rawsonia* community group are *Olyra latifolia* and *Oplismenus hirtellus* (both Poaceae), *Oxyanthus pyriformis* (Rubiaceae) and *Rawsonia lucida* (Flacourtiaceae).

The rejuvenation of *Rawsonia* is extremely good. *Rawsonia* is most abundant in gaps within the formerly undisturbed or less disturbed forests as it is light-demanding. During the late stages of regeneration, *Rawsonia* is replaced by more shade-tolerant understorey trees such as *Olax obtusifolia* (Olacaceae).

The most frequent companions in stratum 1 are *Celtis mildbraedii* (Ulmaceae), *Combretum schumannii* (Combretaceae), *Lecaniodiscus fraxinifolius* (Sapindaceae), *Lovoa swynnertonii* (Meliaceae) and *Mimusops aedificatoria* (Sapotaceae).

Didymosalpinx norae, *Pavetta sansibarica* (both Rubiaceae) and *Majidea zanguebarica* (Sapindaceae) are common in stratum 2.

Among the lianas occuring in the *Olyra - Rawsonia* community group are *Culcasia scandens* (Araceae), *Dichapetalum* cf.*fadenii* (Dichapetalaceae), *Santaloides afzelii* (Connaraceae) and *Adenia gummifera* (Passifloraceae).

The *Lagynias pallidiflora* community is the most original vegetation type on Magarini sands. It occurs throughout Longomagandi Forest but larger areas are found only in the eastern and southern parts of Longomagandi.

Two species are characteristic of the *Lagynias pallidiflora* community: *Lagynias pallidiflora* of the coffee family and *Olax obtusifolia* of the *Olacaceae* family. Lagynias is a tree of about 12 m height which may attain 20 m under favourable conditions. In Kenya, its distribution is restricted to moist coastal forests in Kwale District. Generally, the adult plants significantly contribute to the trees of stratum 2. In spite of its large production of fruits, recruitment was poor in most of the relevés.

Olax obutsifolia is a tree of up to 20 (25)m. The geographical distribution reaches from the Congo Republic to Eastern (Tanzania, Kenya) and Southeastern Africa (Zambia, Zimbabwe, Malawi, Mozambique). Regeneration is good although hardly any fertile specimen was seen. Ecologically, *Olax obtusifolia* has an ample range although it has a clear preference to the multi-storeyed closed-canopy forests.

Companions in stratum 1 are *Albizia glaberrima* (Mimosaceae) and *Celtis philippensis* (Ulmaceae). *Cola octoloboides* (Sterculiaceae) frequently occurs in the lower canopy. A number of large climbers can be found within the *Lagynias pallidiflora* community. *Caesalpinia volkensii* (Caesalpiniaceae), *Tetracera litoralis* (Dilleniaceae), *Entada pursaetha* (Mimosaceae), *Artabotrys modestus* and an unidentified *Uvaria* sp. (Uvaria sp. nov.?.) (both Annonaceae) may all reach the upper canopy. *Turraea mombasiana* (Meliaceae) is a conspicuous plant of the shrub-layer. In the stratum 4, an unidentified species (Coll. No. 1278) is restricted to the *Lagynias pallidiflora* community.

The *Strychnos mellodora* stage occurs very locally. It is restricted to the southeastern and eastern parts of Longomagandi Forest. The characteristic species, *Strychnos mellodora*, is a tree in the Loganiaceae family which generally dominates in stratum 2 (Fig. 3) but it may grow as large as 25 m (35 m). Its occurence in Kenya was unknown before this study. According to White (1983), *Strychnos mellodora* is characteristic for the lower transitional rain forest of the East Usambara Mountains. The rejuvenation is good underneath the adult plants.

Two more species are common in the *Strychnos mellodora* stage: The shade-tolerating shrub *Diospyros amaniensis* (Ebenaceae) is typical for the undergrowth, hardly growing higher than 3 m. *Hunteria zeylanica* (Apocynaceae) is a rare tree up to 15 m in height which occurs in the Northern and Coast Provinces in bush, at forest edges or as a riverine species.

The *Strychnos mellodora* stage is derived directly from the pure *Lagynias pallidiflora* community probably through careful forest use. Alternatively, it may be a very late stage of regeneration towards a vegetation type similar to the original forest.

The *Sclerochiton boivinii* stage is found in small areas of disturbance inside the *Lagynias pallidiflora* community. It is restricted to the eastern part of Longomagandi Forest. *Sclerochiton boivinii* (Acanthaceae) is a weak erect shrub growing up to 3-5 m high. The occurrence of *Sclerochiton boivinii* in Kenya is restricted to moist forests on the coast (Kwale and Taita Districts). The *Sclerochiton boivinii* stage is an early, post-disturbance regeneration stage. The gaps occupied by *Sclerochiton boivinii* are generally smaller than 25 m in diameter. Within these gaps, *Sclerochiton* forms dense thickets partly suppressing the regeneration of larger trees. As soon as the gap is closed from its margins, *Sclerochiton* is replaced by fast-growing trees and more shade-tolerant shrubs. The *Sclerochiton boivinii* stage is therefore generally of short duration. Depending on the size of the treefall gap, it regenerates either to a *Whitfieldia elongata* stage or a *Clematis sigensis* stage.

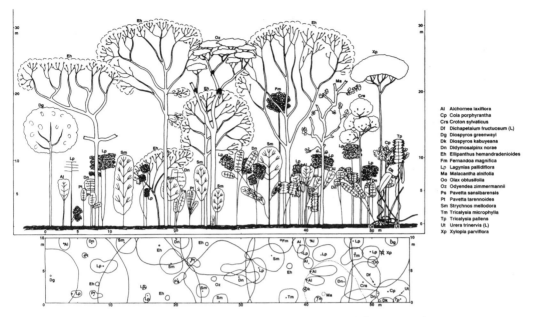

Fig.3. Profile diagram of the *Strychnos mellodora* stage of the *Lagynias pallidiflora* community

The profile diagram of the *Strychnos mellodora* stage (Fig. 3) shows the closed canopy of stratum 1 with a dominance of *Ellipanthus hemandradenioides* (Connaraceae). *Odyendea zimmermannii* (Simaroubaceae) in the centre and *Malacantha alnifolia* (Sapotaceae) belong to the set of the past whereas *Fernandoa magnifica* (Bignoniaceae) and *Xylopia parviflora* (Annonaceae) will form part of the upper canopy in the future. *Diospyros greenwayi* (Ebenaceae) on the left and *Croton sylvaticus* (Euphorbiaceae) on the right have attained their maximum heights.

Stratum 2 encompasses various species. *Lagynias pallidiflora* and *Strychnos mellodora*, the differential species of the community and the stage, respectively, have the highest cover. Apart from *Strychnos mellodora*, there is only one small *Ellipanthus hemandradenioides* that will potentially reach stratum 1.

Stratum 3 consists of *Alchornea laxiflora* (Euphorbiaceae), *Diospyros kabuyeana* (Ebenaceae), *Pavetta sansibarensis*, *Pavetta tarennoides*, and *Tricalysia microphylla* (all Rubiaceae).

The *Clematis sigensis* stage is frequently found in the southern part of Longomagandi Forest near the forest edge. Although *Clematis sigensis* can grow together with *Ipomoea urbaniana* (Convolvulaceae) or *Sclerochiton boivinii* (Acanthaceae), both species of young gaps, its main distribution is in long-standing disturbances.

C. sigensis is a liana in the buttercup family which has been reinstalled to the ranks of a species during this study (Beentje 1989). *C. sigensis* attains a height of 25 m. It is most frequently found climbing up young trees of the upper canopy or large individuals of stratum 2. Indicative of former gaps, *Clematis* is not found in mature undisturbed forest. Other lianas occuring in the *C. sigensis* stage such as *Artabotrys modestus* (Annonaceae) or *Tetracera litoralis* (Dilleniaceae) replace *Clematis sigensis* when regeneration continues. Development to the *Strychnos mellodora* stage is then encountered.

The *Whitfieldia elongata* stage characterizes small natural disturbances in an advanced condition of regeneration. The treefall gaps occupied by *W. elongata* are generally smaller than those dominated by *Clematis sigensis*. *W. elongata* of the Acanthaceae family is an erect or scrambling shrub of up to 6 m height. In older almost closed gaps, *W. elongata* is generally scandent. Continued regeneration of the *W. elongata* stage leads to the *Strychnos mellodora* stage.

The pure *Lagynias pallidiflora* community normally consists of a species-rich mixture of plants in different life-stages. It is characterized by a closed canopy made up of various species of trees and a large number of lianas. Stratum 2 is a combination of *L. pallidiflora, Didymosalpinx norae, Leptactina platiphylla* (all *Rubiaceae*) and *Olax obtusifolia* (Olacaceae). The forest floor is covered with seedlings and saplings of larger trees and shrubs. Only few patches of grass are found and *Geophila repens* is generally the only herb that occurs under a closed-canopy. The pure *L. pallidiflora* community is the final stage of forest succession.

The *Leptonychia usambarensis* community occupies the largest part of Longomagandi Forest covering an area of about 15 ha within this forest. It has evolved from the *Lagynias pallidiflora* community through uncontrolled logging activities.

Fig.4. View of the (pure) *Leptonychia usambarensis* community. Foreground left: *L. usambarensis* with the main trunk ending at a height of 1.5 m as a result of browsing. Large-leaved small tree on the right: *Oxyanthus pyriformis*. Light trunk on the extreme right: *Xylopia parviflora*. (Photo R. Schmidt 18 January 1991)

The *Leptonychia usambarensis* community is characterized by *L. usambarensis* of the *Sterculiaceae* family, a light-demanding soft-wooded tree of up to about 10 m height (20 m elsewhere). *Leptonychia* frequently grows in virtually pure stands although it rarely reaches a total cover of more than 50 percent. Structurally the (pure) community resembles an orchard with grass-covered paths in between the isolated larger trees (Fig.4). The regeneration of *Leptonychia* is generally good even under the parental plants.

A conspicuous feature of the *Leptonychia usambarensis* community is the gapped upper canopy. The trees of stratum 1 hardly ever have interlocking crowns. There are no larger trees among the companions of this community. Understory trees such as *Cola porphyrantha* (Sterculiaceae) may reach a high cover locally and light-demanding shrubs such as *Mussaenda monticola* and *Lamrothamnus zanguebaricus* (both Rubiaceae) are found in the *Leptonychia usambarensis* community. Light-demanding, fast-growing lianas such as *Momordica foetida* (Cucurbitaceae) are favored by the absence of a closed canopy and in stratum 4 an unidentified species (Coll. No. 1580) and a grass, *Panicum trichocladum* are among the companions of the *Leptonychia usambarensis* community.

Within the *Leptonychia usambarensis* community, five stages of forest development can be distinguished. In addition to structural differences, each stage is floristically characterized by one dominant species. The stages are considered as seral stages of regeneration after larger-scale disturbances.

The *Justicia englerana* stage is encountered in some parts of western Longomagandi Forest. In this stage, the vegetation is dominated by *Justicia englerana*, a pubescent shrub of the Acanthaceae family (Fig. 5). Its height reaches up to 4 m and it frequently forms almost pure stands of 0.5 to 1 hectare supressing the germination and growth of other light-demanding species. Grasses such as *Oplismenus* and *Olyra* and small trees such as *Oxyanthus pyriformis* (Rubiaceae) and *Rawsonia lucida* (Flacourtiaceae), otherwise typical for the community group, are rarely found in those stands. Due to the restricted germination of forest species, the *Justicia eglerana* stage is very stable. Within a span of three years, several *Justicia* sites were found to remain almost unchanged. *Croton sylvaticus*, a mostly deciduous, light-demanding tree in the *Euphorbiaceae* family, is always among the pioneer species superseding the *Justicia englerana* stage but it casts little shade and seems not to be very competitive. Otherwise, the lateral expansion of bordering subcanopy trees is slow.

The *Justicia englerana* stage is very conspicuous due to the entire or almost entire lack of larger trees and especially of valuable timber trees. Trunks on the forest floor are absent as well. It is therefore obvious that the community occupies places of earlier timber extraction. Logging tracks which were cut into the forest during the last five years are in the process of being closed by dense tangles of *Justicia*. The stage is thus considered to be the initial regeneration stage after large-scale disturbance. Within the orchard-like *Leptonychia usambarensis* community, the *Justicia englerana* stage forms dense clumps which are not easily penetrable because the plant is avoided by megaherbivores and therefore no elephant tracks render accessibility.

Fig.5. View of the *Justicia englerana* stage. *J. englerana* forms a pure stand on an old logging track. (Photo R. Schmidt 18 January 1991)

The *Ipomoea urbaniana* stage is found in disturbed places mainly in the eastern, southeastern and western parts of Longomagandi Forest. *I. urbaniana* is a fast-growing, light-demanding liana in the Convolvulaceae.

The sites dominated by *I. urbaniana* growth are normally gaps with a diameter of 10 to 30 m. The disturbances in the eastern parts of Longomagandi are obviously of natural origin as one or several fallen trees are found lying on the ground and are frequently in a state of decay. At these gap sites, *Ipomooea* generally forms a dense carpet covering shrubs and smaller trees. In the southern and western parts of the forest, Ipomoea frequently covers abandoned logging tracks. When occuring together with *Justicia englerana*, *Ipomoea urbaniana* is restricted to the shady fringes of the gap while *Justicia occupies* the center.

The *Allophylus zimmermannianus* stage occurs in some areas in the western and southern part of Longomagandi Forest. *A. zimmermannianus*, a rare species in the *Sapindaceae*, is a tree of up to 12 m which is endemic to the Shimba Hills in Kenya. Towards the end of the dry season, *A. zimmermannianus* sheds its trifoliate leaves, a characteristic typical of a canopy species rather than of an understory tree. In fact, it characterizes a forest with a disconnected canopy. Other trees higher than 15 m are rare so that the crown of *Allophylus* is sun-exposed. Regeneration of *A. zimmermannianus* under a closed canopy was not observed. *A. zimmermannianus* is indicative of older disturbances in an advanced stage of regeneration. *Allophylus* saplings or small trees may be found in the *Ipomoea englerana* stage of the *Leptonychia usambarensis* community frequently being accompanied by *Mussaenda monticola* (Rubiaceae). This fact may be interpreted as indicating the succession of older disturbances towards the closed-canopy forest. Still, rejuvenation of trees of the upper canopy is extremely rare. Extreme vapor pressure deficits and high temperatures on the sun-exposed forest floor create conditions which are adverse to the successful germination of larger trees. The main impediment to a proper forest regeneration, however, is the biotic impact through larger wildlife. Signs of browsing, trampling and digging are visible everywhere.

The *Heinsenia diervilleoides* stage is found in the southern and central part of Longomagandi Forest. It is characterized by *H. diervilleoides*, a tree of the coffee family which reaches a height of up to 12 m.

Within this seral stage, regeneration of *Heinsenia* is good; the juvenile plants are frequently found under the adults.

Structurally, the understory trees dominate in the *Heinsenia diervilleoides* stage. Stratum 1 is never closed, producing an intermittent canopy of isolated trees of 30 to 35 m in height. A large number of dead trunks from large trees (set of the past) can be found on the forest floor. Stratum 2 forms a very dense canopy. It is dominated by *Tabernaemontana pachysiphon* (Apocynaceae) and *Oxyanthus pyriformis* (Rubiaceae), two large-leaved trees that frequently dominate areas of older disturbances. *Rawsonia lucida* (Flacourtiaceae), *Rinorea arborea* and *Rinorea ilicifolia* (Violaceae) are frequent companions.

Transitions between the pure *Leptonychia usambarensis* community or the *Allophylus zimmermannianus* stage and the *Heinsenia diervilleoides* stage can be observed. However, recruitment of trees of the *Heinsenia diervilleoides* stage is impeded by the browsing and trampling of large herbivores.

The *Olacaceae* gen. indet. stage occurs in the southern, eastern and central parts of Longomagandi Forest. The characteristic species, a tree up to 20 m in the *Olacaceae* family, could not yet be determined because it is a new record for East Africa. Within the study area, *Olacaceae* gen. indet. is not restricted to this stage but it shows a large range of occurrence in the *Leptonychia* and *Lagynias* communities (*Olyra - Rawsonia* community group). However, it dominates in sites where a regeneration of the closed-canopy forest can be observed. Rejuvenation of this species is excellent especially when the disturbance is not too recent and the gap is in the process of closing. The *Olacaceae* gen. indet. stage develops from the *Heinsenia diervilleoides* stage when natural regeneration continues.

The pure *Leptonychia usambarensis* community is characterized by its open canopy as is illustrated in Figure 6. Obviously the pure *L. usambarensis* community is in a condition of uninterrupted heavy disturbance after the vegetation cover was thinned out by logging companies. This interpretation is supported by the fact that the open bare soil is thoroughly ploughed by elephants and by the East African warthog (*Phacochoerus*

98   R. Schmidt

aethiopicus) searching for bulbs, tubers and roots. *Leptonychia usambarensis* hardly attains a height of 5 m within the pure community because the soft stems are all bitten off at a height of about 1-2.5 m. The community is thus kept in an initial stage of regeneration as rejuvenation is hindered by the activities of wildlife. Under present conditions, there is virtually no chance for this vegetation unit to reestablish its closed canopy.

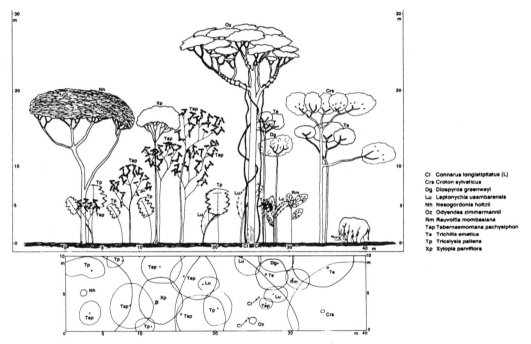

Cl Connarus longistipitatus (L)
Crs Croton sylvaticus
Dg Diospyros greenwayi
Lu Leptonychia usambarensis
Nh Nesogordonia holtzii
Oz Odyendea zimmermannii
Rm Rauvolfia mombasiana
Tap Tabernaemontana pachysiphon
Te Trichilia emetica
Tp Tricalysia pallens
Xp Xylopia parviflora

Fig. 6. Profile diagram of the pure *Leptonychia usambarensis* community

Only a single large tree belonging to the set of the present (*Odyendea zimmermannii*, Simaroubaceae) is found whereas four trees of stratum 1, *Nesogordonia holtzii* (Sterculiaceae), *Xylopia parviflora* (Annonaceae), and two indivuduals of *Trichilia emetica* (Meliaceae) can grow virtually unobstructed by any larger tree and possibly reach 30 m in height or more. *Croton sylvaticus* (Euphorbiaceae), *Diospyros greenwayi* (Ebenaceae) and some *Tabernaemontana pachysiphon* plants (Apocynaceae) have attained their maximum heights of 15 to 20 m. In spite of the openness of the upper canopy, stratum 3 is very sparse. Some plants of *Tricalysia pallens* (Rubiaceae), *Leptonychia usambarensis* (Sterculiaceae), *Tabernaemontana pachysiphon* and a *Rauvolfia mombasiana* (both Apocynaceae) are far from being able to cover the exposed interspaces. It could be expected to find the site in a state of very recent disturbance. But no trunks of fallen trees are found, a fact that indicates extraction of timber some years ago. Still the ground is not covered by a herbal layer and no grass covers the bare soil. Not even quick-growing lianas are to be found and a litter layer is lacking as well.

B. Soil Analysis

The soil profiles of Longomagandi Forest were classified as rhodacric Ferralsols. This classification is in accordance with data provided by the Kenya Soil Survey (1978, 1982).

The soils are generally very deep sandy loams with a reddish brown A-horizon and a dark red B-horizon. The horizon boundaries are diffuse. The CEC is very low (4.8-8.8 me/100g in the topsoil, mostly between 2 and 3 me/100g in the B-horizon). The base saturation is generally slightly above 50 % in the top 5 to 10 cm (A1 horizon) but decreases with increasing depth. The content of Ca_{ex} is low (2.5-4 me/100g), contents in K_{ex} and Mg_{ex} are generally moderate to high (K 0.22-0.44 me/100g, Mg 0.47-1.8 me/100g). Mg may be deficient at some sites (0.1 me/100g). The contents in all essential nutrients that were determined are low to moderate in the B-horizon (Ca 0.3-1.5, Mg 0.06-1.05, K 0.06-0.16). Clay minerals are predominantly well crystallized kaolinite plus traces of illite. The $pH(H_2O)$ in the topsoil is neutral (6.3-7) and slightly acid (4.6-6.1) in the B-horizon. The contents in organic carbon and nitrogen are high in the A-horizon (1.9-3.2 % C, 0.15-0.34 % N).

The soil moisture holding capacity available to plants ranges from 42 to 71 mm. According to a rating proposed by Andriesse and Van der Pouw (1985) for Kenyan conditions, the available moisture is low.

The advanced stage of weathering and the degree of kaolinization of these rather uniform soils has been assumed to be due to the various Pleistocene climates with at times hot and humid conditions.

Discussion

Today's distribution and character of tropical forests is generally considered to be a result of human-induced changes (eg Lugo 1988). The occurrence of two floristically and structurally distinct plant communities in one small forest area in coastal Kenya is attributed to anthropogenic influence. No signs of soil differentiation which might be responsible for the floristic differences could be detected within the study area.

The historical accounts of land use in forest areas around the Shimba Hills are attached with some uncertainty. This is especially true for the time of the Mijikenda settlers. Hawthorne et al. (1981) assumed that the Mijikenda did some enrichment plantings in the undergrowth of the forest which was in use. Certain species seem to have been promoted whereas others may have been exterminated in the vicinity of the kayas. Altogether, there was some influence on the floristic composition by the Mijikenda settlements. The impact on the forest structure, however, remained small. This fact is attributed mainly to religious and military-strategic reasons.

The *Strychnos mellodora* stage of the *Lagynias pallidiflora* community is possibly a result of the Mijikenda settlements. Sites within this type of vegetation are known to be former kaya sites (Mwadzpea, pers. comm. 1988).

The impact of logging activities on the floristic composition as well as on the forest structure is well known from various parts of the world (eg Abdulhadi et al. 1981; Gatto & Rinaldi 1987; Uhl & Guimaraes Vieira 1989; Woods 1989). In Longomagandi Forest, *Milicia excelsa* is the most spectacular example of a formerly very common species, which has become rare in today's forest. Apart from the direct shift in the species composition through removal of timber and damage, there may be an indirect shift as a consequence of the change in the microclimatic and soil conditions.

As a consequence of the respective structures in the *Leptonychia usambarensis* and *Lagynias pallidiflora* communities, the site conditions differ between the two communities. The temperature of the topsoil and vapor pressure deficits are higher at certain times and generally more variable when the forest canopy is open (Bazzaz & Sipe 1987; Denslow *et al.* 1990). Incident light levels and soil moisture levels are highest in the very center of a gap decreasing gradually towards the adjacent forest (Uhl *et al.* 1988). The germination of trees of the upper strata may be impeded under these conditions (Hartshorn 1980). A lack of regeneration of certain canopy species as a consequence of structural and microclimatic differences implies a change in the floristic composition which in turn affects the structure of the community.

The results of the phytosociological analysis indicate the general possibility of a transition from the *Leptonychia usambarensis* community to the *Lagynias pallidiflora* community. Figure 7 shows the transitional paths by which a closed canopy forest could be reinstated from a disturbed site.

The pure *Lagynias pallidiflora* community is considered to be the zonal vegetation type in Longomagandi Forest. The *Leptonychia usambarensis* community has developed through logging activities mainly during the past 90 years. It is a degraded forest type which occupies larger areas than the original vegetation unit. However, further degradation of the *Lagynias pallidiflora* community has stopped since logging was prohibited. The pure *Leptonychia usambarensis* community is found on sites where logging took place selectively whereas the *Justicia englerana* stage occupies larger places of complete forest destruction.

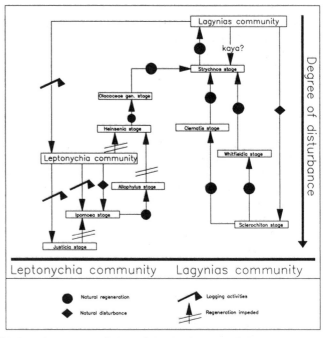

Fig.7. Schematic compilation of the development of the various seral stages of the *Leptonychia usambarensis* and the *Lagynias pallidiflora* communities and their transitions

This type of larger-scale disturbance and complete removal of tall trees in areas exceeding half a hectare was created only very recently. At present, the development of the *Justicia englerana* stage towards the *Ipomoea urbaniana* stage is hindered by the impact of elephants. The same applies to the reinstallation of the *Heinsenia diervilleoides* stage from the *Allophylus zimmermannianus* stage or from the pure *Leptonychia usambarensis* community. Once the *Heinsenia diervilleoides* stage is reached, a slow development back to the pure *Lagynias pallidiflora* community is indicated by transitional phases. These are characterized by regeneration of the canopy tree species of the closed forest. Performance of species such as *Xylopia parviflora* (Annonaceae), *Odyendea zimmermannii* (Simaroubaceae), *Antiaris toxicaria* (Sapotaceae) or *Ellipanthus hemandradenioides* (Connaraceae) in their juvenile stages is good. After establishment of these species, *Heinsenia diervilleoides* is replaced by more shade-tolerant understory trees.

Within the *Lagynias pallidiflora* community, the seral stages follow the more or less accepted schema of natural gap dynamics or chablis of forest rejuvenation (Hallé et al. 1978; Brokaw 1985a, 1985b). After creation of the gap, 'nomad' heliophilous species such as *Sclerochiton boivinii* invade the forest. However, they are outcompeted by more shade-tolerant plants indigenous to the forest. While recovery is in progress, a *Whitfieldia elongata* stage is found whenever the original gap was small, whereas the *Clematis sigensis* stage develops on larger gap sites. Both stages are found to regenerate into a *Strychnos mellodora* stage which structurally shows only small differences to the pure *Lagynias pallidiflora* community as the final stage of homeostatic forest.

The *Justicia englerana* stage as the initial step to a possible regeneration was found to be stable over several years. This is due to elephants who protect *Justicia englerana* from being overgrown by the surrounding forest. The pure *Leptonychia usambarensis* community as well as the *Allophylus zimmermannianus* stage are kept in their actual condition through the browsing and trampling effect of elephants. The *Heinsenia diervilleoides* stage is therefore not reached as long as the impact of elephants remains at the present levels.

It appears, that a forest which was previously disturbed by anthropogenic activities has the potential to regenerate. However, due to the large number of megaherbivores in the area of the National Reserve the natural course of succession is interrupted. The destructive effects of megaherbivores in African forests have been reviewed by Kortlandt (1984), and Schmitt (this volume) presented recent evidence of impeded regeneration due to the concentration of wildlife exceeding tolerable limits (see also contribution of W. Schüle, this volume). Lock (1977) reported better regeneration of trees in grassland vegetation under conditions of elephant exclusion.

At present, the Kenya Wildlife Service, the parastatal organization responsible for nature reserves in Kenya, is examining the necessity of a temporary exclusion of elephants from Longomagandi Forest. Conservation is required to ensure the protection of both wildlife and vegetation and to reinstate a viable balance between the two.

Appendix

Tab.2. Frequency table of the seral stages of the *Lagynias pallidiflora* community (A *Strychnos mellodora* stage, B *Sclerochiton boivinii* stage, C *Clematis sigensis* stage, D *Whitfeldia elongata* stage, E pure community) and *Leptonychia usambarensis* community (F *Justicia englerana* stage, G *Ipomoea urbaniana* stage, H *Allophylus zimmermannianus* stage, J *Heinsenia diervilleoides* stage, K Olacaceae gen. indet. stage, L pure community)

Community	Lagynias pallidiflora					Leptonychia usambarensis					
Seral stage	A	B	C	D	E	F	G	H	J	K	L
Number of relevés	13	3	5	2	18	4	4	3	5	7	2
Differential species of the Lagynias pallidiflora community and its seral stages											
Strychnos mellodora	V	III			I	IV		III	III		
Diospyros amaniensis	V	II	I		I		II		II	III	
Hunteria zeylanica	IV	II					II			I	
Sclerochiton boivinii		III									
Clematis sigensis		II	V	III		II		II	III		
Whitfeldia elongata				V							
Turraea mombassana	I		IV	V	III						III
Lagynias pallidiflora	V	V	V	V	V		II	III	II	II	
Olax obtusifolia	V	V	III	III	III	III	IV	III		III	V
Companions with main distribution in the Lagynias community											
Psychotria tanganyikensis	IV	III	IV	V	III	V			I	I	III
Panicum brevifolium	I	II	IV	III	II	II					
Connarus longistipitatus	V	III	IV	III	III	II	II	III	III	III	III
Cremaspora triflora	IV	II	V	III	III			II	I		III
Synaptolepis kirkii	IV	III	IV	V	V	II		II		I	
Differential species of the Leptonychia usambarica community and its seral stages											
Justicia englerana						V					
Ipomoea urbaniana	I		III	III	I	III	V			II	
Desmodium adscendens	I		I			II	IV		I	I	
Allophylus zimmermannianus					I	III	II	V	I		
Heinsenia diervilleoides		II						II	V	III	
Olacaceae gen. indet.	IV	II			II	II	V	III		V	
Leptonychia usambarensis	II			V	I	V	V	V	V	V	V
Differential species of the Olyra latifolia - Rawsonia lucida community group											
Olyra latifolia	IV	III	V	III	IV		V	II	III	II	III
Oplismenus hirtellus	IV	III	IV	III	V		II		II	I	III
Oxyanthus pyriformis	V	III	II	III	V	II	IV	III	IV	IV	
Rawsonia lucida	V	III	V	V	IV	IV	V	III	IV	IV	V
Differential species of the tropical lowland evergreen seasonal formation											
Tabernaemontana pachysiphon	IV	III	V	V	V	V	V	V	V	V	III
Geophila repens	V	III	III	III	V	III	V	V	V	IV	III
Companions of the tropical lowland evergreen seasonal formation											
Ellipanthus hemandradenioides			IV	III	V		II	II	I	III	III
Memecylon verruculosum	V	III	V	V	V	II	IV	III	I	II	V
Agelaea setulosa	IV	III	II		IV		IV		IV	V	V
Antiaris toxicaria	III	II	IV	III	IV	IV	III		IV	IV	V
Diospyros greenwayi	V	III	IV	V	V	IV	V	V	IV	III	V
Erythrococca usambarica	IV	III	IV	V	IV	V	V	V	III	IV	V
Fernandoa magnifica	IV	II	IV		IV	III	IV	V	III	IV	V
Haplocoelopsis africana	IV		I	III	IV		III	IV	III	III	III
Memecylon mouririifolium	III	III	V		II				III	III	
Odyendea zimmermannii	IV	II	IV	III	III	II	IV	III		V	III
Pavetta tarennoides	IV	III	V	III	III		IV	III	III	V	
Psychotria leucopoda	IV	III	III	V	IV	V	V	III	I	IV	III
Trichilia emetica	V	I	II	III	V	IV	II	II			
Alchornea laxiflora	III	III	II	III	IV		III	III	II	III	V
Species with main distribution in other communities and species that are common throughout											
Croton sylvaticus	II		IV	V	IV	III	IV	V	I	IV	V
Dichapetalum fructuosum	V	III	IV	V	V	V	V	III	V	V	V
Dictyophleba lucida	V	III	III	III	V	III	V	III	III	III	V
Xylopia parviflora	V	III	IV	V	V	V	III	V	IV	IV	III
Allophylus pervillei	III	III	II	V	V	II	III		II		V
Bridelia atroviridis	II		V	III	III	V	III	III	III	III	V
Keetia gueinzii	V	II	III	III	III	III	V	V	V	III	III
Chytranthus obliquinervis	IV	II	II	III	III		III	III	IV	V	
Landolphia kirkii	V	III	V	V	V	III	V	V	V	V	V
Microsorium punctatum	IV	III	I	III	III	III	III	III	II	III	III
Psychotria lauracea	II	III	IV	III	IV	III	I		II	III	III
Psychotria riparia	IV	III	II	III	IV	II	III	II	II	III	V
Tricalysia microphylla	III	III	IV	V	III	IV	III	II	II	III	V
Tricalysia pallens	IV	III	II	III	V	V	V	II	IV	V	V
Triclisia sacleuxii	IV	III	IV	III	II	III	II	III	V	III	V

References

Abdulhadi R, Kartawinata K, Sukardjo S (1981) Effects of mechanised logging in the lowland dipterocarp forest at Lempake, East Kalimantan. Malay For 44(2&3):407-418

Andriesse W, Van der Pouw BJA (1985) Reconnaissance soil map of the Lake Basin Development Authority Area Western Kenya scale 1:250 000. Netherlands Soil Survey Institute, Wageningen in cooperation with Kenya Soil Survey, Nairobi, 56 pp

Bazzaz FA, Sipe TW (1987) Physiological ecology, disturbance, and ecosystem recovery. Ecol Stud 61:204-227

Beentje HJ (1989) The reinstatement of Clematis sigensis Engl. (Ranunculaceae). Utafiti 2:16

Braun-Blanquet J (1964) Pflanzensoziologie. Springer-Verlag Wien, New York, 3rd ed., 865 pp

Brokaw NVL (1985a) Treefall, regrowth, and community structure in tropical forests. In: The ecology of natural disturbance and patch dynamics. Acad Press Inc 53-69

Brokaw NVL (1985b) Gap-phase regeneration in a tropical forest. Ecology 66: 682-687

Denslow JS, Shultz JC, Vitousek PM, Strain BR (1990) Growth responses of tropical shrubs to treefall gap environments. Ecology 71: 165-179

FAO (1977) Guidelines for soil profile description. 2nd ed., Rome, 66 pp

FAO-UNESCO (1988) Soil map of the world. Revised legend, Rome 119 pp

Faden RB (1974) East African coastal - West African rain forest disjunctions. In: East African vegetation (Lind EM, Morrison MES eds.). Longman, London 202-203

Gatto M, Rinaldi S (1987) Some models of catastrophic behavior in exploited forests. Vegetatio 69:213-222

Glover PE (1968) Report on an ecological survey of the proposed Shimba Hills National Reserve. E Afr Wildl Soc, Nairobi, 148 pp

Grubb P (1982) Refuges and dispersal in the speciation of African forest mammals. In: Biological diversification in the tropics (Prance GT ed.). Columbia University Press, New York 537-553

Hallé F, Oldeman RAA, Tomlinson PB (1978) Tropical trees and forests. An architectural analysis. Springer Berlin, Heidelberg, New York, 441 pp

Hartshorn GS (1980) Neotropical forest dynamics. Biotropica 12(Suppl.):23-30

Hawthorne W, Hunt K, Russell A (1981) Kaya: An ethnobotanical perspective. National Museums of Kenya, Nairobi, 126 pp

Hill MO (1979) Twinspan - a Fortran program for arranging multivariate data in an ordered two way table by classification of individuals and attributes. Cornell University, Ithaca

Kenya Soil Survey (1978) Soils of the Kwale - Mombasa - Lungalunga area. Reconnaissance Soil Survey Report No. R3., Nairobi, 300 pp

Kenya Soil Survey (1982) Exploratory soil map and agro-climatic zone map of Kenya. Exploratory Soil Survey Report No E1. Ministry of Agriculture - National Agricultural Laboratories, Nairobi

Knapp R (1965) Pflanzengesellschaften und Vegetations-Einheiten von Ceylon und Teilen von Ost- und Central-Afrika. Geobot Mitt 33:1-31

Kortlandt A (1984) Vegetation research and the 'bulldozer' herbivores of tropical Africa. In: Tropical Rain-Forest: The Leeds Symposium, (Chadwick AC, Sutton SL eds.): Special Publication of the Leeds Philos Lit Soc 205-226

Kuyper JVJM (1982) The human influence on the vegetation in a part of the Kilifi area. Agric. University Wageningen, Preliminary Report 4:2-16

Lind EM, Morrison MES (1974) East African vegetation. Longman, London, 257 pp

Livingstone DA (1982) Quaternary geography of Africa and the refuge theory. In: Biological diversification in the tropics (Prance GT ed.). Columbia University Press 523-536

Lock JM (1977) Preliminary results from fire and elephant exclusion plots in Kabalaga National Park, Uganda. E Afr Wldlf J 15:229-232

Lugo AE (1988) The future of the forest. Environment 30(7):17-20+41-45

Lugo AE, Brown S (1982) Conversion of tropical moist forests: A critique. Interciencia 7:89-93

Moomaw JC (1959) A study of the plant ecology of the Coast Region of Kenya Colony, British East Africa. Rep Agric Dept, Govt Printer, Nairobi, Kenia 1-52

Morton RF (1973) The Shungwaya myth of Miji Kenda origins: A problem of late 19th century Kenya coastal history. AHS 5:397-423

Mueller-Dombois D, Ellenberg H (1974) Aims and methods of vegetation ecology. New York, Wiley, 207 pp

Prins AHJ (1972) The Shungwaya problem: Traditional history and cultural likeness in Bantu North-East Africa. Anthropos 67:9-35

Robertson SA (1987) Prelimary floristic survey of kaya forests of coastal Kenya. Unpublished scriptum, National Museum Nairobi, Kenya

Schmidt R (in prep.) Ecology of a tropical rain forest. Plant communities, soil characteristics and nutrient relations of the forests in the Shimba Hills National Reserve, Kenya. Diss Bayreuth

Schmitt K (this volume) Anthropo-zoogenic impact on the structure and regeneration of a submontane forest in Kenya

Schultka W (1974a) Gebüsch- und Wald-Entwicklung im Grasland und die Flora in den Shimba Hills (Kenia) Oberhess Naturwiss Zeitschr 41:37-56

Schultka W (1974b) Möglichkeiten der Gebüsch- und Waldentwicklung in Grasland und Feuchtsavennengebieten von Kenia. Diss Gießen

Soper RC (1967) Kwale: an early Iron Age site in south-eastern Kenya. Azania 2:1-18

Spear TT (1978) The Kaya complex. A history of the Mijikenda peoples of the Kenya coast to 1900. Kenya Literature Bureau, Nairobi, 172 pp

Uhl C, Clark K, Dezzeo N, Maquirrino P (1988) Vegetation dynamics in Amazonian treefall gaps. Ecology 69:751-763

Uhl C, Guimaraes Vieira IC (1989) Ecological impacts of selective logging in the Brazilian Amazon: A case study from the Paragominas Region of the state of Pará. Biotropica 21(2):98-106

Wildi O, Orloci L (1983) Management and multivariate analysis of vegetation data. Eidgenöss Anst Forstl Versuchswesen Birmersdorf 215

Wildlife Planing Unit (1983) Shimba Hills National Reserve Management Plan. Wildlife Conservation and Management Department, Nairobi, 77 pp

Woods P (1989) Effects of logging, drought, and fire on structure and composition of tropical forests in Sabah, Malaysia. Biotropica 21:290-298

Tropical Forests in Transition
J. G. Goldammer (ed.)
© 1992 Birkhäuser Verlag Basel/Switzerland

Anthropo-Zoogenic Impact on the Structure and Regeneration of a Submontane Forest in Kenya

Klaus Schmitt[*]

Abstract

Submontane forests of the East African high mountains are being threatened by settlement and cultivation. Only small areas of such forests are being protected in the National Parks, although, even there, disturbance cannot be completely prevented.

Reasons for the degradation of submontane forest (c. 80 km^2) in one of the National Parks in which a rhino sanctuary has recently been established, namely in the Salient of the Aberdare National Park, were investigated in the course of a study of the vegetation of this Park.

The vegetation changes which have taken place in the Salient have been principally initiated by man and intensified or maintained by large mammals. Shifting cultivation and livestock grazing have led to the widespread destruction of primary forest. Since the gazetting of the National Park (1950), secondary bushland has developed on previously settled land (c. 25 km^2); to date, no recolonization by forest has taken place here, although considerable regeneration has been observed in adjacent forests.

The structure and composition of the present forest vegetation of the Salient suggests that most forests are secondary, disturbed by both man and wildlife. The forests containing *Juniperus procera* are regarded as a subclimax which has been subject to selective felling of the emergent trees which, in the absence of fire, will develop into *Cassipourea* forest. Primary, or, at least, little-disturbed forest was only found in the higher parts of the Upper Salient.

[*] Department of Plant Physiology, University of Bayreuth, P.O. Box 101251, D-8580 Bayreuth, Germany

The present density of wildlife in the Salient is not enough to cause large-scale destruction of the forest, with the exception of the area around Treetops, where seasonally high concentrations of herbivores build up as a consequence of human activities. Here elephants directly destroy the forest. In addition, herbivores contribute in a catalytic manner to the destruction of forest by extensive trampling which compactss the topsoil so that surface run-off is increased and the oxygen supply to the fine roots is decreased and by debarking of trees (by elephants only). The weakened trees are less resistant to felling by wind and to pushing over by elephants.

The present herbivore density however, does seem to impede the regeneration of forest in areas covered by secondary bushland. Here the tree seedlings are often exposed to browsing and trampling pressure after the removal of fallen trees by man. This, in combination with the slow growth of trees above 1920 m, seems to be responsible for the lack of regeneration.

The shrub-density of the vegetation of the glades in the Salient seems to be dependent mainly on herbivore densities, which in turn are controlled by drought, disease and predators.

Another important factor causing large-scale destruction of forest is fire. However, fire has played only a minor role in the Salient since the cessation of shifting cultivation.

Introduction

Description and Location

The Aberdare Mountains are a broad, meridionally oriented, mountain range located on the eastern side of the Gregory Rift Valley. The range extends southwards from the equator for more than 80 km. The highest peaks are Oldonyo Lesatima (4001 m a.s.l. in the north and Il Kinangop (3906 m a.s.l.) in the south (Fig. 1). The Aberdares constitute four of Kenya's five main drainage basins.

The study area, the so-called Salient, is located on the lower eastern slopes of the Aberdares, which are gently inclined and deeply incised by valleys. Here the Park shares its boundary with densely populated farmland. The Salient stretches from c. 2500 m down to 1920 m and includes a relict of c. 50 km^2 of submontane forest.

History

In 1883 Joseph Thomson became the first European to discover the range of mountains which he named after Lord Aberdare, the then President of the Royal Geographical Society (Thomson 1885).

Before the middle of this century human impact on the Aberdares was essentially limited to the lower slopes, although the Gumba, a hunter-gatherer tribe, found refuge high up in the Aberdares after the Kikuyu had invaded the Gumba hunting areas (Dundas 1908; Matthiessen & Porter 1972; Muriuki 1974).

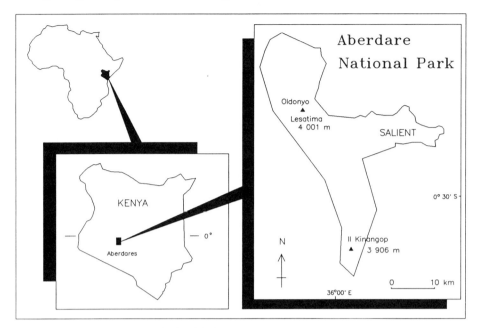

Fig.1. Location of the Aberdare National Park.

The Kikuyu lived outside the forests but cut down and burned huge areas of forest for shifting cultivation, to graze their sheep and goats and to collect honey. The Masai, a nomadic tribe, lived north of the Kikuyu territory, separated from the Kikuyu areas by a fringe of forest which protected the Kikuyu from Masai cattle raiders (von Höhnel 1894; Hutchins 1909; Berger 1910; Troup 1922; Boyes 1926; Kenya Land Commission 1933a; Kenya Land Commission 1933b; Wimbush 1937).

European settlement in Kenya began before the turn of the century and increased rapidly after 1903 (Kenya Land Commission 1933b). Just before 1914 the Europeans began to settle between Mount Kenya and the Aberdares (Walker 1962). An Italian mission had already set up the first saw mill in the Eastern Aberdares in c. 1902 (Logie & Dyson 1962). The demand for timber and firewood rose sharply once the construction of the railway to Uganda had begun (Forest Department Annual Reports, various).

The boundary of the Aberdare forests was demarcated in 1907 (Kenya Land Commission 1933b; Logie & Dyson 1962) and in 1913 a total of 947.5 km^2 were finally gazetted as the Aberdare Forest Area (Forest Department Annual Report 1912-1913). This led to a decrease in shifting cultivation but an increase in forestry.

In 1950 the Aberdare National Park was gazetted (572.2 km^2), it was opened in 1957 and three extensions were added in June 1968 so that it now covers an area of 765.7 km^2. By mid 1953 about 15,000 Mau Mau were living in permanent camps in the forests of the Aberdares (Barnett & Njama 1966; Rosberg & Nottingham 1966). Their demand for food (Simon 1962) and firewood, together with the effect of air raids, machine gun fire (Cowie 1959) and bombs (Prickett 1964; Graham & Woodley 1979), had a significant impact on the flora and fauna of the Aberdares.

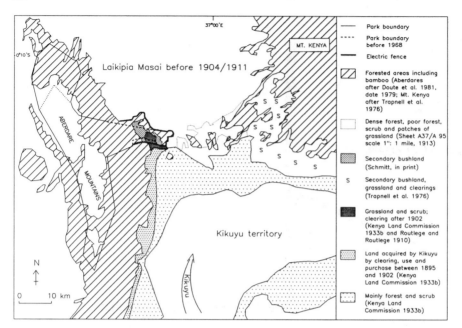

Fig.2. Sketchmap showing changes in the forested areas of the Aberdare Range between 1895 and 1987.

Large mammals, mainly elephants, used to migrate twice a year from the Aberdares, through the Salient to the forests of Mt. Kenya. During the rainy seasons the herbivores left the higher areas of the Aberdares and migrated to the lower forests. In October 1903 Meinertzhagen (1957) recorded a migration of about 700 elephants on their way from Mt. Kenya to the Aberdares.

The migrations and movements of the large mammals caused significant damage to the Europeans' farmland bordering the forests of the Aberdares, necessitating game control. Until the 1950's, game control around the Salient was done by shooting but as this was not a satisfactory solution an electric fence in combination with a ditch was built. Now, since the Salient has become a rhino sanctuary an electrified fence (1.8 m high, 7000 volts) which surrounds the entire Salient from Wandare Gate in the north to Ruhuruini Gate in the south (38 km) has been erected.

Geology

The Aberdares originated from uplift and warping, followed by volcanism and faulting, of the African basement from the early Tertiary to the Pleistocene (Baker et al. 1972).

According to Shackleton (1945) and Thompson (1964) two volcanic formations occur within the area of the Salient:

- The **Sattima Series**: The volcanic lavas of the Sattima Series (mostly phonolites, olivine alkali-trachytes, mugearites and fissile basalts) were laid on a very uneven surface,

which resulted from a period of erosion that followed the previous series. The Sattima Series is thought to be of Middle Pleistocene to Pliocene age.
- The **Laikipian Basalts**: Mainly non-porphyritic basalts were deposited on top of the trachytes and phonolites of the Sattima Series until the upper Middle Pleistocene. The eastern slope of the range (a dissected dip slope) consists of lavas and tuffs of this series.

Soils

The majority of the soils of the Salient are Ando- and Nitisols (FAO-Unesco 1988), rich in nutrients, derived from volcanic ashes and basalts.

Umbric Andosols are found in the upper part (> 2100 m) of the Salient (Sombroek et al. 1982; Maskall 1991). These soils have a dark surface horizon containing significant organic matter. They are very porose and the clay fraction is mainly composed of allophanes.

Ando-humic Nitisols and humic Nitisols, reddish and brownish soils with shiny ped surfaces and without a distinct dark surface horizon, are characteristic of the lower slopes of the Salient (Sombroek et al. 1982; Maskall 1991). Nitisols are strongly weathered kaolinitic soils containing an argic B-horizon (Nicholson 1976; FAO-Unesco 1988). The humic Nitisols of the lower eastern part of the Park are subject to sheet and gully erosion on slopes >10% where protective vegetation cover is lacking (Nyandat 1976).

Climate

The climate of Kenya is of the typical tropical type with large diurnal temperature variations but small variations of the monthly means throughout the year. The equatorial situation also results in a relatively constant number of daylight hours all year round.

A further characteristic of the tropical climate of Kenya is the seasonal moisture regime, with rainy seasons following both equinoxes. East of the Rift valley the 'long rains' last from March to May and are followed by a dry season from June to September. The 'short rains', from October to December, are followed by the short dry season, January to February (Griffiths 1972; Braun 1986).

The annual rainfall in the Aberdares ranges from 940 mm - 3220 mm/yr, and is maximal in the southeast. The rainfall in the Salient varies from 1040 mm in the east to 1500 mm in the west. The northern part of the Salient is influenced by the northeast monsoon, and is drier than the southern part (Fig. 3, Schmitt in print). Additional moisture is provided by low clouds and mist, with mist being very common during the 'Gatano', the foggy period from July to August (Theisen 1966).

The submontane forests of the Salient are confined to areas where the soil temperature ranges between 19.2°C (1920 m) and 15.9°C (c. 2500 m) (Schmitt in print).

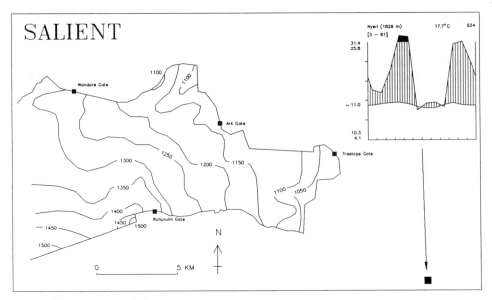

Fig.3. Spatial rainfall distribution in the Salient illustrated by isohyets. Insert climatic diagram (after Walter and Lieth [1960-1976]) shows the temporal rainfall pattern at Nyeri (modified from Schmitt, in print)

Material and Methods

Digitalized rainfall maps were compiled from data obtained from the Kenya Meteorological Department using multiple linear regressions and an algorithm (Schmitt in print).

Soil temperatures were measured at a depth of 70 cm (Winiger 1979; Schmitt in print).

Recording and analysis of the vegetation was based on the method of Braun-Blanquet (1964), as described in detail by Mueller-Dombois and Ellenberg (1974). The combined floristic-physiognomic approach (Mueller-Dombois & Ellenberg 1974) was chosen. A total of 693 individual relevés (stands) were analysed of which 81 were placed in the Salient (Schmitt in print).

The communities were arranged in a hierarchical system. Communities were subdivided into subcommunities and varieties. Several communities were grouped together to form community groups. These neutral terms (Barkman et al. 1976) were used because no syntaxonomic ranking in the sense of Braun-Blanquet (1964) was performed. Subcommunities without additional differential species were called 'typical' (Dierschke 1988).

The nomenclature of the plants followed Turill et al. (1952 -1990), Dale and Greenway (1961), Agnew (1974), Scholz (1981), Haines & Lye (1983), Chi-son & Renvoize (1989) and Beentje (in prep.).

The current vegetation within the Aberdare National Park was mapped using aerial photographs taken in January and February 1987 (scale 1: 50 000).

Vegetation

Two formations, namely **evergreen seasonal forests** and **evergreen forests** were identified within the submontane forests of the Salient. Deciduous species (e.g. *Calodendrum capense* and *Ekebergia capensis*) were commonly found in the former formation, which is represented by two communities (the *Cassipourea malosana - Setaria plicatilis* agg. community and the *Albizia gummifera* var. *gummifera - Croton macrostachyus* community, a riverine forest). The *Cassipourea malosana - Setaria plicatilis* agg. community, a dense, two-storied forest (up to 35 m tall), is dominant in the lower part of the Salient and has been subject to significant disturbance by both man and animals. In addition to *Cassipourea malosana*, canopy species such as *Ekebergia capensis*, *Diospyros abyssinica*, *Nuxia congesta* and *Teclea nobilis* agg. were often encountered. The undergrowth varies, according to the degree of disturbance and the density of the canopy, from dense shrubland containing *Hypoestes forskaolii* and *Ocimum suave* to dense grassland containing occasional herbs.

Two further communities, characterised by *Cassipourea malosana*, were contained in the formation of **evergreen forests**. The *Cassipourea malosana - Olea capensis* ssp. *hochstetteri* community, a dense forest in which up to 36 m high specimens of *Juniperus procera* are conspicuous, is dominant in the Northern Salient. The *Cassipourea malosana - Podocarpus latifolius* community, a single-storied forest of up to 35 m in height, was found in the upper, wetter part of the Salient. All three *Cassipourea malosana* communities were included in the *Cassipourea malosana* community group. A secondary forest (up to 18 m high), dominated by the broad-leaved tree *Neoboutonia macrocalyx* and containing patches of dense undergrowth (*Neoboutonia macrocalyx - Achyrospermum schimperi* community) was found in the Southern Salient, between the secondary bushland and the *Cassipourea malosana - Podocarpus latifolius* forest.

Dense, 2 m - 4 m high, secondary bushland (*Toddalia asiatica - Clutia abyssinica* community), in which only a few trees of the original forest remain (Fig. 6), has invaded an area of c. 25 km², which was subject to shifting cultivation and lifestock grazing. Dominant bushes (in addition to the two species after which this community is named) are *Hypoestes forskaolii* and *Ocimum suave*. The grass *Cynodon dactylon* was particularly common along game-trails.

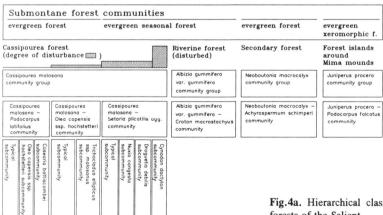

Fig.4a. Hierarchical classification of the submontane forests of the Salient

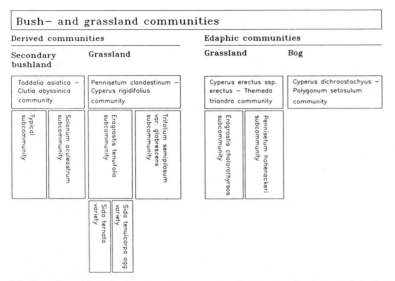

Fig.4b. Hierarchical classification of the secondary bushland and grassland of the Salient

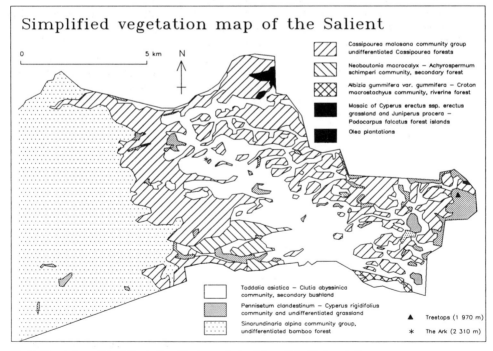

Fig.5. Vegetation of the Salient. Simplified map derived from Schmitt (in print)

Tab.1. List of the vascular plants mentioned in this publication

Achyrospermum schimperi (Hochst.) Perkins	Lamiaceae
Abutilon longicuspe A. Rich.	Malvaceae
Albizia gummifera (J.F. Gmel.) C.A. Sm. var. *gummifera*	Leguminosae
Bersama abyssinica Fres. ssp. *abyssinica* Verdc.	Melianthaceae
Calodendrum capense (L.f.) Thunb.	Rutaceae
Casearia battiscombei R.E. Fries	Flacourtiaceae
Cassipourea malosana (Baker) Alston	Rhizophoraceae
Clausena anisata (Willd.) Benth.	Rutaceae
Clutia abyssinica Jaub. & Spach	Euphorbiacea
Croton macrostachyus Del.	Euphorbiacea
Croton megalocarpus Hutch.	Euphorbiacea
Cynodon dactylon (L.) Pers.	Poaceae
Cyperus dichroöstachyus A. Rich.	Cyperaceae
Cyperus erectus (Schumacher) Mattf. & Kuek. ssp. *erectus*	Cyperaceae
Cyperus rigidifolius Steudel	Cyperaceae
Diospyros abyssinica (Hiern) F. White	Ebenaceae
Dombeya torrida (J.F. Gmel.) P. Bamps ssp. *torrida*	Flacourtiaceae
Dovyalis abyssinica (A. Rich.) Warb.	Flacourtiaceae
Droguetia debilis Rendle	Urticaceae
Ehretia cymosa Thonn. var. *silvatica* (Guerke) Brenan	Boraginaceae
Ekebergia capensis Sparrm.	Meliaceae
Elaeodendron buchananii (Loes.) Loes.	Celastraceae
Eragrostis chalarothyrsos C.E. Hubbard	Poaceae
Eragrostis tenuifolia (A. Rich.) Steud.	Poaceae
Erythrococca bongensis Pax	Euphorbiacea
Ficus thonningii Blume	Moraceae
Hagenia abyssinica (Bruce) J.F. Gmel.	Rosaceae
Hypoestes forskaolii (Vahl.) R. Br.	Acanthaceae
Juniperus procera Hochst. ex Endl.	Cupressaceae
Neoboutonia macrocalyx Pax	Euphorbiacea
Nuxia congesta Fres.	Loganiaceae
Ocimum suave Willd.	Lamiaceae
Ocotea usambarensis Engl.	Lauraceae
Olea capensis L. ssp. *hochstetteri* (Baker) Friis & P.S. Green	Oleaceae
Olea europaea L. ssp. *africana* (Mill.) P.S. Green	Oleaceae
Pennisetum clandestinum Chiov.	Poaceae
Pennisetum hohenackeri Steud.	Poaceae
Podocarpus falcatus Mirb.	Podocarpaceae
Podocarpus latifolius (Thunb.) Mirb.	Podocarpaceae
Polygonum setosulum A. Rich	Polygonaceae
Polyscias kikuyuensis Summerh.	Araliaceae
Prunus africana (Hook.f.) Kalkm.	Rosaceae
Schefflera volkensii (Engl.) Harms	Araliaceae
Setaria plicatilis agg. [*S. plicatilis* (Hochst.) Engl., *S. megaphylla* (Steud.) Th. Dur. & Schinz]	Poaceae
Sida tenuicarpa agg. [*S. tenuicarpa* Vollesen, *S. schimperiana* Hochst. ex A. Rich.]	Malvaceae
Sida ternata L.f.	Malvaceae
Solanum aculeastrum Dunal	Solanaceae
Teclea nobilis agg. [*T. nobilis* Del., *T. trichocarpa* (Engl.) Engl.]	Rutaceae
Themeda triandra Forssk.	Poaceae
Toddalia asiatica (L.) Lam.	Rutaceae
Trichocladus ellipticus Eckl. & Zeyh. ssp. *malosanus* (Bak.) Verdc.	Hamamelidaceae
Trifolium semipilosum Fresen. var. *glabrescens* Gillett	Leguminosae
Vangueria volkensii K. Schum. var. *volkensii*	Rubiaceae
Warburgia ugandensis Sprague ssp. *ugandensis*	Canellaceae

A low grassland, dominated by *Pennisetum clandestinum* (*Pennisetum clandestinum - Cyperus rigidifolius* community) was found on ridges, previously subject to shifting cultivation, and in glades in the Salient, which have been maintained by the activity of herbivores. The density of the shrub layer in this grassland varies inversely with the population density of herbivores. Bogs only cover small areas along rivers.

A grassland mosaic growing on clay-rich Gleysols, consisting of two subcommunities of the *Cyperus erectus* ssp. *erectus* - *Themeda triandra* community and interspersed with round forest islands (*Juniperus procera* - *Podocarpus falcatus* community) which are confined to the immediate vicinity of mole-rat (*Trachyoryctes splendens*) mounds, was found covering an area of 0.4 km² in the Northern Salient.

Anthropo-Zoogenic Disturbance of the Forest of the Salient

The vegetation of the Salient has undergone significant changes over recent decades (Fig. 2). The secondary character of the dense *Toddalia asiatica*-bushland which now covers c. 25 km² of the Salient is indicated by the scattered occurrence of tall trees with straight, unbranched boles which are thought to be remnants of a former submontane forest (Fig. 6).

The submontane forest which still remains in the Salient shows many signs of disturbance, especially towards its lower margins and the Park boundary. The original submontane forests were subject to selective felling of commercial emergent trees such as *Ocotea usambarensis* (Troup 1922), so that boles of non-emergent trees have become visible (Fig. 7).

The vegetation close to the Park boundary and along established tracks was subject to intensive human impact before the Salient became gazetted as part of the Aberdare National Park. This disturbance was then reduced, but has never been abolished completely. An example of vegetation change close to the Park boundary on a slope c. 600 m east-northeast of Ruhuruini Gate is shown in Figure 8. The photographs show a significant increase in the area covered by grassland between 1981 and 1987 despite the fact that the area has not been exposed to significant concentrations of wildlife. This change has probably been due to the illegal grazing of livestock and to firewood collection, which has also been observed in other areas of the Salient by the author.

Comparison of old maps (see Fig. 2), of photographs dating back to the 1930's and of aerial photographs taken in 1947, 1961, 1967 and 1987 reveals changes of vegetation changes which have taken place in the Salient:

• The Lower Salient (to the east) was previously used for the temporary grazing and watering of livestock and exploitation of the forests was only patchy. After the electric fence was erected, the migration of elephants was interrupted and significant vegetation changes followed due to the high concentration of animals found in the eastern tip of the Salient during the times of attempted migration.
• In contrast, the 1947 aerial photographs show that the Upper Salient (to the west) was used primarily for shifting cultivation resulting in the total destruction of the forest. The large areas of *Pennisetum clandestinum* grassland in areas of former forest are a clear indication of this. Edwards (1956) stated that the clearing of forest in areas with annual rainfall above 1000 mm is followed by growth of herb communities composed mainly of the stoloniferous *Pennisetum clandestinum*.

Fig.6. *Ekebergia capensis* tree in secondary bushland (c. 2 200 m, 08.06.1988). From Schmitt (in print)

Fig.7. A disturbed *Cassipourea* forest in the Lower Salient in which exposed boles are clearly visible. The deciduous trees of *Calodendrum capense* can be recognized by their partly shed crowns (light grey). A strip of secondary bushland can be seen in the foreground (c. 2000 m, 07.12.1986). From Schmitt (in print)

Fig.8. Vegetation changes on a slope c. 600 m east-northeast of Ruhuruini Gate (c. 2280 m) between March 1981 and December 1987. From Schmitt (in print)

A: This photo (taken by A. Kortlandt) shows dense bush cover on the slope

B: Many of the bushes have disappeared and Kikuyu grass grassland dominates (photo by K. Schmitt, 10 December 1987)

The Lower Salient

The most significant vegetation change that has taken place in the Lower Salient is the increase in grassland around Treetops Lodge (Fig. 10) and along the Park boundary to the south. The extension of these grassland areas has been due to a combination of fire and the impact of man and of herbivores.

For a long time the Salient has been part of an important migration route for large herbivores. Elephants still try to find their way to Mt. Kenya, although their migration has now been prevented by an electric fence (Reports Warden Aberdare National Park 1960, 1962, 1972, 1973). At the beginning of the long rains (mid March) the elephants start to migrate from the higher areas of the Park to the Salient. They are stopped by the electric fence and are funnelled to the area around Treetops, where a large population of elephants builds up within the next two months. The elephants start their migration back to the higher areas of the Park after the rains. The situation is similar during the short rains and is shown by monthly records of elephant sightings at Treetops (1970 m) and The Ark (2310 m) (Fig. 9). This seasonally high concentration of elephants in a restricted area has led to the destruction of forest around Treetops. The impact of elephants on the conversion of forest to grassland has been described by several authors (e.g. Buecher & Dawkins 1961; Laws 1970; Kortlandt 1984).

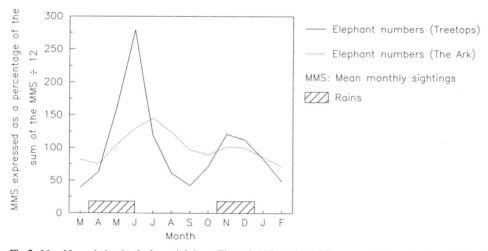

Fig.9. Monthly variation in elephant sightings. The Ark 1970-1988 and Treetops 1981-1987. From Schmitt (in print)

Factors contributing to and enhancing the destruction of forest in the Salient are:

● **Felling of trees:** Extensive trampling by wildlife, mainly by buffaloes and pigs, compacts the topsoil so that surface run-off is increased and the oxygen supply to the fine roots is decreased (c. 50% of the fallen trees around Treetops have dead root systems, Prickett pers. comm. 1987). Debarking of trees by elephants (Tab. 2) allows secondary damage by borers and rots (Holloway 1965). The weakened trees are less resistant to felling by wind and pushing over by elephants. These findings are supported by the results of a study performed in Amboseli Game Reserve (Kenya). Here, Western and van Praet (1973) found that elephants seemed to contribute in a catalytic manner to habitat changes rather than being primarily responsible.

Fig.10.
Vegetation
changes around
Treetops
waterhole
between 1932
and 1988. From
Schmitt (in
print)

A: Treetops pool
in 1932,
photographer
unknown,
reproduced with
the kind
permission of
David &
Charles, Newton
Abbot

B: Aerial
photograph
provided by
F.W. Woodley,
date and
photographer
unknown,
although this
photo must have
been taken after
1957 when
Treetops was
rebuilt following
its destruction in
1954

C: Aerial view,
26 June 1988
(photo K.
Schmitt)

* ● **Removal of fallen trees**: Fallen trees, which contribute to nutrient cycling, erosion protection and soil moisture budget and which provide shelter for seedlings and habitats for insects, are removed either by the Park management or by local people who use them for firewood. The cutting of saplings and young trees for firewood may further contribute to the destruction of the structure of the forest.

● **Fire**: Trampling and browsing of undergrowth allows the invasion of grass into the forest margins so that fires from surrounding agricultural land can penetrate the forests more deeply. In 1953, a fire destroyed trees and bushes south-east of Treetops (Woodley pers. comm. 1987).

Tab.2. List of the trees debarked by elephants in the Salient of the Aberdare National Park, produced with the help of Ass. Warden W. Theuri and Mr. S. Mathenge. From Schmitt (in print)

preferred	occasionally debarked
Dombeya torrida ssp. *torrida* *Elaeodendron buchananii* *Ficus thonningii*	*Polyscias kikuyuensis*
very often debarked	seldom debarked
Albizia gummifera var. *gummifera* *Schefflera volkensii*	*Cassipourea malosana* *Croton megalocarpus* *Olea capensis* ssp. *hochstetteri*
often debarked	*Podocarpus* spec. *Prunus africana*
Dovyalis abyssinica *Ekebergia capensis* *Hagenia abyssinica* *Juniperus procera* *Teclea* spec.	*Vangueria volkensii* var. *volkensii* *Warburgia ugandensis* ssp. *ugandensis*

The combined effect of anthropogenic and zoogenic impact on the structure of a *Cassipourea* forest of the Lower Salient is clearly shown in Figure 11. Figure 11a shows a fairly undisturbed and Figure 11b a heavily disturbed *Cassipourea* forest. All the tall trees have been removed. The resulting gaps have been invaded by secondary bushland and by other species typical of secondary vegetation (e.g. *Abutilon longicuspe, Cynodon dactylon* and *Toddalia asiatica*). The high density of herbivores in this forest, together with the removal of fallen trees and collection of firewood, hinders the regeneration of forest and maintains the seral stage of the bush vegetation.

Factors which, in addition to anthropogenic activities, affect the density of herbivores are disease, predation and droughts:

From the mid-1960's to the end of the 1970's bushland almost completely disappeared from glades in the Salient. Since then the number of shrubs, especially of *Abutilon longicuspe*, has increased again. During this period herbivore populations have decreased in size (Fig. 12). The density of the shrub cover of the glades appears to be affected by the periodic fluctuations in herbivore numbers which, in turn, are dependent on disease (Rinderpest in buffalo, e.g. Percival [1928], Holloway [1965]) and on the abundance of predators (Sinclair 1974a; Yoaciel 1981). No significant proof of the extent of predation by lions and by hyaenas on the population of herbivores has been documented in the Salient yet (Sillero-Zubiri & Gottelli 1987), but Yoaciel (1981) concluded that in the Mweya Peninsula of the Ruwenzori National Park in Uganda, predation, especially by lions, appeared to be a major regulatory mechanism on the buffalo population.

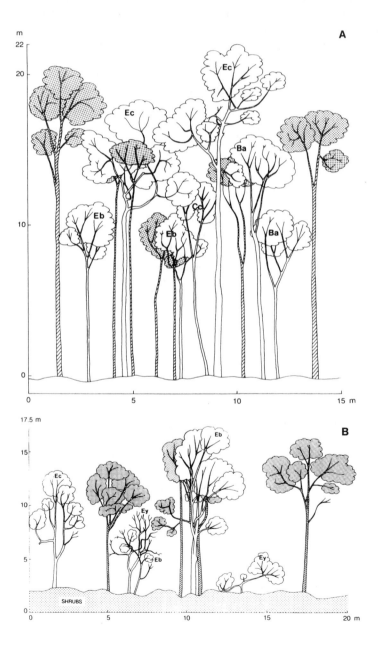

Fig.11. Profile diagrams of two *Cassipourea* forests of the Lower Salient. From Schmitt (in print)

A: *Nuxia congesta* subcommunity of the *Cassipourea malosana - Setaria plicatilis* agg. community (2030 m). Shaded trees: *Cassipourea malosana*, Ba: *Bersama abyssinica* ssp. *abyssinica*, Eb: *Elaeodendron buchananii* and Ec: *Ekebergi a capensis*

B: *Cynodon dactylon* subcommunity of the *Cassipourea malosana - Setaria plicatilis* agg. community (2060 m). Shaded trees: *Cassipourea malosana*, Eb: *Elaeodendron buchananii*, Ec: *Ekebergia capensis* and Ey: *Ehretia cymosa* var. *silvatica*

Exceptional climatic events such as droughts have a significant, but only short-term impact, on vegetation and on the movement of game. They lead to a shortage of food for grazers, which causes mortality and in turn reduces the grazing pressure (Sinclair 1974b).

Long-term climatic shifts do cause changes in vegetation. In the Aberdares, a general decrease in rainfall is suggested from the results of a water-balance model of Lake Naivasha (southeast of the Park) which receives 90% of its total river inflow from the Aberdare Mountains (Vincent *et al.* 1989), from observations by people with long-term knowledge of the area and from long-term rainfall records (Schmitt in print).

The combination of a decrease in rainfall and an increase in deforestation caused by man has resulted in vegetation changes in the Aberdares which, in addition, have had a serious impact on the watercatchment function of the Range, e.g. previously permanent rivers have become seasonal.

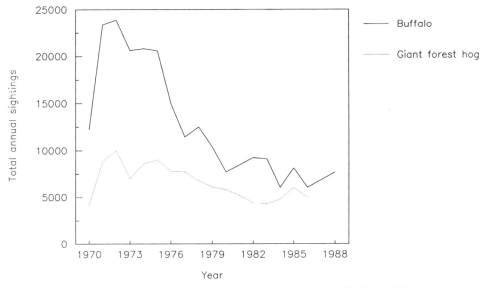

Fig.12. Annual sightings of buffaloes and giant forest hogs at The Ark. Modified after Schmitt (in print)

The Upper Salient

The 1947 aerial photographs of the Upper Salient show large areas of grassland on ridges and moderate slopes surrounded by areas of secondary bushland. The general distribution of forest and secondary bushland has changed very little since that time.

The grassland, which is the result of shifting cultivation and livestock grazing, has now become almost completely overgrown by secondary bushland. Some clearings in the Lower Salient, further away from the Park boundary, have become similarly overgrown. This development can be ascribed to the cessation of significant impact by man and livestock following the gazetting of the Park.

Most of the grassland in the Salient has developed into secondary bushland in the space of 40 years, although wildlife was (Meinerzhagen 1957; Hessel pers. comm. 1987; Woodley pers. comm. 1987) and still is very concentrated in this part of the Park, suggesting that wildlife alone, even when present in significant numbers, cannot transform large areas of forest into savanna unless wood-cutting, bushfires and agriculture also contribute (Aubréville 1947). However, small-scale vegetation destruction is possible in areas with seasonally high concentrations of herbivores.

Fig.13. Profile diagram of *Cassipourea malosana - Olea capensis* ssp. *hochstetteri* community (Lower Salient 2180 m). From Schmitt (in print)

Shaded trees: *Cassipourea malosana*, Da: *Diospyros abyssinica*, Eb: *Elaeodendron buchananii*, Ec: *Ekebergia capensis*, Jp: *Juniperus procera* , Oa: *Olea europaea* ssp. *africana*, Oh: *Olea capensis* ssp. *hochstetteri* and Tn: *Teclea nobilis*

The large numbers of herbivores in the Salient do, however, seem to contribute to the persistence of the secondary bushland, by impeding the regeneration of forest through trampling and eating of tree seedlings. This assumption is supported by the fact that seedlings of forest trees were only found inside forests, but not in the adjacent secondary bushland. Hatton and Smart (1984) showed that after 24 years of exclusion of large herbivores from a grassland plot in Murchison Falls National Park, Uganda, tree species were able to re-establish to a considerable degree. The floristic composition of the ground layer changed dramatically at the same time and important grazing grasses disappeared completely.

Secondary bushland with scattered glades is capable of supporting much more wildlife than submontane forest, because it provides a wider diversity of food plants and habitats (Vesey-FitzGerald 1972, 1973). The higher density of herbivores supported by the secondary bushland in turn maintains an early stage of the sere.

Gaps in tropical lowland rain forest arise naturally when trees fall down. They are recolonized by secondary vegetation and a mosaic of decline and renewal results. No regeneration of trees was observed in gaps in the forests of the Lower Salient or in the secondary bushland of the Salient, which is more than 40 years old. Either regeneration of tropical submontane forest is much slower than that of tropical lowland rain forest (Budowski 1965; Hallé *et al.* 1978), or it is impeded by the high concentration of herbivores. Presumably a combination of both factors is responsible for the absence of regeneration stages. Removal of fallen trees, (i.e. the removal of the crowns which can protect the tree-seedlings during the first years of slow growth) exposes seedlings to browsing and trampling pressure.

The structure of the forest of the Northern Salient has changed due to selective felling of emergent *Juniperus procera* trees for railway sleepers and fence posts and the subsequent regeneration of broad-leaved trees (Fig. 13). According to Wimbush (1937) in the absence of repetitive fire Cedar forest is only a seral stage in the succession to a broad-leaved forest, because Cedar trees cannot regenerate without fire. Numerous small trees and seedlings of *Cassipourea malosana*, a common understory tree (Dale & Greenway 1961), have become established in the gaps created by the selective felling of emergent trees in the Northern Salient, suggesting that the former *Juniperus procera - Olea capensis* ssp. *hochstetteri* forest will eventually develop into a *Cassipourea malosana* forest as a result of selective felling and the absence of fire.

The forest of the higher part of the Salient, in contrast, shows few signs of disturbance and species typical of secondary forests and forest edges (e.g. *Bersama abyssinica* ssp. *abyssinica, Clausena anisata, Ehretia cymosa* var. *silvatica* and *Erythrococca bongensis*) are almost completely absent.

References

Agnew ADQ (1974) Upland Kenya wild flowers. Oxford: Oxford University Press, 827 pp
Aubréville A (1947) Les brousses secondaires en Afrique Equatoriale. Bois et Forêts des Tropiques 2: 24-49
Baker BH, Mohr PA, Williams LAJ (1972) Geology of the Eastern Rift system of Africa. Geogr Soc of America
    Special Paper 136, Boulder Colorado, 67 pp
Barkman JJ, Moravec J, Rauschert S (1976) Code of phytosociological nomenclature. Vegetatio 32(3): 131-185
Barnett DL, Njama K (1966) Mau Mau from within. Autobiography and analysis of Kenya's peasant revolt.
    London: MacGibbon & Kee, 512 pp
Beentje HJ (in prep) Kenya trees shrubs and lianas
Berger A (1910) In Afrikas Wildkammern als Forscher und Jäger. Berlin: Paray, 430 pp
Boyes J (1926) John Boyes King of the Wakikuyu - 6th edition (1st edition 1911) London: Methuen & Co, 240 pp
Braun HMH (1986) Seasonal distribution of rainfall in Kenya. Misc paper M 14 revised edition 1986 (1st edition
    1977) Kenya Soil Survey: Nairobi, 16 pp
Braun-Blanquet J (1964) Pflanzensoziologie. 3rd edition. Wien, New York: Springer, 865 pp
Budowski G (1965) Distribution of tropical rainforest species in the light of successional process. Turrialba 15:
    40-42
Buechner HK, Dawkins HC (1961) Vegetation change induced by elephants and fire in Murchison Falls National
    Park Uganda. Ecol 42(4): 752-766
Chi-son CHAO, Renvoize SA (1989) A revision of the species described under *Arundinaria* (Gramineae) in
    Southeast Asia and Africa. Kew Bull 44(2): 349-367
Cowie M (1959) The Aberdare National Park. Wild Life 1(2): 49-52
Dale IR, Greenway PJ (1961) Kenya trees and shrubs. Nairobi: Buchanan, 654 pp
Dierschke H (1988) Zur Benennung zentraler Syntaxa ohne eigene Kenn- und Trennarten. Tuexenia 8: 381-382
Doute R, Ochanda N, Epp H (1981) Forest cover mapping in Kenya using remote sensing techniques. Nairobi
    Ministry of Environment and Natural Resources: KREMU, 130 pp
Dundas KR (1908) Notes on the origin and history of the Kikuyu and Dorobo tribes. Man 8(76): 136-139
Edwards DC (1956) The ecological regions of Kenya. Empire Journal of Experimental Agriculture 24(94): 89-108
FAO-Unesco (1988) Soil map of the world revised legend. Rome: FAO, 119 pp
Forest Department Annual Reports. Nairobi Govt Printer
Graham A, Woodley FW (1979) An unusual type of waterhole. Azania 14: 139-142
Griffiths JF (1972) Eastern Africa. In: Griffiths JF (ed): Climates of Africa Vol 10. Amsterdam London New
    York: Elsevier: 313-347
Haines RW, Lye KA (1983) The sedges and rushes of East Africa. Nairobi: E A Nat Hist Soc, 404 pp
Hallé F, Oldeman RAA, Tomlinson PB (1978) Tropical trees and forests. An architectural analysis. Berlin
    Heidelberg New York: Springer, 441 pp
Hatton JC, Smart NOE (1984) The effect of long-term exclusion of large herbivores on soil nutrient status in
    Murchison Falls National Park Uganda. Afr J Ecol 22(1): 23-30
Holloway CW (1965) The impact of big game on forest policy in the Mount Kenya and North-East Aberdare forest
    reserves. E Afr Agric For J 30(4): 370-389
Hutchins DE (1909) Report on the forests of British East Africa. London: Darling & Son for HM Stationery
    Office, 155 pp
Kenya Land Commission (1933a) Kenya Land Commission Evidence Vol 3. Nairobi: Govt Printer: 2129-3458
Kenya Land Commission (1933b) Report. Nairobi: Govt Printer, 618 pp
Kortlandt A (1984) Vegetation research and the "bulldozer" herbivores of tropical Africa. In: Chadwick AC &
    Sutton CL (eds): Tropical rain-forest. Spec Publ Leeds Phil Lit Society: 205-226

Laws RM (1970) Elephants as agents of habitat and landscape change in East Africa. Oikos 21: 1-15

Logie JPW, Dyson WG (1962) Forestry in Kenya. A historical account of the development of forest management in the colony. Nairobi: Govt Printer, 34 pp

Maskall JE (1991) The influence of geochemistry on trace elements in soils and plants in wildlife conservation areas of Kenya. PhD thesis, University of London

Matthiessen P, Porter E (1972) The tree where man was born. The African experience. London: Collins, 247 pp

Meinertzhagen R (1957) Kenya Diary 1902-1906. Edinburgh London: Oliver & Boyd, 347 pp

Mueller-Dombois D, Ellenberg H (1974) Aims and methods of vegetation ecology. New York: Wiley, 547 pp

Muriuki G (1974) A history of the Kikuyu: 1500-1900. Nairobi Oxford New York: Oxford University Press, 190 pp

Nicholson MJL (1976) Soils and land use on the northern foothills of the Aberdare Range Kenya. Thesis presented towards BSc(Hons) degree: Dept of Soil Science University of Aberdeen Scotland U K, 54 pp

Nyandat NN (1976) Nitosols and rhodic ferralsols in Kenya Morphological and chemical properties - use and management. Miscellaneous soil paper M9 Nairobi: Kenya Soil Survey, 18 pp

Percival AB (1928) A Game Ranger on Safari. London: Nisbet & Co, 305 pp

Prickett RJ (1964) The living forest. Nairobi: East African Publishing House, 163 pp

Reports Warden Aberdare National Park. Quarterly half-yearly and annual reports. Mweiga: Aberdare National Park Headquarters

Rosberg CG, Nottingham J (1966) The myth of "Mau Mau" nationalism in Kenya. Nairobi: E Afr Publishing House, 427 pp

Routledge WS, Routledge K (1910) With a prehistoric people. London: Frank Cass, 392 pp

Schmitt K (in print) The vegetation of the Aberdare National Park

Scholz U (1981) Monographie der Gattung Oplismenus (Gramineae). Phanerogamarum Monographiae 13 Vaduz:J Cramer, 213 pp

Shackleton RM (1945) Geology of the Nyeri Area. Geological Survey of Kenya Report no 12. Nairobi Govt Printer, 26 pp

Sillero-Zubiri C, Gottelli MD (1987) The ecology of the spotted hyaena in the Salient Aberdare National Park and recommendations for wildlife management. Report for the Wildlife Conservation and Management Dept of the Ministry for Tourism and Wildlife of Kenya, 73 pp

Simon N (1962) Between the sunlight and the thunder: the wildlife of Kenya. London: Collins, 384 pp

Sinclair ARE (1974a) The natural regulation of buffalo populations in East Africa. E Afr Wildl J 12(2): 135-154

Sinclair ARE (1974b) The natural regulation of buffalo populations in East Africa. E Afr Wildl J 12(4): 291-311

Sombroek WG, Braun HMH, van der Pouw BJA (1982) Exploratory soil map and agroclimatic zone map of Kenya 1980 1: 1 000 000. Exploratory soil survey report E1 Nairobi: Kenya Soil Survey, 56 pp

Theisen A (1966) Der Mineralbestand saurer tropischer Böden auf vulkanischem Ausgangsmaterial in Kenya. Dissertation: Universtät Giessen, 84 pp

Thompson AO (1964) Geology of the Kijabe area. Report no 67 Nairobi: Geological Survey of Kenya, 52 pp

Thomson J (1885) Through Masai Land. London: Sampson Low, 580 pp

Trapnell CG, Birch WR, Brunt MA, Lawton RM (1976) Kenya vegetation 1: 250 000 sheet 2. DOS (LR) 3006

Troup RS (1922) Report on forestry in Kenya Colony. London Dustable and Wafford: Waterlow & Sons, 47 pp

Turill WB, Milne-Redhead E, Hubbard CE, Polhill E (eds) (1952-1990) Flora of Tropical East Africa. East African Community Crown Agents and Balkema Rotterdam

Vesy-FitzGerald DF (1972) Fire and animal impact on vegetation in Tanzania National Parks. Proc Tall Timbers Fire Ecology Conf 11: 297-317

Vesy-FitzGerald DF (1973) Animal impact on vegetation and plant succession in Lake Manyara National Park Tanzania. Oikos 24: 314-324

Vincent CE, Davis TD, Brimblecombe P, Beresford AKC (1989) Lake levels and glaciers: indicators of the changing rainfall in the mountains of East Africa. In: WC Mahaney (ed): Quaternary and environmental research on East African Mountains. Rotterdam Brookfield: Balkema: 199-216

Von Höhnel L (1894) Discovery of Lakes Rudolf and Stephanie. London: Longmans, 435 pp

Walker ES (1962) Treetops Hotel. London: Robert Hale Ltd, 190 pp

Walter H, Lieth H (1960-67) Klimadiagramm Weltatlas. Jena: Gustav Fischer Verlag

Western D, van Praet C (1973) Cyclical changes in the habitat and climate of an East African ecosystem. Nature 241: 104-106

Wimbush SH (1937) Natural succession in the Pencil Cedar forests of Kenya Colony. Emp For J 16: 49-53

Winiger M (1979) Bodentemperaturen und Niederschlag als Indikatoren einer klimatisch - ökologischen Gliederung tropischer Gebirgsräume. Methodische Aspekte und Anwendbarkeit diskutiert am Beispiel des Mt Kenya (Ostafrika). Geomethodica 4: 121-150

Yoaciel SM (1981) Changes in the populations of large herbivores and in the vegetation community in Mweya Peninsula, Rwenzori National Park, Uganda. Afr J Ecol 19: 303-312

Tropical Forests in Transition
J. G. Goldammer (ed.)

Tropical Mountain Ecology in Ethiopia as a Basis for Conservation, Management and Restoration

Siegfried K. Uhlig[*]

Abstract

The results of several surveys in the forest and alpine region in southwest Ethiopian mountains are used for the demonstration of various ecological problems, mainly the gradual or abrupt changes of some features of the plant formations with increasing altitude. The need for taking fundamental ecological data as a basis for a "disturbance management" is emphasized.

Introduction

The major part of the Highlands in Eastern Africa is located in Ethiopia, that is nearly half of the area of this country covering about 1.22 million square kilometers. There are 57 mountains surmounting 3000 m a.s.l. and 25 with the summit above 4000 m a.s.l. The natural vegetation of these highlands has its particular features which are of regional significance. The altitudinal range as well as the orographic effects on the intensity of

[*] Institute of Tropical and Subtropical Forestry, Dresden Technical University, P.O. Box 10, D-O-8223 Tharandt, Germany

winds, cloudiness, radiation etc. induce a great diversity of ecological conditions with steep gradients in decisive factors which is reflected by the natural vegetation. On the one hand, these complicated mountain ecosystems may be regarded as marginal environments. They are fragile and sensitive. The range of possible responses to perturbations and disturbances is narrow. On the other hand, these forests and alpine plant formations have to fulfill essential functions. They equalize the water balance, which is important for the irrigation of the adjacent lowlands, and provide wood, which is the main source of energy in the country. The geographical isolation and the large distance of the East African mountains from other mountain systems have created much endemism, making the indigenous vegetation a unique reservoir of genes of extraordinary importance.

However, a growing population exerts increasing pressure on the landscape by expanding agricultural cultivation and an increasing demand of wood for domestic consumption. The forests which formerly covered the major parts of these sub-humid highlands were, therefore, largely deforested by fire, cultivation, overgrazing and inadequate removal of wood. Forests in their original state are now represented only by few remnants, and the alpine region beyond the forest limit will also become increasingly devastated by anthropogenic impact. Further destruction urgently needs to be stopped. But this can only be achieved by a complex and integrated program of sustainable land use which does not go beyond the limits set by ecological factors. For this purpose much understanding is needed to assess the consequences of interference or disturbances and to improve management options. Therefore there are many reasons for learning more about the mountain vegetation and the environmental factors which control them.

Methods

Studies were carried out at several places in Ethiopia, mainly on the highlands and mountains southeast of the Rift Valley to augment availability of basic research information on the subject. They included numerous surveys on occurrence, floristic composition, structure, stock, yield, regeneration and successional dynamics of different forest and afro-alpine plant communities: different mixed broadleaved forests, conifer forests dominated by *Juniperus procera* and *Podocarpus gracilior*, mountain bushes, the ericaceous belt and the afro-alpine zone, rich in herbs like *Helichrysum* spp., *Senecio* spp., *Alchemilla* spp. and others as well as primary and secondary (tussock) grasslands. These formations have their particular distribution pattern as described elsewhere (Uhlig, 1988; Uhlig & Uhlig 1989, 1990a, 1990b). This report, however, is not a specification of the detailed local data. It is rather focussed on the conclusions and it tries to reveal some basic ecological problems of this mountain vegetation as a review on a higher level of generalization and a more extended validity. This has to be put into the broader context of a general tropical mountain ecology which is basically aimed at conservation and "disturbance management" as well as restoration of degraded and devasted areas.

Fig.3. Elfin forest with epiphytic lichens covering the trees on Gara Mulatta

Fig.4. Cushions of *Helichrysum spicata* and *Erica arborea* at about 3700 m in the Bale Mountains

Ecological Background

The most striking climatic factor in tropical mountains is the wide daily fluctuation of temperature with low seasonality. The long winter blockade of growth under snowcover is absent. In the East African Mountains rainfall increases only up to mid-altitudes and decreases toward the summits. Maximum precipitation occurs during the summer, so that snowfall in the Ethiopian mountains is only occasional neither causing a permanent snow cover nor glaciers. The influence of the prevailing winds is decisive. The Southwest monsoon winds bring clouds and moisture, while the dry Northeast trade winds have a desiccating effect.

Results

The most species-rich and luxuriant montane forests have already disappeared. Single or scattered tall trees on cultivated or abandoned ground are the last remains. Only a few forests are left mainly in refuges on stony soils at the pediment or on steep slopes. The numerous fragmented data of the surveys can be condensed to some general features of the changes with increasing altitude:

- The species composition changes in a specific way leading to the well-known altitudinal vegetation zonation. Each plant formation has its particular performance as is already described (Knapp 1973; Lind and Morrison 1973).

- The borders of dispersal of the various species are caused by different barriers: competition to other species, mesoclimatic, orographic or edaphic factors. The upper and the lower boundary line of occurrence of one particular species is usually determined by different constraints. Not all species show a similar reaction to the same limiting factors. The species at higher elevation tend to be more stenochor in their distribution. Their areas are mainly refuges.

- The diversity of woody plants diminishes with increasing altitude. But there is no coincidence in diversity and abundance between the different strata. For the development of ground vegetation, structure and density of the shelter is the most important factor. Openings in the forests, therefore, promote undergrowth. In that way alpine plants have their best performance in the subalpine zone when they are not "shaded out" by taller cover plants.

- The structure of plant formations loses their complexity. There are gradual or abrupt transitions from the multistory mixed lower montane forests to the single-layered upper forests, to the bush, grassland or herbaceous formations. The dominating plants become smaller, the internodia shorter etc. There is a mutual connection between the structure and the regeneration pattern which is accomplished in a more or less complicated space-time mosaic dynamics of the different internal development stages (gap, building and mature stages). Dependent on an altitudinal gradient of changes in diversity and abundance, interspecific competition is largely replaced by intraspecific competition. Under the prevalence of limiting climatic factors competition loses significance.

Fig.5. Giant rosettes of *Lobelia rhynchopetalum* with *Alchemilla johnstonii* at about 4100 m in the Bale Mountains

Fig.6. *Carex* bogs in depressions at about 4100 m on the Sanetti Plateai, Bale Mountains

- Near the upper limits positive coexistence of different species becomes essential for regeneration. In this respect mountain bush associations have to be evaluated in different ways with regard to regeneration of other species under their shelter. It was observed, that *Hypericum revolutum* frequently serves as a "nurse" for seedlings of several species (Uhlig & Uhlig 1989). A contrast to this phenomenon is the legume *Indigofera rothii*, which aggressively occupies forest openings and grasslands and which easily suppresses other species. Life forms adapted to this environment, such as cushions, giant rosettes, acaulescent rosette plants and sclerophyllous shrubs, become more dominant (Hedberg 1964; Hedberg & Hedberg 1979).

- Local endemics become more frequent. The disjunct areas of some of these species are isolated and the population is already so small that the survival of some species is acutely endangered, e.g. *Lobelia rhynchopetalum, L. gibberoa, Echinops ellembecki* and others. This also refers to various animals like the Simen fox *(Canis simensis)*, the gelada baboon *(Theropithecus gelada)* etc.

These changes are not always exhibited in a gradual transition. There are also extreme alternations causing sharp contrasts as can be seen at the limits of the cloud or the elfin forest. The most interesting ecotone, however, is the timberline. In the surveyed area the timberline is mainly reached by the following tree species: *Hypericum revolutum, Hagenia abyssinica* and *Juniperus procera*. These forests, if undisturbed, reach their upper limit as closed stands and cease abruptly as a sharp line against the treeless alpine zone. They generate a mircro climate which enables seedlings to develop. Once the closed structure of this forest is destroyed, its reinvasion upwards into exposed areas becomes extremely difficult. It was observed that shade-tolerant species like *Rapanea simensis*, which in few cases also reach the timberline, form a sharper border by dense cover as compared to those more light-demanding species, such as *Hypericum* or *Juniperus*. Single or scattered trees above the timberline are generally not "outposts" but "remains", indicating that this line was artificially lowered by human impact.

There are different successional developments in relation to the intensity, the duration and the frequency of the disturbance, and the site conditions or the potential ("climax") plant formation with respect to the local seed pool. But there is little available basic research information for diagnostic assessment. An identification of the critical components in the cause-effect relations is needed to evaluate situations of imbalance before the regulating mechanism can counteract effectively. There are different modes and intensities of recovery. That makes it difficult to select the optimal management option for protection, conservation or restoration. The given examples and considerations should demonstrate that conservation and management of tropical mountain ecosystems in all their heterogeneity need a very distinct and differentiated approach, which has to be based on a broad foundation of ecological data.

References

Hedberg O (1964) Features of afroalpine plant ecology. Acta Phytogeographica Suecica 49: 144 pp

Hedberg I, Hedberg O (1979) Tropical-alpine life forms of vascular plants. Oikos 33: 297-307

Knapp R (1973) The vegetation of Africa. G. Fischer: Stuttgart

Lind EM, Morrison MES (1974) East african vegetation. Longmann: London

Uhlig SK (1988) Mountain forests and the upper tree limit on the Southeastern Plateau of Ethiopia. Mountain Research and Development 8: 227-234

Uhlig SK, Uhlig K (1989) On the ecology and vegetation of the plateaus of East Ethiopian isolated mountains. Archiv für Naturschutz. Berlin. 29: 173-177

Uhlig SK and Kate Uhlig (1990a) The floristic composition of a natural montane forest in Southeast Ethiopia. Feddes Repertorium. 101: 85-88

Uhlig SK, Uhlig K (1990b) Die Höhenstufen am Gara Mulatta, Äthiopien. Feddes Repertorium. 101: 651-664

Tropical Forests in Transition
J. G. Goldammer (ed.)
© 1992 Birkhäuser Verlag Basel/Switzerland

Forests for Integrated Land-Use Development in an Eastern Ethiopian Water Catchment

Holm Uibrig[*]

Abstract

Although forest has diminished to a few relics, the Eastern Ethiopian highlands are still relatively rich in scattered tree occurrences. Results of a land use survey in the Alemaya catchment comprising 20,000 ha show that natural forest vegetation has remained on only 0.5 % of the reference area.

The density of woody plants and the tree species composition of remnants of the natural forest render possible restoration without any enrichment planting by minimizing the intensity of use. The establishment of woodlots on the basis of a voluntary and participatory approach by the local farmers shows promising initial results. The use of indigenous tree species should be favoured in order to avoid the risks of establishing monocultures with exotic *Eucalyptus* spp. and *Acacia saligna*.

On the one hand, increasing mechanization of agricultural production tends to cause the number of the scattered trees of various species to decline. On the other hand, the expansion of irrigated agriculture facilitates the integrated management of agricultural crops and trees. Non-conflicting tree planting may also contribute to wood production and biological diversity.

---

[*]Institute of Tropical and Subtropical Forestry, Dresden Technical University, P.O. Box 10, D-O-8223 Tharandt, Germany

Introduction

The natural forest ecosystems of the Ethiopian highlands are known as extensively exploited, degraded and converted to other mostly unsustainable ecosystems. Improper land use by pressures to feed a rapidly growing population causes a continuing process of declining soil fertility, water holding capacity, and leads to erosion.

Ecologically based land-use development is generally recognized as a measure to solve these problems. A land-use survey and investigations within remnants of natural forests and planted woodlots were carried out in a water catchment in the Hararghe Highlands. Pilot forest management plans were prepared at community level. This was to establish and execute the integration of forest land-use with the agricultural land use pattern on a low cost approach.

Location, Site and Methods

The eastern Ethiopian highlands are located on the southern escarpment of the Great Rifft valley. They are subdivided into the Chercher Highlands in the western and the Hararghe Highlands in the eastern part. The Hararghe Highlands cover an area from Kulubi eastwards to the boundary of the country. Figure 1 provides a general view on the geographical situation.

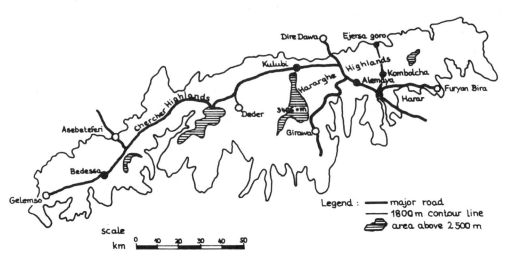

Fig.1. Sketch map of the eastern Ethiopian highlands above 1800 m contour line (Center: 9°18'N/41°26' E)

The highland consists of the crystalline bed-rock of the pre-cambrian Gondwana continent. Granite prevails. Rarely is gneiss found. During the Triassic, sands and limes were deposited forming layers of varying consistency and thickness. Volcanic basalt, the uppermost layer in extensive areas of the Ethiopian highlands, is absent in the surroundings of Alemaya. Limestone and sandstone have been weathered intensively, exposing granite boulders mainly in the lower sections of the catchments (Tamirie Hawando 1982).

The reference area is an internal catchment. It covers about 20,000 ha around Alemaya. The altitude ranges from 2000 to 2400 m a.s.l. According to the records at Alemaya meteorological station, the mean annual temperature is 15.9°C (1960-1987). The area receives 827 mm of rainfall per annum on the average (1960-1987) with a peak of 120 mm in April and another one of 131 mm and 143 mm in July and August. The annual precipitation varies distinctly between the extremes of 522 mm (1980) and 1260 mm (1967) (Verjux 1987). The agroclimatic zone is to be identified as dry to sub-humid Woina Dega (Hurni 1986).

The climatic climax of the vegetation is the montane dry evergreen forest (Daniel Gamachu 1977). The upper layer of trees is described as moderately dense with rather tall trees. The lower layer is characterized as very dense. *Juniperus procera* Hochst. is the dominating species. Applying the classification of Marklund & Odenyo (1984) the area belongs to the Juniper forest with some tendency to the *Podocarpus* forest in more humid sites and the Juniper woodland in drier sections.

The land-use system of the landscape is the Sorghum plough complex of Hararghe (Westphal 1975). Sorghum, maize, pulses etc. are grown. In addition, livestock is herded by the families. Depending on the location, several cash crops, like chat (*Catha edulis* Forsk.), coffee (*Coffea arabica* L.) and vegetables, play a certain part in the local economies (Langlais *et al.* 1984).

The ethnic group of Oromos counts for about 90 % of the population of altogether 330 persons per km^2 in the region. Amharic people predominantly live in towns. Rural families manage small individual farms of 0.7 (0.1-3.0) ha on the average (Schmitt 1988).Co-operative farms cover about 40 % of the entire catchment (Uibrig 1989). In the whole area of the Hararghe Highlands natural forests were diminished to a few small sized and degraded remnants. Wood for fuel and poles can hardly be produced. Recently, efforts have been made to establish community woodlots and to plant trees according to various non-competitive designs (Poschen-Eiche 1987; Schrempp 1987; Badege Bishaw & Uibrig 1989).

Within the Alemaya water catchment, land use was recorded by sampling. Inventories covering the total area were conducted on a community basis. Investigations on natural and planted forests were carried out applying sampling techniques and also 100 percent enumerations.

Results and Discussion

The major land use types identified in the reference area are enlisted in Table 1. It clearly shows that fillage is the major land-use within the catchment.

Tab.1. Major land-use types in Alemaya catchment in 1988 (Source: Uibrig [1989])

Key No.	Description of the land use type	Proportion (%)	Area (ha)
1.	Dwelling site or other technical infrastructure	5.5	1,075
2.	Agricultural land	74.2	14,499
2.1.	Rainfed agriculture	68.1	13,307
2.2.	Irrigated agriculture	4.9	957
2.3.	Fallow	1.2	235
3.	Grassland	7.3	1,426
4.	Bushland	2.9	567
5.	Forest land	4.5	879
5.1.	Natural forest	0.5	98
5.2.	Planted forest	4.0	781
7.	Waste land	1.0	195
8.	Swamp	0.5	98
9.	Water bodies	4.1	801
Total		100.0	19,540

About 2000 ha of the agricultural land are slopes of more than 16 percent of inclination. According to a land capability classification of the Forestry and Wildlife Conservation and Development Authority (1983) this land should be converted into permanent vegetation, preferably forest. Ploughed land sloping 8 to 16 percent, i.e. almost one third of all agricultural land, should be managed by applying techniques of soil conservation like bunds, terraces and agroforestry systems.

Irrigation of ploughed land is a new technique in the region. It has preferably been established in co-operative farms to get more than only one harvest per year and to produce vegetables for export and fruits at an increasing rate.

Bushland is charcterized by a poor production of biomass. Generally, it covers sections formerly ploughed and left fallow for reasons of soil erosion. However, bushland serves as a natural grazing land providing a minimum fodder resource especially for goats.

Forest land embodies natural and also planted forests. The extremely small proportion of 0.5 % of a natural forest cover exclusively occurs on remote slopes of over 30 % of inclination. The stocking attributes to long lasting exploitation producing small-sized timber and fuelwood. Grazing is a common practice, as well (Uibrig & Abdu Abdulkadir 1989).

Table 2 characterizes the natural stocking of the forest at Hubota mountain. This mountain is located in the very north of the catchment at an altitude of between 2100 m and 2330 m a.s.l. The remaining forest area directed towards the catchment comprises about 50 ha. Figure 2 provides a general view on the forest vegetation.

Tab.2. Number of trees and shoots of the natural stocking of the *Juniperus procera* forest at Hubota mountain, Alemaya catchment (Source: Uibrig [1990].

Species	Number of trees per ha	%	Number of shoots per tree	per ha	%
Juniperus procera Hochst.	835	60.2	2.2	1802	72.1
Olea africana Mill.	228	16.4	1.0	235	9.4
Celtis africana Burm.	112	8.1	1.1	126	5.0
Croton macrostachyus Del.	93	6.7	2.1	193	7.7
Peremna schimperi Engl.	61	4.4	1.4	83	3.3
Vangueria apiculata K. Schum.	21	1.5	1.0	21	0.8
Rhus glutinosa A. Rich.	12	0.8	1.0	12	0.5
Maesa lancoelata Forsk.	9	0.7	1.3	12	0.5
Pittospermium viridiflorum Sims.	9	0.7	1.0	9	0.4
Vernonia amygdaline Del.	4	0.3	1.0	5	0.2
Cordia africana Lam.	2	0.2	1.0	2	0.1
Total	1,386	100.0	-	2500	100.0

Mathematic-statistical parameters

Arithmetic mean	x	14	25
Coefficient of variability	sx%	+ 65.43 %	+ 61.94 %
Accuracy (= 0.05)	k	+ 20.00 %	+ 18.90 %

The density of trees amounts to almost 1400 per ha. *Juniperus procera* is the dominating species. Initial natural regeneration may be observed three years after closing the area from grazing. The associated tree species of *Olea africana* and *Croton macrostachyus* belong to the natural Juniper forest (Marklund & Odenyo 1984). Other tree species have been identified as immigrants. *Rhus glutinosa* and *Vernonia amygdalina* originate from the Juniper woodland and *Acacia xiphocarpa* woodland, *Maesalanceolata*, *Pittospermium viridiflorum* and *Cordia africana* from the *Olea* forest (Breitenbach 1963; Marklund & Odenyo 1984).

Broadleaved species were browsed heavily in the past. The consequence is that only small habitats and few shoots sprouting from the stumps are left.

Enrichment planting was executed on a food-for-work basis using the exotics *Eucalyptus globulus* Labill., *Eucalyptus camaldulensis* Dehn., *Acacia saligna* Wendl., *Schinus molle* L. and *Cupressus lusitanica* Mill. The indigenous *Juniperus procera* and *Erytherina burana* Chiov. contribute to about 50 % of trees planted. *Eucalyptus* spp. perform the highest growth rates. This corresponds to all expectation (Uhlig 1983; Poschen-Eiche 1987; Uibrig 1988). Until now, no further management has been planned or employed.

Fig.2. View at the
Juniper forest on
Hubota mountain,
Hubota Peasants'
Association,
Alemaya catchment

Fig.3. Afforestation
of *Eucalyptus
camaldulensis* and
E. globulus on a
degraded site over
limestone in
Legeambo Peasants'
Association,
Alemaya catchment
(Age: 6 years, h =
6.5 m, DBH = 6
cm)

Fig.4. A single tree
of *Cordia africana*
in a farmers' field.
Farmers relax under
its shade. Legeambo
Peasants'
Association,
Alemaya catchment

Planted woodlots were mostly identified on slopes. About two thirds of them were established on denuded slopes of more than 16 % of inclination. Figure 3 shows a six-year old stand of *Eucalyptus* spp. on denuded limestone. Only few of the woodlots grow on highly productive sites.

Principles and plans of forest management by the Ministry of Agriculture have not been available. Therefore, pilot forest management plans were prepared by the Faculty of Forestry of Alemaya University of Agriculture (Uibrig 1987, 1989). Certain follow-ups have been undertaken (Badege Bishaw & Uibrig 1989). The main idea of the plans is to expand the afforested area to all land attached to the worst land capability classes and to contribute to self-sufficiency in wood production at the community level. In general, management of woodlots was based on sustained yield principles and experience gained from station and field trials.

According to the records tree species preferred by farmers are *Eucalyptus* spp. and *Acacia saligna*. The employment of indigenous species is still at trial stage.

The summarized activities two years after the introduction of a planned forest management are as follows:

- Voluntary planting has carefully been protected from browsing. No care was taken to afforestations through "food for work".

- Continued afforestation weeding and replanting under a voluntary program was executed according to the management plan .

- Thinning needs repeated and time-consuming demonstration, advice and supervision. The procedure seems hardly to be fully understood by the farmers.

- Final felling has been carried out according to the extensive house construction program.

- Because the farmers did not measure the trees harvested it was difficult to assess the yields.

Trees found on different used lands refer to the former natural vegetation as well as to some planting. Results are summarized in Table 3. With regard to the separate survey forests are included, as well.

Table 3 shows that about 30% of the total number of trees are *Euphorbia* spp., a species traditionally used as fencing material in farms, homesteads and trails.

Since *Juniperus procera* is the major tree species of the natural forest vegetation, it occurs in all tree bearing land use types.

Olea africana is an indigenous tree species, which is frequently found as relics scattered in agricultural fields. It regenerates fairly under the shade of older trees preferably when protected from browsing by thorny bushes.

Tab.3. Frequency of tree species in the land use types in the Alemaya catchment as to a sampling survey 1988 (for land-use types refer to Table 1). Source: Uibrig (1989).

Tree/bush species	1	2	3	4	5.1	5.2	7	9.4	Total
				Number					
Acacia abyssinica	-	1	-	-	9	8	1	-	19
Acacia albida	-	12	-	-	-	-	-	-	12
Acacia saligna	-	1	3	-	-	295	2	-	301
Brucea antidysenteria	-	2	-	-	-	-	-	5	7
Calpurnia aurea	-	14	-	4	-	-	1	-	19
Carissa edulis[1]	-	5	-	59	-	219	27	11	321
Casuarina equisetifolia	-	2	-	-	-	-	-	-	2
Casuarina montana	-	2	-	-	-	-	-	-	2
Celtis kraussian	2	-	-	-	-	-	-	-	2
Cordia africana	4	84	-	-	-	-	1	-	89
Croton macrostachyus	2	19	1	3	-	7	3	-	35
Cupressus sp.	29	2	-	-	-	324	-	-	355
Dovyalis abyssinica[2]	-	9	-	1	-	42	7	-	59
Dovyalis caffra[2] -	-	-	-	-	30	-	-	30	30
Ekebergia capensis	-	-	-	-	-	-	3	-	3
Erythrina burana	-	-	-	-	-	1	-	-	1
Eucalyptus camaldulensis	1	40	-	-	-	305	-	1	347
Eucalyptus globulus	18	35	32	10	-	177	-	2	274
Eucalyptus saligna	-	-	-	-	-	14	-	-	14
Euphorbia sp.	311	168	14	171	23	385	46	71	1189
Ficus vasta	-	1	-	-	-	-	-	-	1
Grevillea robusta	2	2	-	-	-	-	-	-	4
Hagenia abyssinica	-	1	-	-	-	-	-	-	1
Juniperus procera	3	71	3	13	6	192	18	4	310
Maesa langcoelata	-	-	-	-	-	-	4	-	4
Mangifera indica	-	6	-	-	-	-	-	-	6
Maytenus sp.	-	-	-	-	-	-	-	3	3
Milletia ferruginea	-	2	-	-	-	-	-	-	2
Musa sp.[3]	-	1	-	-	-	-	-	-	1
Myrsine africana	-	-	-	-	-	3	-	-	3
Olea africana	8	71	6	16	5	43	14	10	173
Peremna schimperi	1	-	-	2	-	4	4	2	13
Prunus persica	4	74	-	-	-	-	-	-	78
Rhamnus prinoides	-	1	-	-	-	-	-	-	1
Rhus glutinosa	-	1	-	-	-	-	-	-	1
Ricinus communis	17	61	-	-	-	3	4	-	85
Rosa abyssinica[1]	-	5	-	12	-	-	21	20	58
Salix subserrata[2]	-	4	-	-	-	-	10	4	18
Schinus molle	1	7	1	-	-	-	-	-	9
Vangueria apiculata	1	1	-	-	-	-	-	-	2
Vernonia amygdalina	-	37	-	1	-	-	2	-	40
Total	404	742	60	292	43	2052	168	133	3894

[1] Bush   [2] Bush or tree   [3] *Gramineae*

Cordia africana is well known for shading. The species produces multiple usage, fixes atmospheric nitrogen and increases the content of humus of the soil through shedding leaves annually. Figure 4 shows a shading specimen in a farmer's field.

Ricinus communis is well appreciated by local people. It is a conspicuous woody plant in newly established villages.

A few more indigenous tree species like *Vernonia amygdalina, Croton macrostachyus* and *Calpurnia aurea* occur especially on farmers' fields serving preferably multiple usage.

Carissa edulis, Dovyalis sp. and *Rosa abyssinica* are the most frequent bushes found. Generally, *Dovyalis abyssinica* is intensively browsed and grows bush-like. Only a few specimens were classified as trees.

The large number of *Eucalyptus* trees attributes to the good performance of several *Eucalyptus* species introduced into the Hararghe Highlands. Due to the low susceptibility to browsing, the high quality of construction poles produced in short rotation periods, fair coppicing, easy handling of seeds, high germination rate and short periods to raise seedlings, the species have experienced general acceptance by farmers and high overall success. However, *Eucalyptus* spp. are preferably grown in woodlots. About half of the total number was identified to be *Eucalyptus globulus*. Presently, mainly seedlings of *Eucalyptus saligna* are desired.

Thirs in frequency of trees are *Cupressus* spp.: For about 15 years planting of *Cupressus* spp. has been a common practice to establish woodlots. Despite the extensive failures of *Cupressus* spp. in the eastern highlands these species are still planted.

The exotic *Acacia saligna* is preferably used in afforestations for soil and water conservation. *Acacia saligna* is characterized by an aggressive root system and relatively low susceptibility to browsing by cattle. However, goats and also sheep may completely damage newly planted stands. Another disadvantage is that in this ecological zone this species does not coppice. Hence, certain lopping trials have been undertaken and show promising initial results (Uibrig 1990). *Prunus persica* is the most widely grown fruit tree species in the catchment and preferably planted in fields, irrigated land and in homesteads.

Table 4 provides a general view on the number of trees per unit of area of the major land use types. According to this data settlements rank number three in tree density. Till now, the number of *Euphorbia* spp. is impressive as compared to other ligneous plants. A change towards shade spending and especially fruit trees is to be expected with the continued consolidation of the recently established villages.

On agricultural land most trees (45 per hectare) are found in irrigated fields. This attributes to the increasing fruit production in combination with agricultural crops, especially vegetables. The relatively low number of ca. 14 trees/ha on land managed without irrigation can be explained by the general objection to trees on agricultural fields. The number even tends to decline due to "zero-planting" and the removal of trees from fields that are cultivated by tractor.

Only a few trees can survive on marshy land, because frost and grazing damage the young seedlings. Other unimproved grassland and even fallow tend to be covered by a bushy vegetation if the woody plants are not subjected to browsing pressure.

A large number of almost 1300 trees per hectare next to creeks etc. may be assessed as an indicator of zero-use of the banks and even some tree planting for soil conservation. More than 50 percent of the total number consists of *Euphorbia* spp., which again hints to previous demarcation lines of farms, trails etc.

Tab.4. Occurrence of trees (individuals per ha) on the major land-use types within the Alemaya catchment (Source: Uibrig [1989]).

Land use type	Number of trees and bushes		
	Euphorbia sp.	other species	Total
		Number per ha	
Settlements	109.5	32.7	142.2
Agricultural land	3.8	24.4	28.2
Annual crops	3.4	10.9	14.3
Perennial crops	8.0	17.1	25.1
Irrigated agriculture	0.4	44.6	45.0
Fallow	3.3	24.8	28.1
Marshy grassland	.	2.1	2.1
Other unimproved grassland	6.0	18.5	24.5
Bushland	112.5	79.6	192.1
Forest land	173.6	717.9	891.5
Unproductive land	87.6	232.4	320.0
Swamp	.	.	.
Water bodies	.	.	.
Creeks etc.	676.2	590.5	1 266.7

Conclusion

The results of the land-use inventory confirm the general assessment that the tree-bearing character of the Hararghe Highlands still exists. Although natural forests have been extremely diminuished, trees are a conspicuous and appreciated element of the landscape. Increasing mechanization will, however, reduce the number of trees in agricultural land. But development of irrigated agriculture will render the growing of fruit trees profitable. Another tendency to increase number of trees in non-competitive planting designs is to be expected with the further consolidation of recently established villages, for example tree planting on new roads and as a measure of soil conservation along gullies, creeks etc.

The very small area of natural forest remaining on extreme sites presents a challange for careful protection and restoration. As pilot studies show, only closing the area may fulfill all requirements to rehabilitate the mountain forest. However, a longer period of time will be needed as compared to the enrichment of the degraded forest vegetation. Due to the lack of professional forest managers and financial funds, advanced silvicultural techniques cannot be applied properly. To a very limited extent rotation grazing and a minimum felling of trees seem to be applicable to ensure the active participation of local people in the programs.

The establishment of woodlots is considered to provide a valuable type of land use and will increase the proportion of forest land within the region. According to previous experiences within the communities the selection of good quality land will render positive economic results within very short time. The afforestation of low-quality land will primarily be devoted to soil and water conservation.

Planting *Eucalyptus* spp. may produce more than 50 m³ ha⁻¹ yr⁻¹ on fertile sites and distinctly less than 5 m³ ha⁻¹ yr⁻¹ on poor sites. Ecological risks of *Eucalyptus* spp., however, should be beared in mind. *Acacia saligna* has proved an applicable exotic tree species on relatively poor sites for multiple purpose and usage.

Field trials have to be intensified and extended applying indigenous species. With regard to the capacity of extension services it may be advisable to limit the number of species to a few. Initial experience collected from forest management plans in the communal sector may encourage the idea to extend the pilot projects by varying methodology and areas.

References

Badege Bishaw, Uibrig H (1989) Management of community woodlots in Hararghe Highlands, eastern Ethiopia. Paper presented to the 1st Natural Resources Improvement Conference. Addis Ababa, February 7-8. 24 pp

Breitenbach F von (1963) The indigenous trees of Ethiopia. 2nd ed. Addis Ababa: Ethiopian Forestry Association. 305 pp

Daniel Gamachu (1977) Aspects of climate and water budget in Ethiopia. Addis Ababa University Press. 71 pp

Forestry and Wildlife Conservation and Development Authority (1983) Forestry under respect of land use in Hararghe region. Addis Ababa. 15 pp

Hurni H (1986) Guidelines for development agents on soil conservation in Ethiopia. Addis Ababa: Community Forests and Development Department, Ministry of Agriculture, Ethiopia. 100 pp

Langlais C, Weill M, Wibaux H (1984) Farming systems research - preliminary survey and future programme. Alemaya College of Agriculture, Department of Agricultural Economics. 41 pp

Marklund SE. Odenyo VAO (1984) Assistance to land-use planning. Ethiopia. Vegetation and natural regions and their significance for land-use planning. Rome: UNDP/FAO, AG:DP/ETH/78/003, Technical Report 4. 75 pp

Poschen-Eiche P (1987) The application of farming systems research to community forestry. A case study in the Hararghe Highlands, eastern Ethiopia. Tropical Agriculture, TRIOPS, Langen. 250 pp

Schmitt C (1988) Khat (Catha edulis, Forskal) als Bestandteil des Ackerbaus und des Marktgeschehens in der Region Alemaya im östlichen Hochland Äthiopiens. Giessen: Diplom-Arbeit, Justus-Liebig-Universität, Wissenschaftliches Zentrum Tropeninstitut, Abteilung Pflanzenbau und Pflanzenzüchtung. 79 pp

Schrempp B (1987) A pilot project on non-conflicting multipurpose tree integration in the agricultural land-use system of the Hararghe Highlands, eastern Ethiopia. Alemaya: Alemaya University of Agriculture and Ministry of Agriculture, Addis Ababa, Report. 70 pp

Tamirie Hawando (1982) Summary results of soil science research program. Alemaya: Alemaya College of Agriculture. 132 pp

Uhlig SK (1983) Untersuchungen über die Ertragsfähigkeit verschiedener Baumarten in Ost-Äthiopien. Beiträge zur tropischen Landwirtschaft und Veterinärmedizin, Leipzig, 21: 459-463

Uibrig H (1989) Forest management plan. Tinike Peasants' Association 1.1.1989 to 31.12.1993 (23. Tahsas 1981 bis 22.Tahsas 1986 E.C.). Alemaya:Alemaya University of Agriculture, Faculty of Forestry. 20 pp (plus App: 1 Management book, 1 map)

Uibrig H (1987) Preliminary forest management plan for the Legeambo Farmers Producers' Cooperative 12.9.1987 to 11.9.1992 (1980 to 1984 E.C.). Alemaya: Alemaya University of Agriculture, Faculty of Forestry. 22 pp

Uibrig H (1988) Yield investigation of selected stands of several tree species in the Alemaya catchment for afforestation planning. A.U.A. Newsletter, Alemaya 2: 21-25

Uibrig H (1989) Report on a land-use survey in the Alemaya catchment, Hararghe Highlands, eastern Ethiopia. Alemaya: Alemaya University of Agriculture, Faculty of Forestry, Research Report. 68 pp

Uibrig H (1990) Wege zur Integration der Waldlandnutzung in die landwirtschaftlichen Nutzungssysteme im ostäthiopischen Hochland - ein Beitrag zur ländlichen Entwicklung in Entwicklungsländern. Dresden: Dissertation(B), Technische Universität Dresden. 160 S. Anhang 1-43

Uibrig H. Abdu Abdulkadir (1989) Natural forest inventory in the eastern Ethiopian highlands for decision making in management planning. Addis Ababa: Paper presented to the 1st Natural Resources Improvement Conference, Addis Ababa, February 7 and 8 1989. 20 pp

Verjux E (1987) Characterization of the climate at the Alemaya weather station. Alemaya: Alemaya University of Agriculture, Department of Agricultural Economics, Report. 53 pp

Westphal E (1975) Agricultural systems in Ethiopia. Wageningen: Centre for Agricultural Publishing and Documentation, Research Report No. 826

Tropical Forests in Transition
J. G. Goldammer (ed.)
© 1992 Birkhäuser Verlag Basel/Switzerland

Geoecological Consequences of Human Impacts on Forests in Sri Lanka

Christoph Preu* and Walter Erdelen**

Abstract

Between 1900 and 1988 Sri Lanka's forest cover was reduced from 70% to about 20%. Major causes were colonization schemes, increasing demand for timber, extension of agricultural land and expansion of tourism. Besides the quantitative removal of forests there has been reforestation which has led to qualitative changes in forest cover. These human impacts on the forests in Sri Lanka have caused not only a general degradation of land in the areas directly affected, but have also caused geoecological changes in distant areas. This paper presents (1) general considerations on the impact of human activity on tropical forests and the resulting geoecological consequences, as well as (2) specific information on the situation in Sri Lanka.

---

* Department of Physical Geography, University of Augsburg, Universitätsstr. 10, D-8900 Augsburg, Germany

** Department of Biogeography, University of the Saarland, D-6600 Saarbrücken, Germany

Introduction

Deforestation has been one of the traditional and significant ways in which humans modify their environment. Flenley (1979) indicated that clearing of rain forest for agriculture occurred since at least 3000 BP in Africa, since about 7000 BP in South and Central America, and possibly since 9000 BP or earlier in New Guinea and India. At present, however, deforestation has reached new dimensions. Annual deforestation rates for tropical forests are about 11 million ha/yr or 20.9 ha/min (FAO 1982).

In Sri Lanka, a tropical island in the Indian Ocean, natural forests covered 70% of the country in 1900 when the population was about 3.5 million. But increased population growth has led to drastic deforestation, particularly in the last few decades. By the time of national independence, in 1948, natural forest cover was already reduced to about 50%, and by 1988, when the population of Sri Lanka had reached 18 million, forest cover was reduced to about 20%. Both lowland and montane forests have been cleared to extend settled agriculture and cash crop cultivation, for shifting cultivation and planting of tobacco, tea and rubber plantations, and timber and fuel. Colonization schemes, urbanization and expansion of agricultural land within the scope of large-scale development projects, such as "The Accelerated Mahaweli Development Programme" (TAMS 1980), have further reduced the remaining natural forest cover. In addition, reforestation of grasslands, which partly covered previously deforested steep slopes in the central highlands, with exotic tree species such as Pinus and Eucalyptus, which are believed to prevent soil erosion by quickly establishing ground cover, has qualitatively changed the forest cover. The impact of human activity has also affected the coastal ecosystems. Coastal vegetation has been removed, particulary mangroves, to expand the infrastructures for tourism, and provide land for fisheries and coconut plantations. Further disturbance and pollution pose a threat to the remaining patches of natural coastal vegetation.

The human impacts on forests have caused not only a general land degradation in areas where those human impacts have taken place, but have also resulted in medium to long-distance effects with important geoecological consequences in other areas. This paper presents (1) general considerations on the impact of human activity on tropical forests and the resulting geoecological consequences, as well as (2) specific information on the situation in Sri Lanka.

Human Impacts on Tropical Forests - Some General Considerations

As indicated by the interrelations between them and their physical and chemical environment, tropical forests are the most complex extant ecosystem (e.g. Wischmeier 1975; Jansson 1982). Even more complex are the relationships between the abiotic and biotic components within tropical forest ecosystems (e.g. Kittredge 1948; Smith & Wischmeier 1965; Meyer & Monke 1965; Young 1976; Hewlett et al. 1984). The disturbance of these relationships due to human impacts leads to phenomena such as soil degradation and erosion.

Often overlooked are impacts on tropical ecosystems such as coastal vegetation which has multi-functional importance for plants and animals (for details cf. Mercer and Hamilton 1984). On a systems level coastal vegetation contributes to exporting decomposible plant debris into adjacent coastal waters, thus forming an important energy source for tropical estuaries and functioning as a buffer that prevents coastal erosion (Stoddart 1971).

Both deforestation and reforestation affect water budgets through interception of non-rainfall precipitation (Henderson-Sellers & Gornitz 1984) and contribute to surface albedo values (Gornitz 1987), which is an essential parameter in the global climatic system. Reduction in tropical forest cover has been considered one of the major factors contributing to global climatic changes (Jacobeit 1991).

The change of forested areas to agricultural land in the tropics has led to phenomena such as accelerated podzolization, acidification, and lateritization (for details cf. Goudie 1988). Shifting cultivation, possibly one of the earliest forms of land use in the tropics, originally aimed at maintaining "the general structure of the pre-existing natural ecosystem into which it is projected, rather than creating and sustaining one organized along novel lines and displaying novel dynamics" (Geertz 1963). The main idea behind shifting cultivation has been "the transfer of the rich store of nutrients locked up in the vegetation of the rain forest to a botanical complex whose yield to people is a great deal larger" (Swan 1987). Successful shifting cultivation depends on the optimal rotation of fallow and cultivation periods. If, mostly due to population increase, fallow periods are shortened soil characteristics may change drastically as a consequence of repeated burning (Morgan 1986). Changed microclimatic conditions may even prevent the re-establishment of forest communities. As a result, many tropical areas formerly under dense forest are now dominated by open vegetation dominates or grassland.

In addition to these changes in climatic conditions and in soil characteristics, such as soil structure, deforestation may also affect the hydrological patterns of catchments. It has repeatedly been shown that increased runoff follows deforestation (Gregory & Walling 1979; Jansson 1982). The opposite effect may occur in cases where forest is replaced by irrigated land (Lvovitch 1970). According to Pereira (1973), if carefully managed, deforested areas may be replaced by "hydrologically effective" substitutes.

Several studies have demonstrated how changes in forest cover influence erosion in the tropics (e.g. Douglas 1967; Roose 1971; Young 1976). The erosive power associated with high precipitation in the tropics has become particularly evident in areas where the forest has been removed completely.

Naturally, soil that is eroded is always deposited elsewhere. Though this statement may seem trivial, sedimentation processes following erosion are poorly understood in the tropics. Eroded soil may, in principle, be deposited anywhere between the extremes of the place of origin and the sea. In eroded uplands, sedimentation and damage associated therewith often occurs a long distance downstream. Although the amount of information on sediment load in tropical rivers has increased enormously, this information is mostly related to suspended load (e.g. Bosch and Hewlett 1982) rather than to bed load, which is much more difficult to measure (for details cf. Gregory & Walling 1979). Sedimentation on bottomlands caused by the overtopping of rivers, which is better understood, has created world-wide concern about countermeasures to be taken (FAO, 1965).

Situation in Sri Lanka

Physical setting

Sri Lanka located off the southern tip of the Indian subcontinent between 5°54'-9°52' N and 79°39'- 81°53'E, covers an area of some 64.000 km^2 (Fig. 1). Topographically, Sri Lanka consists of the central highlands in the south central part, which are subdivided into midlands (300-900 m a.s.l.) and uplands (900 m to about 2500 m a.s.l.), from which most of the rivers radiate coastwards. The central highlands are surrounded by an extensive lowland (0-300 m) which is narrow in the west and south but widens towards the north and east. The 1920 km long coastline is characterized by numerous bays and headlands, lagoons, estuaries, salt marshes and mangrove swamps. In the northwest and southeast, sand dunes and spits are well developed. Coral reefs are found off the southern, south western, and eastern coasts. Geologically, nine tenths of Sri Lanka is composed of highly metamorphosed crystalline rocks of Precambrian and Cambrian age; the remainder includes limestone, sandstones and shales of Tertiary and Quaternary origin (Cooray 1984).

The climate of Sri Lanka is characterized by seasonal changes in wind direction and rainfall patterns. During the southwest monsoon (mid-May to September), westerly to southwesterly winds prevail and heavy convectional rains occur in the southwest when average precipitation is between 1500 mm and 3000 mm. In the remaining parts of the island rainfall is less and droughts are a common feature. During the northeast monsoon (December to February), the relatively dry and stable air masses of the northeasterly winds predominate and lead to rainfall maxima in the north and east. Thus considering the intermonsoonal periods between the southwest monsoon and the northeast monsoon (October to November, March to mid-May), Sri Lanka's climate comprises four seasons. Based on the seasonal and spatial rainfall patterns, Domrös (1974) subdivides Sri Lanka into two main hygroclimatic zones, viz. the wet zone (mean annual rainfall higher than 1900 mm) in the southwest, including the western and south western slopes of the central highlands, and the dry zone (mean annual rainfall less than 1900 mm) covering the remaining parts of the island. The boundary of the hygroclimatic zones coincides with the climatic shed in the central highlands. Average temperatures vary little from month to month. Mean annual temperatures are about 27°C at sea level, 24°C at 500 m, and 15°C at 1900 m (Domrös 1974). Humidity is generally high throughout the year; annual averages are between 80 - 85%.

The spatial rainfall patterns reflect the distribution of the major vegetational communities. However, small-scale spatio-temporal differences in amounts of precipitation are important for the classification of the vegetation (Fernando 1968). For this study we adopted the subdivision with four zones (cf. Mueller-Dombois 1968; see Fig. 1): (A) Monsoon scrub jungle; (B) Semi-evergreen forest; (C) Intermediate forest; (D) Rain forest and grassland. Whereas zones A to C are comparatively uniform in floral composition zone D is differentiated into lowland forest (sea level to approx. 900m), montane forests (900-1500m), and cloud forest (above 1500m). Area D is more or less congruent with the wet zone, the remaining areas belong to the dry zone (see above).

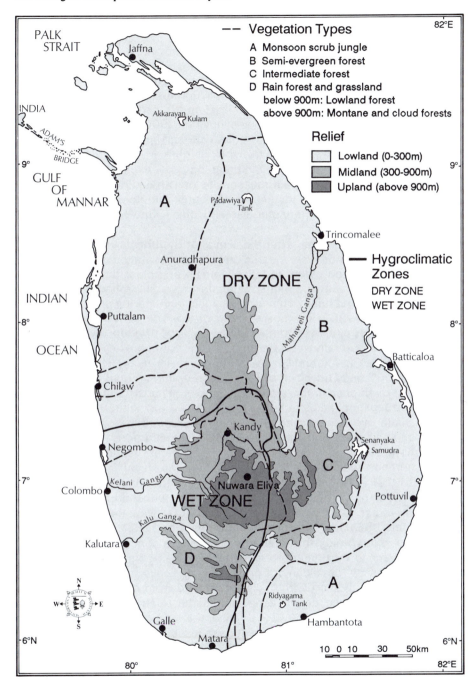

Fig.1. Relief, hygroclimatic zones and vegetation types of Sri Lanka

Historical background

When man first came to Sri Lanka, about 25 centuries ago, most of the island was covered to a varying degree by either natural forest or grassland (Silva 1986). Up to the "Kandyan Period" (1509 - 1815), "chena cultivation", a form of shifting cultivation, was practised only in some restricted areas of virtually all the provinces and therefore human impacts on the forests were negligible. Except where village settlements existed and shifting cultivation was practised, the watersheds of the central highlands remained largely in their natural state (Tennent 1859). Around the villages, which were mostly located in the valley bottoms, the population was not large enough to extend shifting cultivation into the hills. Fallow periods following shifting cultivation were undoubtedly much longer at that time. In the E where the density of settlements was higher, an irrigation system had evolved in which the central highlands functioned as a "reservoir" feeding the irrigation ditches which provided water for the paddy fields in the valleys (Panabokke 1988).

With the introduction of plantations, after the arrival of the British in 1815, much of the forests in the central highlands were cleared and environmental conditions changed drastically. "Money was sent to Ceylon, to fell its forests and plant them with coffee, and it was returned in the shape of copious harvests to some capitalists, leaving in some cases only the bare hillsides from where their rich harvests were drawn" (Ferguson 1903). Ferguson (1903) states that most of the forests were removed and very little remained in regions below 1500m. Much of the land that was cleared and not replanted and where no soil conservation measures were taken, changed into grasslands. During that period soil erosion reached a level which required the colonial government to impose a "Land Order" in 1873 to preserve the area above 1500 m.

Despite of the above mentioned deforestation Sri Lanka still had an approximate forest cover of 70% in 1900 when the population was 3.5 million. Although there were various attempts made at soil conservation and reforestation, land degradation continued unabated. The floods and landslides of 1947 generated a new concern to seek solutions to the problem of land degradation. This interest resulted in a Cabinet paper on soil conservation which was finally translated into legal form by the "Soil Conservation Act" of 1951. However, forest cover had further diminished to 50% in 1953 while the population had grown to 8.1 million. In 1982 with a population of nearly 15 million the natural forest cover was estimated to be 25% (Nanayakkara 1982) and was reduced to 23% in 1985 (Governmental Land Commission 1985). Further reduction in forest cover has been due firstly to the energy crisis and a concomitant demand for fuel, secondly to the demand for timber brought about by the boom in the construction industry, thirdly to large-scale development projects, and finally to the extension and intensification of shifting cultivation with cycles shortened from over 10 years to less than 3 years. The present forest cover, especially in the upper watershed areas, is estimated to be only approximately 9% (Governmental Land Commission 1989). One example of that rapid deforestation within recent decades is the catchment area of the Mahaweli Ganga. Nanayakkara (1982) quotes some 22% as being under forest in 1956. By 1971 this was reduced to 8% and has since then deteriorated further (Governmental Land Commission 1985). Jansen (1981) reports that only 9% of the Upper Mahaweli Ganga Catchment is covered by forest or forest plantations, which is well below the critical level for ensuring protection from erosion. The remainder is intensively managed land (51%), unmanaged agricultural land (15%) and unused or misused land, mostly scrub, areas under shifting cultivation, grassland and abandoned tealands (24%). Jansen points out that 40% is affected by extreme erosion, well above the "tentative standard of acceptable loss", and that 11% of the Upper Mahaweli Ganga Catchment is degraded to such an extent that rehabilitation is urgently needed.

The problem of land degradation is confined not only to the catchment areas, but also to the coastal zone. Although Sri Lanka boasts of a culture dating back 2500 years, its inhabitants had very little use for its surrounding ocean and coastal zone resources in the precolonial era. Therefore, even at the beginning of British colonization, vast areas of the coastal zone were covered with mangroves and "littoral woodland" (Tennent 1859). At present, Sri Lanka's coastal land, especially in the southwest, is densely populated and most of the natural vegetation has been removed for various kinds of high density land use systems and for infrastructures (Preu 1991).

In terms of traditional coastal land use, fisheries are very important. In particular the beaches and nearshore areas are used for fisheries. Although centralization of these activities has taken place with the establishment of fishery harbors in some areas, fishing activity in general has been extended along a narrow strip of coastal land. The intensity of activity has increased most markedly in key fishing areas such as Negombo, Ambalangoda and Dondra. This process has led to a significant reduction in natural vegetation cover. In many areas natural coastal vegetation has been replaced by coconut plantations or has been cleared for construction or fuel. More recently, urbanization has become a threat establishing areas of shanty housing, eg. south of Colombo between Dehiwala and Panadura, as well as industrial plants, energy installations and tourist facilities, even up to the high water mark (Preu 1989).

Geoecological consequences

Although the effects of the changes in the forest cover of Sri Lanka are obvious and are recognized by the governmental authorities and the national, as well as international scientific communities (Erdelen *et al.* 1992), very few systematic studies providing reliable data on geoecological consequences have been conducted out or are available.

Modifications of climatic patterns

Although modifications of climatic patterns resulting from changes in forest cover were already recognized by the Sri Lankan government in 1929, and forest conservation measures were labeled as a main objective of the forest policy in Sri Lanka (Perera 1975), only a few studies have been conducted on that topic.

For the Horton Plains, a plateau at an altitude of approximately 2000 m in the central highlands, the influence of forest cover on distribution and amount of precipitation has been shown (Mueller-Dombois 1968; Mueller-Dombois & Ellenberg 1974). Based on daily rainfall data the authors demonstrated that the rain gauges in forests received more precipitation during March and April (intermonsoon) compared to the gauge stations in the open grasslands adjacent to the forests. At the beginning of the Southwest monsoon (May) the amount of rainfall was about equal at both sites, and during June and July (southwest monsoon) more precipitation was recorded in the rain gauges of the grasslands compared to those in the forests. These differences are explained by the fact that clouds moving across the Horton Plains do not always result in precipitation during March and April, but that the trees comb out the supersaturated air masses and droplets precipitate on tree branches and leaves. So, according to this study, some 100 to 150 ltr/m² are supplied to the forest floor during the relatively dry period before the southwest monsoon. In contrast, during the southwest monsoon when the annual rainfall reaches its maximum the forest seems to receive less precipitation than the open grassland. This effect may be due to alternations between intensive shower activity and sunshine, the latter causing greater transpiration in the canopy of the forest (Mueller-Dombois 1968; Mueller-Dombois & Ellenberg 1974).

Hamamori (1967), in his analysis of the "Climate and Hydrology of the Mahaweli Basin", also considers how forests affect or "attract" rainfall and refers to the "considerable decrease in the average annual rainfall of Nuwara Eliya during the period between the last quarter of the 19th century and the second quarter of the 20th century". He points out that "this tendency seems to be common to most of the places in the upstream areas of the Upper Mahaweli Ganga. A simple question might be raised as to whether it is a consequence of tea plantations, since this phenomenon is more or less coincident with the intensification of tea plantation in its extent and period as well". However, Arulananthan's (1982) study on the relationship between rainfall characteristics and deforestation in the Sinharaja Forest proves that although vegetation does affect precipitation patterns, there is no evidence that it can affect the amount of precipitation.

There is much evidence that deforestation in the central highlands has frequently caused soil erosion, which is further increased by stronger winds in cleared areas (Nanayakkara, 1982). Experiments conducted by the Forest Department in the Uva Basin through the planting of *Eucalyptus* as shelter wood and timber show that during the southwest monsoon, when this region experiences strong winds, the average wind velocity was reduced to a quarter of that in the deforested area at distances up to 10 times the height of the trees (Governmental Land Commission 1985). Such "forest belts" have also contributed considerably to the conversion of grassland into areas of vegetable cultivation, particularly around Palugama (Keppetipola), because deliberate planting of trees has provided not only a windbreak, which has brought about protection from damaging winds, but has also resulted in higher humidity and reduced rates of evapotranspiration.

Modifications of hydrological patterns

In Sri Lanka, the importance of forestry for the conservation and management of watersheds were recognized as early as the 1930s. Apart from attempts in 1873 to preserve forests above an elevation of 1500 m, many government commissions have emphasized the role of forestry in watershed conservation since that time. However, only a limited number of studies on that topic have been conducted and only very little reliable data is available.

Soil moisture in the central highlands depends on type and density of the vegetation cover (Mueller-Dombois 1968; Mueller-Dombois & Ellenberg 1974). Consequently runoff of all rivers with headstreams in this region is also controlled by the forests of the central highlands. These rivers provide the water for irrigation schemes, reservoirs and hydro-electric power projects. Therefore, land use management in upper river catchment areas has become an important task and should aim at (1) maximizing water yields, (2) minimizing fluctuation of base flow, (3) minimizing sediment transport, and (4) maintaining drinking water quality.

The effects of forest cover on hydrology, in particular on the timing and distribution of streamflow, is still widely misunderstood (Lee 1980). Summarizing the state of present knowledge on the protective role of tropical forests Hamilton et. al. (1985) conclude that " ... reducing forest cover of a forested catchment increases the water yield from the catchment, with the majority of this increase occuring as baseflow. Planting trees in non-forested environments will tend to decrease the water yield with the majority of the decrease occuring in the baseflow component. Changing forest cover in headwater catchments will have only a minor impact on downstream flooding, particularly on large river basins. Reducing forest cover often leads to an increase in erosion and stream sedimentation". The limited number of studies conducted on that topic in Sri Lanka indicates that water yields from many catchments increased after deforestation and led to a steady increase in the runoff/rainfall ratios of the river catchment areas. According to Abernathy's (1976) and Madduma Bandara's (1977) studies the average annual increase in runoff/rainfall ratio between 1953 and 1974 was about 0.75% in dry zone catchments, whereas the increase in runoff/rainfall ratio in wet zone catchments reached nearly 1.4%. Based on these data the authors concluded that the increase of runoff/rainfall ratios over the years is a direct consequence of increased deforestation and land degradation in the upper catchment areas.

The results of the only study on the effect of forest cover on the occurrence of floods in Sri Lanka contradict the conclusions of Hamilton *et. al.* (1985) as quoted above. Ponnadurai *et al.* (1979), who studied the effects of selective logging in two catchment areas in the Sinharaja Forest, concluded that peak flows are significantly higher and tend to occur at shorter intervals in "exploited" catchment areas compared to "unexploited" ones.

During the past decade many development projects related to the hydrological effects of changes in the forest cover have been launched in Sri Lanka, but neither data nor results have been published or are available.

Modifications of geomorphological processes

Soil erosion

The problem of land degradation caused by deliberate deforestation, particularly in the central highlands, was recognized by the Sri Lankan government soon after the introduction of plantation agriculture at the beginning of the 19th century and remedial measures were taken. However, few systematic and detailed studies on the loss of soil under natural forest or in areas where forest has been removed for the extension of agricultural land have been undertaken. One such study by Krishnarajah (1984) concludes that the areas with highest soil erosion are the midlands and uplands in the wet zone areas of the central highlands. He estimates that 30 cm of the top soil in this region has been lost since the beginning of the century. TAMS (1980) studied the loss of soil in the area around Hanguranketa located in the upper Maha Oya catchment area on the western hillslopes of the central highlands, where natural forest had been cleared for cultivation. Loss of soil was between 308 and 913 $mt \cdot ha^{-1} \cdot yr^{-1}$ in areas where tobacco was cultivated. Higher rates were reported only from abandoned tealands and scrubland. On other cultivated land, even on steep terrain (slopes up to 40%), maximum soil loss was estimated at only 570 $mt \cdot ha^{-1} \cdot yr^{-1}$.

More detailed studies on soil erosion were conducted in the Nuwara Eliya district in the central highlands. The district has a total area of 1745 km^2, altitude ranges from 300 m to 2000 m. 78% of the land used is situated on slopes steeper than 30% and 15% on slopes steeper than 60%. The southwest part receives rain during the southwest monsoon and northeast monsoon as well as during the intermonsoon periods. The drier northeast part receives rainfall only during the northeast monsoon and the two intermonsoon periods.

In the precolonial era and even in the colonial periods of the Portuguese (1505-1658) and the Dutch (1658 - 1796) only some areas under forest were used for shifting cultivation and paddy cultivation in the Nuwara Eliya district (Werner, 1984). With the arrival of the British in 1815, the situation changed drastically. From 1820 onwards, vast areas were cleared for the cultivation of coffee, later substituted by tea. As the coffee plantations were only partly replaced by tea, the remaining areas left fallow developed into grasslands, where, even after a period of 100 years, forests have not established themselves. With the increasing international demand for tea, remaining forests were removed to extend tea plantations even into the peak regions of mountains. At the same time, the population density here increased from about 21 inhabitants per km^2 in 1870 to about 170 per km^2 in 1989. This has been due to both an increase in population growth and to an increased demand for laborers. Out of the district's total population of 604,000 in 1989, only 7% lived in urban areas, almost 60% on tea plantations and 33% in rural areas (NORAD 1989). The resulting increased demand for land for food production and infrastructural measures has led to further deforestation, in addition to that caused by the extension of tea plantations. Zijlstra (1989a) estimated that in 1989 cultivated land covered an area of 95,000 ha composed of (1) 325 state managed tea plantations covering almost two thirds of the cultivated area (64,000 ha) and (2) the smallholder or village agricultural sector (31,000 ha) with land use categories such as shifting cultivation and tobacco cultivation (35%), mixed gardens (26%), paddy cultivation (18%), tea smallholdings (11%), and homesteads (10%). The remaining 40% (70,000 ha) of the district was still covered with woodlands and grasslands, but only some 29,000 ha were "dense forest", whereas the remaining 41,000 ha comprised "degraded forests" (20,000 ha), scrubland (8,700 ha) and grassland (13,000 ha).

The specific geomorphological situation, the high pressure on agricultural land together with inappropriate agricultural methods (shifting cultivation), and poor management in some of the tea plantations have led to serious land degradation in the past few decades. Stocking (1986) estimates that in tea lands about 30 cm of the topsoil, corresponding to 40 $t \cdot ha^{-1} \cdot yr^{-1}$, has been lost during the past century. Panabokke's (1988) estimates range between 100 - 150 $t \cdot ha^{-1} \cdot yr^{-1}$ in poorly managed seedling tea plantations and 0.3 $t \cdot ha^{-1} \cdot yr^{-1}$ in well managed vegetatively propagated (VP) tea plantations. Estimates of erosion in the village and agricultural sectors range between 18 and 70 $t \cdot ha^{-1} \cdot yr^{-1}$ in vegetable cultivation areas (Panabokke 1988) and 100 and 200 $t \cdot ha^{-1} \cdot yr^{-1}$ in shifting cultivation areas (Zijlstra, 1989a). By contrast soil erosion rates in areas under "dense forest" are very low and range between 0.1 $t \cdot ha^{-1} \cdot yr^{-1}$ and 1.0 $t \cdot ha^{-1} \cdot yr^{-1}$ (Zijlstra 1989b).

No quantitative empirical studies have investigated the relation between changes in forest cover and the occurrence of earthslips and landslides in Sri Lanka (Preu 1986; Mohns 1988). Although opinions about the stabilizing effect of forest cover on steep slopes differ (for details cf. Morgan 1986) it is generally agreed that such mass movements are less frequent in forested areas than in areas cleared of forests (Goudie 1988). In, for example, the Katmandu-Kakani area of Nepal which is similar to the central highlands of Sri Lanka, Bajracharya (1983) concludes that "serious damages are clearly related to intensive cultivation especially in steep terrain. ... Deforestation of steep slopes to provide additional land for cultivation, resulting from the population pressure, is a major reason for heavy losses from erosion, earthslips and landslides."

Before the introduction of plantation industries, human settlements and agricultural land use in the central highlands were largely confined to the valley bottoms. Earthslips and landslides triggered off by heavy rainfall were a recurrent natural phenomenon in various parts of the central highlands. Damage from such mass movements has been minimal as they mostly occurred in uninhabited areas. The extension of human settlements and the rapid and uncontrolled opening of the forests for plantation agriculture, e.g. for tea, since the mid 19th century, particularly in steep terrain and geologically vulnerable areas, foreshadowed the present problems of earthslips and landslides in the central highlands. Responding to the growing pressure on the forests, the Forest Department warned of the possible consequences of indiscriminate clearing. The convention "Standing Orders to Surveyors and Administrators" restricted cultivation activities to areas below 1500 m (Nanayakkara 1982).

As a remedial measure to settle landless people in the central highlands the alienation of land for village expansion and cultivation schemes began in the 1930s, particularly under the "Land Development Ordinance" of 1935. In areas where there were resettlement schemes, villagers moved to vulnerable steep terrain between plantations and villages where, as a result, the impact on the remaining forest patches increased drastically. The records available since 1930 bear ample evidence of the frequent occurrence of earthslips and landslides in planned settlements in the central highlands as examplified by colonies such as Goodwood, Elangahapitiya and Mahawewa (Nanayakkara 1982).

The intensity and frequency of earthslips and landslides have increased in recent times. However, this assertion is based on qualitative information rather than on empirical scientific studies. Based on records of the Geological Survey Department (1987) it appears that over 60% of reported earthslips and landslides have taken place after 1978 and can be attributed to changes in forest cover and subsequent more widespread land use in steep terrain. But even more important, shifting cultivation has spread to geologically as well as geomorphologically unstable slopes and fallow periods have decreased with the growth of the rural population. Landlessness and the poverty crisis forced people to encroach on steep terrain and grow cash crops such as vegetables and tobacco. A considerable proportion of leaf supplied to the two major tobacco companies in Sri Lanka originates from farmers growing tobacco on shifting cultivation lands and encroached areas (Department of Census and Statistics 1985; Zijlstra 1989a). Most farmers are aware of the fact that they are cultivating land vulnerable to soil erosion and earthslips, but they continue in this fashion to earn their living in the absence of alternative incentives.

Tobacco cultivation is often considered the main cause of land degradation, particularly of soil erosion, earthslips and landslides in hill country areas (Morgan 1986). However, many of the earthslips and landslides in the central highlands of Sri Lanka are not directly associated with tobacco cultivation (Geological Survey Department 1987), but rather occur in areas where vegetables are grown, shifting cultivation is practised and even where tea plantations are located, especially on slopes steeper than 20% (Preu 1986). As soil loss in areas under tobacco cultivation is high (TAMS 1980; Mohns 1988; see also above), tobacco cultivation should be discouraged on steep slopes in the central highlands. Apart from shifting cultivation and tobacco cultivation, occasional reference is made to areas where forests were replaced by irrigated arable land and where the terracing of paddy fields is considered a possible cause of earthslips and landslides (Gorrie 1954; Vitanage 1992).

Apart from the many earthslips and landslides in the central highlands in 1947, which caused devastating floods in many valleys (Gorrie 1954), some of the worst earthslips and landslides were recorded in the wet zone area of the central highlands in January 1986. The Governmental Land Commission (1989) reported that "there is hardly any doubt that the immediate cause ... was the spell of unusually heavy rain and continued rainfall in the areas concerned". Certainly in the period between 4 to 16 January 1986, the central highlands received an amount of rainfall which was over four to five times the average monthly rainfall for January (Nildandahinna: 1195 mm, Udapussellawa: 924 mm, Walapone: 695 mm), with 508 mm of rainfall being recorded within 20 hours at the Watalawa climatological station (Department of Meteorology 1990). It also appears that periods of high intensity rainfall lasting 7 to 14 days occur from time to time in the central highlands (Domrös 1974). However, heavy rainfall alone cannot cause earthslips and landslides of devastating dimensions if other conditions favorable for sliding are not met. In addition to the natural factors in the central highlands - such as the geological, structural, geomorphological and topographical features which favour the occurrence of earthslips and landslides - the human impacts on the forest and subsequent improper land use over the past 100 years were the main reasons for these mass movements. Removal of the protective forest decreases rainfall interception and transpiration while increasing the amount and velocity of rainfall that reaches the surface. In addition, deforestation diminishes soil thickness and, as a consequence, decreases the infiltration capacity of the soil. Thus, the removal of the forest cover causes a general slope destabilization followed by earthslips and landslides on steep slopes.

Sedimentation

Land degradation in the central highlands has led to a serious disturbance in the ecological balance, particularly in watersheds. Although siltation and sedimentation processes caused by changes in forest cover in Sri Lanka are poorly understood, siltation of "Lake Gregory" in Nuwara Eliya, "Kandy Lake", Polgolla and Norton reservoirs and several irrigation canals such as Waduwawela Ela, Bodi Ela and Murapola Ela and others in the area of Walapane, Hanguranketa and Hewaheta may be related to the human impacts on forests in the respective watersheds. In addition, springs and streams have dried up after the reduction of forest cover in watersheds, particularly along the eastern slopes of the central highlands (Nanayakkara, 1982).

The information presented above adequately highlights the sedimentation problem and its relation to deforestation and subsequent land degradation. However, studies which have been conducted on that topic, mainly concentrate on the changes in sediment transport of rivers due to changes in forest cover and focus on the catchment area of the Mahaweli Ganga. One of the earliest estimates of silt load carried by the upper Mahaweli Ganga (above Peradeniya/Kandy) ranges from about 130,000 to 820.000 $t \cdot yr^{-1}$ (Joachim & Pandithasekera 1930). More recent studies have estimated a soil loss of 0.2 $mm \cdot yr^{-1}$ or 417 $t \cdot km^2 \cdot yr^{-1}$ in this catchment area, and they indicate that the average annual sediment transport of the upper Mahaweli Ganga was about 486.000 $t \cdot yr^{-1}$ in the period between 1950 and 1982 (Lauterjung & Platz 1985). Sediment transport of the Mahaweli Ganga at Weragantota (located off the central highlands' east slope) was estimated at 618,000 t in 1975 and 1540,000 t in 1982 (Lauterjung & Platz 1985). These figures indicate just how drastic the human impacts are on forest cover in the Upper Mahaweli Ganga Catchment. However, these assumed sediment loads are based on the interpretation of the sedimentation in some small upland reservoirs, but not on actual sediment and bed load data. Reliable data on bed load and suspended load in the rivers of the Upper Mahaweli Catchment are not available. Sediment transport has been measured only sporadically and does not allow extrapolation on annual dynamics. The Water Resources Board (1985) maintains that the sediment transport figures tend to be underestimated. Contrary to that, TAMS (1980) concluded that sedimentation will not affect the functioning of water reservoirs in the Upper Mahaweli Ganga Catchment and will not reduce their life span (estimated at 50 years) "because the dead volumes of these reservoirs are large enough" (Lauterjung & Platz 1985).

Modifications of coastal development

Siltation of lagoons has become a serious problem affecting the productivity of most of the lagoons in Sri Lanka. Major causes have been clearing peripheral areas of vegetation and deforestation in watersheds. Both result in increased runoff and soil erosion and hence the closure of lagoon outlets. Siltation and related problems have altered the physical and chemical characteristics of some and have affected some that are economically important such as Valachchenai Lagoon (East-coast) and Negombo Lagoon (West-coast). Fine sediments have formed a thin layer and have caused excessive oxygen reduction both within the sediments and the overlying water (Preu 1991). In some lagoons high quantities of sediment also increased water temperatures beyond critical levels for aquatic animal species (Wickramaratne 1985).

Although the formation of seasonal sand bars across mouths of rivers and lagoons is a common phenomenon in Sri Lanka, their size and continuity has increased in recent decades. Although the causes of sand bar formation differ from site to site, deforestation and land-use changes in the catchment areas have supported the development of sand bars. Such closures affect the productivity of estuaries by decreased salinity levels, siltation, concentration of pollutants beyond acceptable levels and insufficient flushing and water exchange (Swan 1987). They also cause downstream flooding and prevent navigational accesses to and from the sea (Preu, 1991). In some cases, where water of such estuarine areas has been used for agriculture and irrigation the opening of such outlets by artifical means has also caused an increase in salinity thus creating a number of ecological problems in near-by areas under cultivation (Preu et al. 1989). An example of a formerly productive lagoon that has become a dead lake due to sand bar formation is "Mundel Lake" located on the West coast. Its outlet was closed by a sand bar and subsequent stagnation. Serious pollution and siltation problems and resulting reduced productivity in the Batticaloa Lagoon (East coast), which was one of the most productive lagoons, was also associated with the formation of sand bars at its outlet (Preu 1991).

The coastal vegetation performs an important function in regulating climatic conditions and maintaining hydrological characteristics. Increased runoff and sediment load of rivers, for instance, may destroy coral reefs and associated life forms as well as cause excessive siltation. Increased runoff can also lead to increased concentrations of pollutants which are washed off the agricultural lands in the catchment areas and are transported to the coastal waters. Vegetation also helps to stabalize coastal land forms and reduce coastal erosion. Clearing of coastal vegetation is a serious problem in Sri Lanka. In urban areas such clearing occurs as a result of construction activities. In rural areas coastal vegetation is cleared for fuel. Along the East coast the demand for fuelwood has resulted in even mangrove areas being denuded. The seasonal timing of the rate of freshwater discharge to the coastal zone governs salinity and circulation which in turn affects productivity, stability and overall carrying capacity of the coastal ecosystems. Natural seasonal flow rates in these systems are generally optimal for plants and animals as they have synchronized their life cycles to such seasonality. Denudation of coastal vegetation and increased runoff and sediment load of rivers, however, may radically alter the natural rhythm of organisms typical for coastal ecosystems, especially their breeding, feeding and migration, thereby affecting overall productivity of coastal waters.

The human impacts on coastal vegetation and its geoecological consequences are illustrated with two representative examples below. In the case of Negombo, a tourist resort north of Colombo (west coast), about 95% of the tourist hotels built in and around Negombo are located in close proximity of the coast and Negombo Lagoon. These hotels are located on a 100-150 m wide strip of land between Negombo town and Kuda Paduwa. Hotel owners have cleared the coastal vegetation and have built hotels very close to the beach considering the preference of tourists for the beach. More than 50% of the hotels are located less than 20 m from the high water mark. Only 10% of the hotels are more than 30 m away. Presently, some 80% of these hotels facing the coastal strip are confronted with the problem of coastal erosion (Preu 1991). In addition to various protective structures which the government has built to protect these hotels from erosion, the hoteliers themselves have undertaken coast protection measures on their own. All these protection efforts, while providing only a temporary solution, have destroyed the scenic attraction of the coastal stretch. Apart from this, the hotels are faced with an enormous financial burden since the destruction of the scenic value has reached such an extent that tourists are no longer attracted.

A second example is on the coast near Hikkaduwa, 20 km north of Galle, an area representative of the coastal zone in southwest Sri Lanka outside towns and larger settlements. The coastal section may be subdivided into (1) raised beach with main road and various types of land use, (2) present-day beach, and (3) the near-shore zone. During the NE-monsoon low waves 0.5-1.5 m high and the southeast setting swell cause a southward sand drift resulting in accumulation and an increasing width of the present day beach. During the southwest monsoon, however, strong southwesterly to westerly winds prevail and high waves of 1.0 - 3.0 m occur. The oncoming waves reach up to the front of the raised beach and reform its edge by erosion. Mainly in places where the vegetation was removed and destroyed, the swash runs in canal-like footpaths further landwards, reaches the raised beach, and washes over it. Subsequently, the receding water removes unconsolidated raised beach sand, widens the "canals", and lateraly erodes the raised beach (Preu 1991). Although the beach profile seems to show a similar appearance in the following NE-monsoon period as in the preceding one, the annual net sediment balance is negative and, therefore, poses an increasing threat to settlements and public installations in years to come.

Conclusion

The human impacts on the forests in Sri Lanka have caused land degradation which has reached serious dimensions, particularly in the central highlands and the coastal zone. If present trends continue irreversible changes in the availability and quality of natural resources may occur in the near future. Present management activities should focus on the landscape mosaic of Sri Lanka as a whole rather than on units which, as shown above, may lie far apart from each other but are in fact interlinked through the flow of energy and matter. Understanding long-distance and often time-delayed effects may be crucial for the formulation of integrated management plans for montane and coastal ecosystems in Sri Lanka. Our poor understanding of patterns and processes that characterize these highly complex systems, at the same time requires detailed basic and applied research programs which have not been formulated to date. Within its environmental programs and activities conservation and management of natural resources in montane and coastal landscapes should be given higher priority by the decision making community of Sri Lanka.

References

Abernathy CL (1976) Report on a visit in Sri Lanka. National Committee for the IHP Irrigation Department, Colombo, 21pp (unpublished report)

Arulananthan J (1982) The effects, if any, on rainfall due to deforestation of the Sinharaja Forest. Tropical Environments 5:17-131

Bajracharya D (1983) Deforestation in the flood/fuel context: historical and political perspective from Nepal. Mountain Research and Development 3:227-240

Bosch JM, Hewlett JD (1982) A review of catchment experiments to determine the effect of vegetation changes on water yield and evapotranspiration. J Hydrology 55:3-23

Cooray PG (1984) An introduction to the geology of Sri Lanka. National Museums of Sri Lanka, 340pp

Cronin LE (1967) The role of man in estuary processes. American Association for the Advancement of Science 83:667-689

Department of Census and Statistics (1985) Statistical abstract of the Democratic Socialist Republic of Sri Lanka. Ministry of Plan Implementation (Colombo)

Department of Meteorology (1990) Summary of meteorological observations in Sri Lanka. Colombo

Domrös M (1974) The agroclimate of Ceylon. Geoecol Res 2:1-265

Douglas I (1967) Natural and man-made erosion in the humid tropics of Australia, Malaysia and Singapore. Int Assoc Sci Hydrol 75:17-30

Ellenberg H (1979) Man's influence on tropical mountain ecosystems in South America. J Ecol 67: 401-416

Erdelen W. Preu Chr. Ishwaran N. Madduma Bandara CM (eds.) (1992) Ecology and Landscape Management in Sri Lanka. Proceedings of the international and interdisciplinary Symposium, Colombo/Sri Lanka, Josef Margraf Publishers (in press)

Ferguson J (1903) Ceylon in the jubilee year. London: Haddon

Fernando SNU (1968) The natural vegetation of Ceylon. Colombo: Swabasha

Flenley JR (1979) The equatorial rain forest: a geological history. London: Butterworth

Food and Agriculture Organization of the United Nations (FAO) (1965) Soil erosion by water. Rome, 284pp

Food and Agriculture Organization of the United Nations (FAO) (1982) Tropical forest resources. FAO Forestry Paper 30, Rome, 106pp

Geertz C (1963) Agricultural involution: the process of ecological change in Indonesia. Berkeley: University of California Press

Geological Survey Department (Colombo) (1987) Disaster in the Hills. Colombo, 49pp (unpublished report)

Gornitz V (1987) Climatic consequences of anthropogenic vegetation changes from 1880-1980. In Rampino MR. Sanders JE. Newman WS. Königsson LK. (eds.) Climate - History, periodicity, and predictability, pp 47-69. New York: Van Nostrand Reinhold Company

Gorrie ML (1954) Kotmale landslides and adjoining river catchments. Sessional paper No. XVII, Ministry of Agriculture and Irrigation, Colombo, 37pp

Goudie AS (1973) Duricrusts of tropical and subtropical landscapes. Oxford: Clarendon Press

Goudie AS (1988) The human impact on the natural environment. Basil Blackwell, 338pp

Governmental Land Commission (1985) First interim report of the land commission. Ministry of Agriculture, Colombo, 47pp

Governmental Land Commission (1989) Second interim report of the land commission. Ministry of Agriculture, Colombo, 52pp

Gregory KJ, Walling DE (1979) Drainage basin: form and process. Ewward Arnold, London, 458pp

Hamamori A (1967) Mahaweli Ganga irrigation and hydropower survey. FAO and Irrigation Department (Colombo), 109pp

Hamilton LS, Bonell M, Cassels DS, Gilmour DA (1985) The protective role of tropical forests: a state of knowledge review. Environment and Policy Institute, Hawaii (USA), 208pp

Henderson-Sellers A, Gornitz V (1984) Possible climatic impacts of land cover transformations, with particular emphasis on tropical deforestation. Climatic Change 6:231-257

Hewlett JD, Post HE, Doss R (1984) Effect of clear-cut silviculture on dissolved ion export and water yield in the Piedmont. Water Resources Research 20:1030-1038

Jacobeit J (1991) Climatic impacts of tropical land use practices. In Erdelen W. Ishwaran N. Müller P. (eds.) Tropical Ecosystems. Proceedings of the International and Interdisciplinary Symposium, Saarbrücken/FRG. Verlag Josef Margraf, Weikersheim/FRG: 65-82

Jansen MAB (1981) The Upper Mahaweli Catchment. Case study report, Sri Lanka. Watershed Management Training Course, Chiang Mai, Thailand, 39pp (unpublished report)

Jansson MB (1982) Land erosion by water in different climates. Uppsala University, UNGI Rapport 57:1-151

Joachim AWR. Pandithasekera DG (1930) Sediment transport in the Mahaweli Ganga. Tropical Agriculturist 74:203-209

Kittredge J (1948) The effects of woody vegetation on climate, water and soil with applications to the conservation of water and the control of floods and erosion. Mc.Graw-Hill, 139pp

Krishnarajah P (1984) Erosion and degradation of the environment. Paper presented at the annual session of the Soil Science Society of Sri Lanka (unpublished)

Lanly JP, Clement J (1979) Present and future natural forest and plantation areas in the tropics. Unasylva 31:12-20

Lauterjung H. Platz H (1985) Watershed management project for the upper Mahaweli Ganga. Irrigation Department, Colombo, 73pp (unpublished report)

Lee R (1980) Forest hydrology. New York: Columbia University Press

Lvovitch MI (1970) World water balance. Intern Assoc Sci Hydrol 93:401-415

Madduma Bandara CM (1977) Water resources of SE Sri Lanka. Asian regional meeting of the national committee of the IHP, Colombo, 52pp

Mercer DE, Hamilton LS (1984) Mangrove ecosystems: some economic and natural benefits. Nature and Resources 20:14-19

Meyer LD, Monke EJ (1965) Mechanics of soil erosion by rainfall and overland flow. Trans Am Soc Agric Eng 8:572-577

Mohns B (1988) Land use and erosion control planning for hydro-project catchments in the upcountry of Sri Lanka. 3rd Regional GTZ Symposium on Long-term Power System Planning, Colombo (Sri Lanka), Technical Papers 2:32-46 (unpublished report)

Morgan RPC (1986) Soil erosion and conservation. Longman, UK, 298pp

Mueller-Dombois D (1968) Ecogeographic analysis of a climate map of Ceylon with special reference to vegetation. Ceylon Forester 8:39-58

Mueller-Dombois D, Ellenberg H (1974) Aims and methods of vegetation ecology. New York: John Wiley

Nanayakkara VR (1982) Forests: Policies and strategies for conservation and development. Sri Lankan Forester 15:32-47

NORAD (1989) Environmental study of Sri Lanka. NORAD, Colombo (Sri Lanka), 239pp (unpublished report)

Panabokke CR (1988) Land use planning for Sri Lanka. Ministry of Agriculture, Colombo, 47pp (unpublished report)

Pereira HC (1973) Land use and water resources in temperate and tropical climates. Cambridge University Press, 215pp

Perera AS (1975) Natural resources development. Economic Review 7:3-13

Ponnadurai DK. Gomez GEM. Kandiah A (1979) Effect of selective felling on hydrological parameters of a wet zone catchment. Asian regional meeting of IHP national committee, Colombo, 41pp

Preu C (1986) Geomorphological observations in the tea-growing areas of the wet zone of Sri Lanka's uplands with special regard to the problem soil erosion. Sri Lankan Forester 17:157-162

Preu C (1989) Zur Problematik der rezenten Morphodynamik an den Küsten Sri Lankas - Ursachen und Auswirkungen der Küstenabrasion an der W- und SW-Küste zwischen egombo und Dondra Head. Forschungen auf Ceylon III, Franz Steiner Verlag: 23-42

Preu C (1991): Zur Küstenentwicklung Sri Lankas im Quartär. Untersuchung der Steuerungsmechanismen und ihrer Dynamik im Quartär zur Ableitung eines Modells der polygenetischen Küstenentwicklung einer Insel in den wechsel-feuchten Tropen. Augsburger Geographische Hefte 10

Preu C. Sterr H. Zumach WD (1989) Monitoring of the coastal environments by means of a remote controlled balloon-borne camera (LAP-technique). Proceedings of 6th Symposium on Coastal and Ocean Management/ASCE, Charleston, SC:4847-4861

Roose EJ (1971) Influence des modificationes du milieu naturel sur l'erosion: le bilan hydrique et chimique suite Ña mise en culture sous climat tropical, Cyclo. ORSTOM, Adiopodoumé Ivory Coast, 307pp

Scott PA (1978) Tropical rain forest in recent ecological thought: The reassessment of a non-renewable resource. Progress in Physical Geography 2:80-98

Silva P (1986) The need for land use planning in Sri Lanka. Sri Lanka Foundation Institute, 63pp

Smith DD, Wischmeier WH (1965) Rainfall erosion. Adv in Agron 14:109-148.

Stocking MA (1986) Land use planning - Phase II. UNDP/FAO Project SRL/84/032, 83pp

Stoddart DR (1971) Coral reefs and islands and catastrophic storms. In JA Steers (ed) Applied coastal geomorphology, Macmillan:154-197

Swan B (1987) Sri Lanka mosaic: environment, man, continuity and change. Marga Institute, Colombo, 473pp

TAMS (1980) Environmental Assessment: Accelerated Mahaweli Development Programme. Ministry of Mahaweli Development (unpublished report)

Tennent E (1859) Ceylon: an account of the island. London, 439pp

Vitanage PW (1992) Impact of landslide hazards in Sri Lanka and preventive and mitigating measures. In Erdelen W. Preu C. Ishwaran N. Madduma Bandara CM (eds.) Ecology and Landscape Management in Sri Lanka. Proceedings of the international and interdisciplinary Symposium, Colombo/Sri Lanka, Josef Margraf Publishers (in press)

Water Resources Board (1985) Watershed management survey (unpublished report)

Werner WL (1984) Die Höhen- und Nebelwälder auf der Insel Ceylon (Sri Lanka). Tropisch-subtropische Pflanzenwelt 46:467-504

Wickramaratne HJM (1985) Environmental problems of the coastal zone in Sri Lanka. Economic Review:8-16

Wischmeier WH (1975) Estimating the soil loss equatation's cover and management factor for undisturbed areas. US Dep Agric, Agric Res Serv, 137pp

Young KK (1976) Erosion potential of soils. Proceedings 3rd Sediment Conference Denver (Colorado):567-583

Zijlstra PJ (1989a) Erosion hazard and suitability of the present land use. Integrated Rural Development Project, Ministry of Agriculture (Colombo), 47pp (unpublished report)

Zijlstra PJ (1989b) The need for land use improvement in the Nuwara Eliya district. Integrated Rural Development Project, Ministry of Agriculture (Colombo), 53pp (unpublished report)

Tropical Forests in Transition
J. G. Goldammer (ed.)
© 1992 Birkhäuser Verlag Basel/Switzerland

Structure and Dynamics of the Upper Montane Rain Forests of Sri Lanka

Wolfgang L. Werner* and Sinnathamby Balasubramaniam**

Abstract

The upper montane rain forests of Sri Lanka occur above 1500 m in the Central Highlands and Knuckles mountains of Sri Lanka. There is a marked difference in floristic composition and physiognomy against the lower montane rain forests of middle elevation. The most frequent plant families are Lauraceae (*Cinnamomum, Litsea, Actinodaphne*) and Myrtaceae (*Syzygium, Eugenia, Rhodomyrtus*), followed by Clusiaceae (*Calophyllum, Garcinia*), Theaceae (*Gordonia, Ternstroemia*), Elaeocarpaceae and Symplocaceae. Gymnosperms and Fagaceae, which are prominent in the mountains of Asia and other regions of the world, are lacking in South India and Sri Lanka. This makes the mountain flora of Sri Lanka very peculiar, as the montane species derive from the rain forest flora of the lowland (cf. Werner 1984, 1985). The analysis of trace elements in leaves of forest trees in Sri Lanka shows, that those of lowland rain forest and upper montane rain forest are very similar in contrast to deciduous forest and mangrove. The content of aluminium in trees of the upper montane rain forest is ten times higher than in other forest types. Canopy-dieback has been observed on the western slopes, where heavy winds increase the effect of dry spells. Frost damage sometimes occurs along the edge of the forest and in open gaps (cf. Werner 1988). The dynamics of the UMRF still have to be studied in permanent plots. Regeneration seems to be poor, as the trees grow slowly and the seedlings are suppressed by the dense undergrowth of *Strobilanthes*. Knowledge about natural regeneration of these forests is essential for proper conservation management, as they have been heavily disturbed above many tea estates and settlements.

* South-Asia Institute, University of Heidelberg, Im Neuenheimer Feld 330, D-6900 Heidelberg, Germany

** Department of Botany, Peradeniya University, Peradeniya, Sri Lanka

Location of the Upper Montane Rain Forests of Sri Lanka

Evergreen rain forests are the natural vegetation of the "wet zone" of the island. Lowland rain forests once covered the coastal plains and lower hills up to 900 m. The typical plant family are Dipterocarpaceae with more than 30 endemic species and 2 endemic genera (*Stemonoporus* and *Doona*). The rain forest flora must have survived the partly drier conditions during Pleistocene.

Between 600 and 900 m lowland rain forest passes through a wide ecotone into lower montane rain forest. These are still dominated by Dipterocarpaceae of the genera *Doona/Shorea* and *Stemonoporus. Doona gardneri* reaches up to 1500-1600 m in the Peak Wilderness. Forests, which were dominated by this species, once covered the mountain slopes between 900 and 1500 m but were converted into coffee plantations, and later tea, during the last century. The lower montane rain forests are still very similar to lowland rain forests in floristics and structure. Buttressed stems do not occur and the undergrowth of *Strobilanthes* is much denser. Many genera of the lowland no longer exist, and lowland-species are replaced by montane species within the same genus. In addition the size of the leaves is decreasing. Trees of the families Lauraceae and Theaceae become more prominent than in the lowland. Annual rainfall of more than 5000 mm in the average has been measured. The lower montane rain forests of the eastern slopes of the highlands differ from those of the western slopes because of lower rainfall (2000-2500mm) and a pronounced dry season. Dipterocarps of the genus *Doona* do not occur. Lauraceae, e.g. *Cinnamomum verum*, are typical as well as *Myristica dactyloides* and *Calophyllum tomentosum*. Typical elements of the "intermediate zone", such as *Filicium decipiens* and *Dimocarpus longan* occur.

The upper montane rain forests occur above 1500 m occur and stretch up to the highest peak, Pidurutalagala (2524 m). The original area must have been about 600 km², of which almost 400 km² have survived. This area, however, is sometimes heavily degraded by illicit felling above tea estates and vegetable farms. The largest intact area stretches along Horton Plains National Park and Peak Wilderness Sanctuary, around Pidurutalagala and in the upper elevations of the Knuckles mountains. This "mossy" or "elfin" forest is very different from the the rain forests of lower elevation, although many genera are the same. The most prominent families are Lauraceae (*Cinnamomum, Litsea, Neolitsea, Actinodaphne*), Myrtaceae (*Syzygium/Eugenia, Rhodomyrtus*), Theaceae (*Adinandra, Ternstroemia, Gordonia*), Clusiaceae (*Calophyllum, Garcinia*), Symplocaceae (*Symplocos*) and Elaeocarpaceae (*Elaeocarpus*). *Syzygium/Eugenia* and *Symplocos* have developed the highest number of species. Besides the flora, which obviously has developed from the lowland plants during the gradual uplift of the mountains during Tertiary, typical montane elements exist, which have invaded from the north via the mountains of South India. Such genera are *Rhododendron, Ilex, Michelia, Vaccinium, Prunus* etc. Conifers (Pinaceae, Podocarpaceae) are totally absent from Sri Lanka. The same applies to Fagaceae, which are prominent in the mountain forests of southeast Asia.

Balasubramaniam *et al.* (in press) have studied the species composition of plots on Horton Plains. These revealed that Lauraceae are the dominant plant family, while Symplocaceae, Myrtaceae, Rubiaceae, Ericaceae and Clusiceae are leading families. The dominant species in the plots was *Cinnamomum ovalifolium. Calophyllum walkeri*, which followed in fifth place, can be dominant elsewhere and normally forms the tallest trees on Horton Plains, sometimes overtopping the dense canopy with umbrella-shaped crowns. The mean density of the plots was 2861 individuals per hectare. An explanationfor the dominance of *Cinnamomum ovalifolium* could be the age of the community studied. As this species can be observed as a frequent sapling in stands, dominated by *Calophyllum walkeri*, the plot studied, may be in a young stage.

Balasubramaniam *et al*. (in press) found that 50% of individuals were endemic for Sri Lanka, and more than 40% endemic for the mountains of Sri Lanka and South India. This proves that the montane vegetation of Sri Lanka is very isolated, although it is a continental island, and that the montane forests of South India and Sri Lanka form a biogeographical unit. Moreover this proves, that the indigeneous element of the flora is much more vigorous than the "holarctic" elements, which may have invaded during he Pleistocene. The importance of Lauraceae and Myrtaceae is typical for a tropical montane forest, especially as Fagaceae are lacking, but the importance of Symplocaceae is surprising. *Symplocos elegans* with its small leaves has the highest density in the plots studied.

The height of the trees is very variable and depends on wind exposure and soil. The tallest trees, mostly *Calophyllum walkeri*, reach 20m and overtop the dense canopy. Such tree stands can be observed in some sites of Horton Plains, Hakgala Strict Natural Reserve and Great Western. The trees of the "typical" upper montane rain forest of Sri Lanka normally reach less than 5 m height. Besides some emergents, the tree stands form a single story, and only very few young trees can be observed below the canopy. *Actinodaphne speciosa* ("Elephant ear") with its large and coriaceous leaves, normally does not form part of the dense canopy. Only the uppermost branches reach that height.

The crowns of most trees are "umbrella"-shaped, with gnarled branches, and all leaves, flowers and fruits are confined to the upper surface of the crown. Species of *Symplocos* and *Actinocaphne speciosa* are an exception. The crowns are often wind-shaped by the southwest monsoon.

On exposed peaks and ridges the trees of the upper montane rain forest can be compressed to 1.5 or even 1 m. In that case, only few tree species of the genera *Calophyllum*, *Syzygium* or *Symplocos* form stands with bushes like *Rhodomyrtus tomentosa* or *Osbeckia* sp.. The most extreme stand can be observed on Hakgala, where the shrubs reach 30-50 cm only, although the same species can form bushes or trees of several meters in height in less exposed sites.

The dense undergrowth of *Strobilanthes* spp., which reaches 3 m in height, plays an important role in the dynamics of these forests, as it suppresses the establishment and growth of tree saplings. These get a chance, when the *Strobilanthes* population dies after flowering. This phenomenon will have to be studied in permanent plots. It may provide a mechanism for rehabilitation measures, to encourage the regrowth of saplings, by cutting back the *Strobilanthes*. Once *Strobilanthes* stands have grown up, they make these forests impenetrable. When they die after flowering, the forests are easy to walk through. In former days, elephants used to form tunnel-shaped paths through these forests. This can still be observed on Handapanella Plains, south of Rakwana. *Strobilanthes* is not only a competitor for tree saplings, but also for herbs on the forest floor, such as *Impatiens* sp., *Amomum involucratum* or ferns. But sometimes it is replaced by dwarf-bamboo,for example *Ochlandra stridula*, *Indocalamus debilis* or *I. wightianus*, which has a similar life-cycle and dies back after the flowering of a whole stand.

Soil samples of three sites in upper montane rain forest have been compared with samples from lower montane rain forest, lowland rain forest and deciduous forest.

Tab.1. Soil samples of Namunukula, World's End, Totupolakanda on Horton Plains, Le Vallon Estate (Galaha), Ritigala SNR, Kottawa Arboretum

	N (%)	K (%)	Ca (%)	Mg (%)	Na (%)
Le Vallon	0.43	17.12	59.2	45.8	7.75
Namunukula	0.46	31.5	174.1	78.9	7.16
World's End	0.4	12.26	45.9	40.7	6.61
Totupola	0.58	12.81	33.7	32.5	6.62
Ritigala	0.17	44.8	337.5	71.3	5.63
Kottawa	0.05	7.59	25.05	20.9	6.01

	Zn (ppm)	Mn (ppm)	Fe (ppm)	Al (ppm)
Le Vallon	1.09	5.03	742	597
Namunukula	1.31	4.81	893	1063
World's End	0.69	5.5	1560	1180
Totupola	0.9	3.4	1074	1014
Ritigala	1.74	6.1	268	177
Kottawa	0.23	0.38	263	511

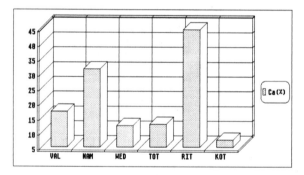

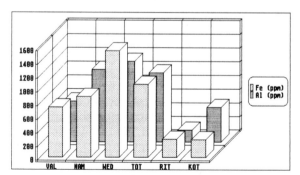

Fig.1.   Content of calcium, iron and aluminium in the soil samples of Table 1

The nutrient-content of soils of lower and upper montane rain forest is higher than in the lowland. The content of Fe and Al is strikingly higher than in lowland soils. The high content of Al can have a poisonous and thus selective effect on various plants. Analysis of elements in leaves of forest trees from various forest types reveal an extremely high content of Al in the leaves from UMRF. Such a high content of Al is known from trees in the Cerrados

Tab.2. Content of aluminium in leaves of forest trees in Sri Lanka

	Al (ppm)
Lowland Rain Forest	161
Montane Cloud Forest	1043
Season.Dry Forest	149
Mangrove	135

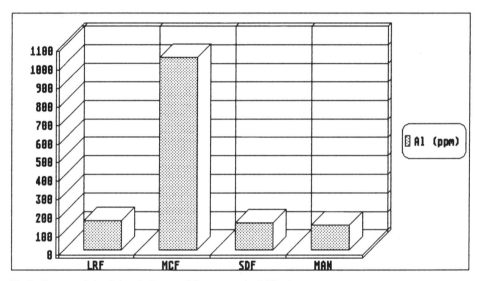

Fig.2. Content of aluminium in leaves of forest trees in Sri Lanka

The Dieback Phenomenon

A forest patch comprised of dead and dying trees was first observed on the slope of Thotupolakanda, above Horton Plains, in 1977/78. Further patches have been found around Kirigalpota and in the Knuckles mountains (Werner 1984, 1988; Wijesundera in prep.). The dieback-areas were confined to wind-exposed gaps or western slopes with stunted trees.

The first observation of canopy-dieback followed several exceptional droughts since 1972, especially in 1976. The last prolonged drought was in early 1983, which coincided with a severe drought in Hawaii and a "Giant El Niño" in Peru. In the following years, high precipitation resulted in a partial recovery of trees, that had been affected by the drought before (cf. Werner 1988).

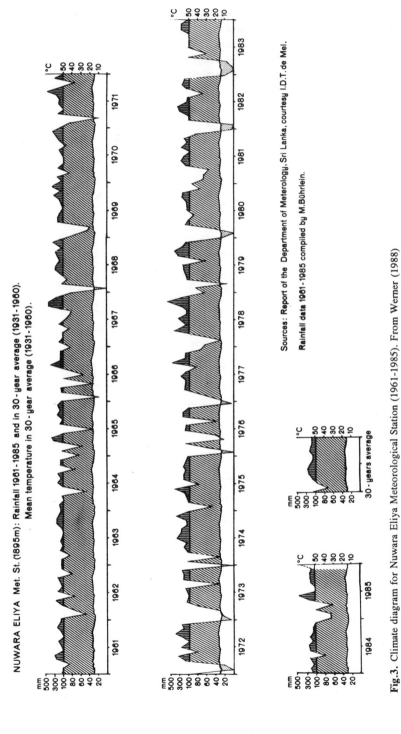

Fig. 3. Climate diagram for Nuwara Eliya Meteorological Station (1961-1985). From Werner (1988)

Air pollution is one factor, which has been assumed as a reason for the dieback-phenomenon in Sri Lanka. But why are the dieback-stands confined to wind-exposed sites only? If canopy dieback were common in the dynamics and life cycle of these forests, it should have been observed on other sites as well. The different water balance since the occurrence of dieback and the partial recovery after the heavy rains in 1985/86 were reflected in an increase of moss and lichen cover on the trees, which was hardly visible around 1980, and in the establishment of seedlings of trees like *Cinnamomum ovalifolium*.

In addition to the dieback phenomena, an exceptionally severe frost occurred on Horton Plains in February 1986. Slight ground frost sometimes occurs on the open "patana" grassland, where it may kill seedlings of trees from the neighbouring forest. In the Nilgiris it has been observed, that "tropical" tree species grow inside the dense forest, while more frost tolerant "holarctic" elements grow on the edge of the forest (i.e. *Rhododendron, Berberis, Mahonia, Vaccinium*) (cf. Meher-Homji 1984).

Many questions arose, which proved, that our knowledge on the montane-vegetation of Sri Lanka, which had first been surveyed in 1980-81 (Werner 1984), is still sparse. We know about the extent and geographical differentiation of the montane vegetation, and about the vertical and horizontal distribution of various plant-species, but quantitative studies on structure and dynamics have just begun (Balasubramaniam in prep.).

Both authors intend to continue their studies on Horton Plains, for to observe the species composition and growth rate over the course of several years.

References

Ashton PS, Gunatilleke CVS (1987) New light on the plant geography of Ceylon. J Biogeogr 14: 249-285
Balasubramaniam S, Ratnayake S, White R (in press) The montane forests of the Horton Plains Nature Reserve. In: Tropical Ecology 2 (W Erdelen et al., eds.)
Erdelen W, Preu C (1990) Quaternary coastal and vegetational dynamics in the Palk Strait region. In: Vegetation and Erosion (JB THORNES, ed.), 491-504. Chichester: John Wiley & Sons
Erdelen W (1988) Forest ecosystems and nature conservation in Sri Lanka. Biol Conserv 43: 115-135
Greller AM, Balasubramaniam S (1988) Vegetational composition, leaf size, and climatic warmth in an altitudinal sequence of evergreen forests in Sri Lanka (Ceylon). Trop Ecol 29: 121-145
Meher-Homji VM (1984) Udagahamandalam: a biogeographic perspective. Indian Geogr J 59: 205-213
Werner WL (1984a): Die Höhen- und Nebelwälder auf der Insel Ceylon (Sri Lanka). Trop u subtrop Pflanzenwelt, Wiesbaden : Steiner
Werner WL (1985a) Naturreservate im Hochland der Insel Ceylon (Sri Lanka). Natur und Museum 115: 65-76

Werner WL (1985b) The upper montane rain forests of Sri Lanka. The Sri Lanka Forester 15: 119-135
Werner WL (1988a) Human impact on natural environment in the Central Highlands. Universitas 30: 29-37
Werner WL (1988b) Canopy dieback in the upper montane rain forests. Geojournal 17: 245-248
Werner WL (1989b) Die Wälder des östlichen Hochlandes von Ceylon. Erdkundl Wissen 97: 43-72

A Research Perspective on Disturbance and Recovery of a Tropical Montane Forest

Robert B. Waide* and Ariel E. Lugo**

Abstract

Studies of disturbance in tropical forest ecosystems have been important in developing the new paradigm that views these ecosystems as dynamic in structure and function rather than constant. Long-term investigations in the Luquillo Experimental Forest in Puerto Rico are designed to evaluate the relative importance of the four principal types of disturbance within the forest and to analyze the importance of the biota in restoring the ecosystem after disturbance. Puerto Rico is an excellent site to conduct such investigations because of the availability of long-term weather and growth records, the detailed understanding of historical land use, and the long tradition of ecosystem research.

Research is driven by the concept that the response of an ecosystem to disturbance is a function of the type, intensity, periodicity, and extent of the disturbance. Recovery is influenced by a complex interaction among the soil, biota, hydrosphere, and atmosphere, but we hypothesize that the biota plays a key role in conditioning the return to the previous level of productivity after disturbance. With increasing severity of disturbance, the role of the biota becomes more important.

A patch dynamics model is being used to guide research on disturbance and regeneration at the ecosystem level. Results from this work are being linked to the landscape level of organization through simulation models generalized to each cell of a geographic information system covering the forest.

* Terrestrial Ecology Division, University of Puerto Rico, GPO Box 363682, San Juan, PR 00936

** Institute of Tropical Forestry, USDA Forest Service, Call Box 25000, Rio Piedras, PR 00928-2500

Introduction

Studies of response of forested ecosystems to disturbance have been historically important in ecology and have contributed to a developing view of forest systems as dynamic
in structure and function. Forest ecosystems are subject to a variety of disturbances,
differentiated along scales of severity, spatial extent, frequency, and duration (e.g., Karr
& Freemark 1985; White & Pickett 1985; Jordan 1985; Lugo et al. 1986; Foster 1988a
and b). Many studies of forest disturbance and its consequences have been undertaken,
some with a long-term perspective; however, relatively few such studies have occurred
in the humid tropics. Extending studies of forest disturbance to the tropics is potentially
valuable because: (1) comparison of a wider variety of ecosystems will assist in forming
generalizations about disturbance, (2) tropical forests are different from temperate
forests in many aspects that may affect response to disturbance, such as type of soil,
amount and half-life of organic matter, and community complexity, and (3) anthropogenic disturbance is occurring widely in tropical forests.

Most investigations of disturbance in tropical forests focus on a limited subset of the
broad spectrum of ecosystem disturbances, partly because most tropical research is
short-term due to logistic difficulties and lack of long-term institutional support. Long
temporal series of observations are necessary to unravel short- from long-term responses
to events with complex return frequencies. Hence, long-term research is a necessary tool
for the eventual understanding of tropical forests. The National Science Foundation's
Long-Term Ecological Research (LTER) program provides an ideal framework for
examining ecological events that occur on a temporal scale of decades or centuries.

We are conducting long-term studies of the relationship between disturbance regime
and forest structure in the Luquillo Experimental Forest (LEF) of Puerto Rico (Fig. 1). Our
objectives are (1) to investigate the relative importance of different types of disturbance
within the four life zones (Ewel & Whitmore 1973) constituting the landscape of the LEF,
and (2) to analyze the importance of the biota in restoring ecosystem productivity after
different types of disturbance within representative watersheds in one of these life
zones.

The history of disturbance in the LEF is well known through measurements of long-
term plots, although ecosystem responses have not been well studied for each type of
disturbance (Brown et al. 1983). Frequent human-related and natural disturbances to the
forest have created a mosaic of areas in various stages of succession. The major forms
of disturbance in this humid tropical forest are natural treefalls, landslides, hurricanes,
and selective cutting. The integral role of disturbance in the LEF was shown by Doyle's
(1982) close simulation of actual relative abundances of tree species, using a forest
dynamics model that incorporated treefalls and hurricanes (Fig. 2).

Components of the current research include examination of:

1. Pattern, frequency, and intensity of disturbance in the LEF (e.g., treefalls, landslid-
    es, and hurricanes).
2. Environmental properties that are expected to vary with disturbance size, age, and
    origin (e.g., light, nutrient availability, moisture, temperature, and soil organic
    matter).

3. Biological properties that are expected to vary with environmental properties (e.g., species composition, growth, nutrient dynamics, reproductive success, carbon fixation, and food web structure).

4. System properties that emerge from the effects of disturbance pattern and frequency on the mutual interaction of abiotic environment and biota (e.g., nutrient cycling, phases of recovery, rates of recovery, and displacement from and return to steady state).

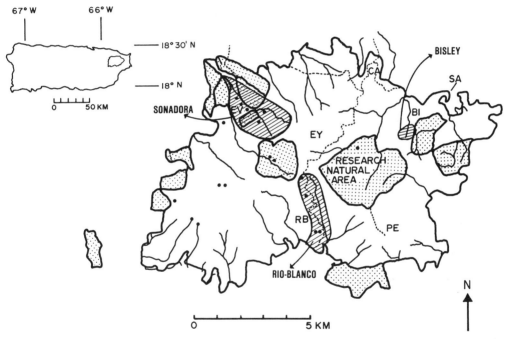

Fig.1. Map of the LEF showing (1) 12 reserved research tracts (dotted areas), (2) the Bisley, Sonadora, and Rio Blanco watersheds (shaded areas), (3) long-term growth plots under study by the Institute of Tropical Forestry (points), and (4) other sites for which long-term data sets exist (EV = El Verde, CA = Catalina, BI = Bisley, SA = Sabana, EY = El Yunque, RB = Rio Blanco, PE = Pico del Este). The inset shows the location of the LEF in Puerto Rico

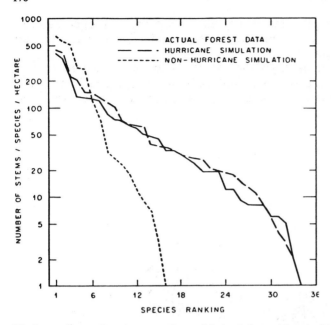

Fig.2. Dominance-diversity curves for model simulations with and without hurricane effects compared to tabonuco (*Dacryodes excelsa*) forest data. Species rank ranges from most abundant (1) to least abundant (36). Species abundance is represented as the total number of stems (> 4 cm dbh) per hectare (Doyle 1982)

The new Paradigm of Disturbance in Tropical Ecology

Speciation and hence high biotic diversity in the tropics is driven by "environmental challenges" that, according to Dobzhansky (1950), stem chiefly from "the intricate mutual relationships among the inhabitants." This quotation reflects a central idea of tropical ecology, namely, that the benign and relatively constant tropical environment allows biotic interactions to be the dominant factor in determining the structure and function of forest ecosystems (Giller 1984). This view has led to impressive progress in evolutionary tropical biology and has resulted in particular emphasis being given to the importance of predation, competition, pollination, and fruit dispersal (Leigh *et al.* 1982; Janzen 1983; Giller 1984; den Boer 1986).

This traditional paradigm of tropical ecology, however, is now under close scrutiny (Ho *et al.* 1986). For example, Sousa (1984, p. 338) stated: "There is a growing realization that disturbance may play as great a role in community dynamics as do biological interactions such as competition and predation, which have received far more empirical and theoretical attention from ecologists. The interplay between disturbance and these biological processes seems to account for a major portion of the organization and spatial patterning of natural communities." Several types of evidence have triggered alternative interpretations of the driving factors of ecosystem structure and function in the tropics.

For example: (1) the possibility that extraterrestrial forces caused mass species extinctions (Alvarez *et al.* 1980) and that such extinctions follow recurrent cyclic patterns (Fischer 1981) has stirred considerable debate over traditional thinking about speciation and extinction in the tropics (Raup 1984, Spepkoski & Raup 1986, Officer *et al.* 1987); (2) the debate over the existence of species refugia in the tropics (Haffer 1982, Benson 1982, Endler 1982) has challenged the assumption that the tropics were not affected by glaciations; (3) the formulation of a "new concept" in ecology ("patch dynamics"; Pickett & White 1985) and the realization of the importance of canopy gaps for the regeneration of canopy tree species (Whitmore 1975, Hartshorn 1978, Brokaw 1982) has caused a re-evaluation of the way tropical ecologists view forest succession; and (4) the recent fire that burned millions of hectares of tropical moist forest in Borneo (Leighton 1984; Goldammer & Seibert 1990), the discovery of charcoal in the soil profiles at La Selva, Costa Rica, San Carlos, Venezuelan Amazon, and many other locations (Sanford *et al.* 1985; Goldammer & Seibert 1989), and paleoecological data from lake sediments (Covich 1978; Deevey 1984) have forced a re-examination of the concept of what a primary tropical forest is or is not.

Parallel to this change in paradigms, and implicit in the evidence that motivates the change, is the realization that disturbances are stressors that operate at many scales, frequencies, and intensities (Fig. 3). Scale can vary from very local (e.g., the small area affected by a falling branch) to global disturbances (e.g., biomes affected by meteorite impacts [Raup 1984] or human deforestation of the tropics [Lanly 1982]).

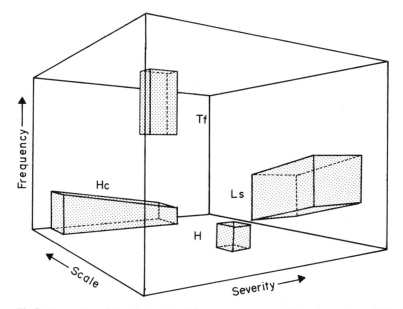

Fig.3. Conception of the relationship of four common types of disturbance in the LEF along dimensions representing disturbance severity, scale, and frequency. Tree fall (Tf), landslides (Ls), hurricanes (Hc), and harvest (H) are the four kinds of disturbance. In this figure, the relationships among the disturbance types can be seen. For instance, tree falls are frequent, but low in severity and scale, while hurricanes are infrequent (especially severe hurricanes), have moderate to very severe effects, and act on a large scale. The effects of these disturbances and the responses of ecosystems should be equally dissimilar

Severity of disturbance (the impact of the stressor on the ecosystem; Lugo 1978; White & Pickett 1985; Jordan 1985) may or may not be related to scale. For example, a tree fall gap is a less severe stress than a landslide of similar size because only structure is removed from the system and the productive capacity of the soil is unaffected (Lugo 1978). The evaluation of the impact of a given type of disturbance event is complicated further by the frequency of return of the event. Usually, less severe events have higher frequencies of return than do more severe ones (Fig. 3). A less severe disturbance, however, could be highly stressful to a system if its period of return is sufficiently frequent. The challenge to ecologists is to unravel the mechanisms of ecosystem response to disturbances that differ in scale, frequency, and severity of action.

Most tropical research in the area of disturbance ecology is focusing on systems dominated by small gaps whose frequency of occurrence is high (Denslow 1980; White & Pickett 1985; Denslow 1987). Although small gaps are important in maintaining diversity in certain forest types, this situation represents only one end of a continuum of disturbance severity and frequency. Tropical forests comprise large numbers of species that must face natural disturbances of all scales and intensities, each with a different frequency of return, yet relatively little is known about the effects of infrequent, large-scale disturbance. Forest response to small-scale, low-severity disturbance with a frequency of 10 years is likely to be much different from response to large-scale, high-severity disturbance with 100-year frequency.

Treefalls are the most common form of natural disturbance in tropical forests. Landslides also occur in many tropical forests, but differ in their importance based on geology and topography. In the Caribbean, southeast Asia, Australia, and some parts of Central America, hurricanes are the disturbance events that operate at scales and intensities that are most conducive to long-term ecological research and that offer an opportunity to answer questions about the mechanisms of action of physical forces relative to long-term behavior of the biota. Hurricanes occur in the Caribbean with predictable frequencies (Fig. 4), on the order of centuries for hurricanes with very severe effects and on the order of several decades, decades, or years for lesser storms (Weaver 1986).

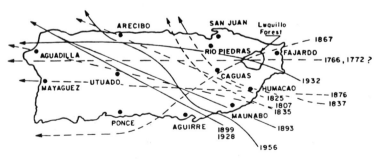

Fig.4. Paths of severe hurricanes over Puerto Rico from 1700 to 1960. Solid lines are known trajectories and dashed lines are assumed trajectories based on literature descriptions (Weaver 1986)

Tropical forestry research in Puerto Rico has already produced observations that suggest certain patterns of biotic response to both large- and small-scale phenomena. For example, the estimated age of large colorado trees (*Cyrilla racemiflora*; Fig. 5) and palms (*Prestoea montana*; Fig. 6), can be related to hurricanes in 1867 and 1932, respectively (Weaver 1986; Lugo & Rivera-Battle 1987). Studies show that frequently measured forest parameters such as biomass, tree density, number of tree species, basal area, wood volume, wood density, above ground primary productivity, and complexity index will change in predictable patterns over periods of 40 years following a hurricane (Crow 1980; Weaver 1986; Fig. 7).

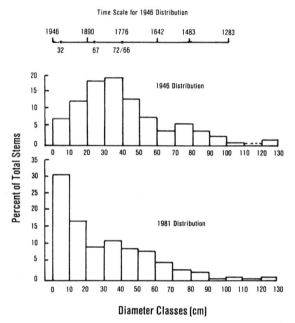

Fig.5. Diameter class distribution of *Cyrilla racemiflora* on undisturbed long-term research plots within the colorado forest of the Luquillo Mountains in two different years. The time scale indicates the years to which the diameter class corresponds as well as the years that severe storms passed directly over the LEF (Weaver 1986)

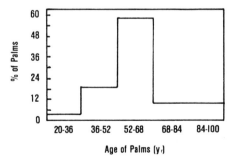

Fig.6. Age of palms (*Prestoea montana*) in the LEF. Individuals in the dominant age class were seedlings at the time of passage of the 1932 hurricane (from Lugo and Rivera-Battle 1987)

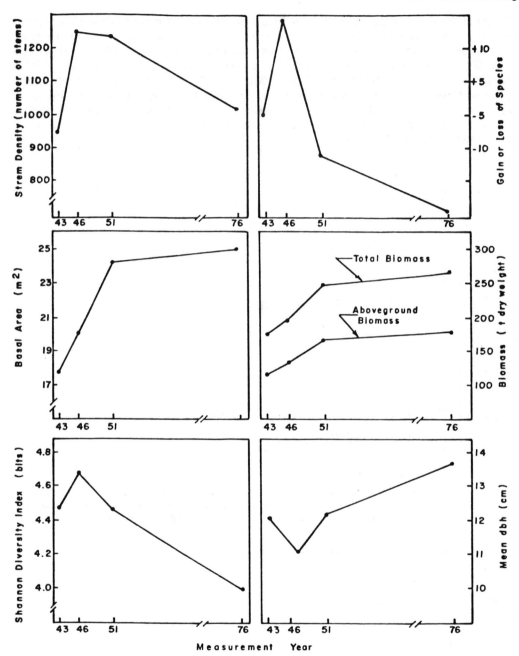

Fig.7. Changes in stand characteristics for the El Verde plots during the period 1954-1976. Measurements are based on all trees with dbh > 4 cm in a 0.75 ha plot (Crow 1980). The graphs show patterns of increasing biomass, basal area, and mean dbh and decreasing stem density, species richness, and diversity, reflecting recovery from hurricanes that struck the LEF in 1928 (San Felipe), 1931 (San Nicholas), and 1932 (San Ciprian)

Variation in annual rainfall that is unrelated to hurricane events can also elicit biotic responses since periods with more frequent and higher rainfall increase the probability of landslides and can result in a doubling of annual stream runoff (Fig. 8). Because hydrologic fluxes are critically important to many ecosystem processes (Lugo 1986), infrequent but large fluctuations in rainfall will have significant effects on ecosystem functions such as organic matter export (Lodge & Asbury 1988), nutrient cycling, and productivity. Long-term records are necessary to measure and understand infrequent events (Fig. 8). Clearly, both time and spatial scale are critical factors in the design of any ecological research in tropical forests subjected to such types of disturbances. The LEF offers significant background understanding and sufficient records of long-term ecosystem processes to permit the formulation of specific hypotheses for long-term ecological research (Brown *et al.* 1983).

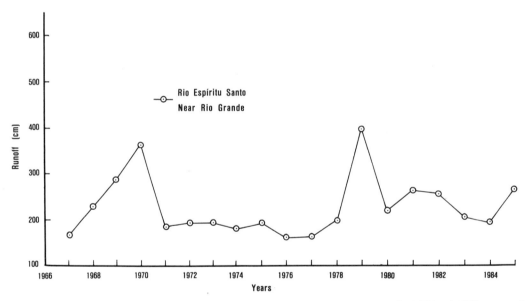

Fig.8. Long-term records of annual runoff in the Espiritu Santo River show recurrent peaks (1970 and 1979) separated by eight years of low flow. This pattern occurs in other gaged rivers in the forest (Brown *et al.* 1983). This record illustrates the need for long-term data collection in this forest which is greatly affected by infrequent meteorological events (data are from US Department of the Interior)

Long-Term Ecological Research in the Luquillo Mountains

The Luquillo Experimental Forest

Four life zones occur in the LEF (subtropical wet forest, subtropical rain forest, lower montane wet forest, and lower montane rain forest; Ewel & Whitmore 1973), and four major vegetation types occupy these life zones (Table 1). Below 600 m the dominant tree is the tabonuco (*Dacryodes excelsa*), which is best developed on protected, well-drained ridges. Above the average cloud condensation level (600 m), palo colorado (*Cyrilla racemiflora*) is the dominant tree except in areas of steep slope and poorly drained soils, where the sierra palm (*Prestoea montana*) occurs in nearly pure stands. The dwarf forest occupies ridge lines and is composed of dense stands of short, small diameter trees and shrubs that are almost continually exposed to winds and clouds. Both the palm and dwarf forests are dominated by only a few plant species.

Tab. 1. Distribution of forest types within the Luquillo Experimental Forest (adapted from Brown *et al.* 1983)

SITE	Approximate area (ha) of each forest type*					
	1	2	3	4	5	TOTAL
Higher elevation (600-1,070 m)	5,868					5,868
Medium elevation (300-600 m)	59	1,076	2,499	215	76	3,925
Lower elevation (100-300 m)		56	1,094	163	125	1,438
Increasing human disturbance	-->					
Total	5,927	1,132	3,593	378	201	11,231

*
1. Colorado, palm, and dwarf forest
2. Old growth tabonuco forest
3. Secondary tabonuco forest
4. Plantations
5. Deforested

The tabonuco forest has been the subject of the most extensive ecological studies of any of the four forest types. Long-term studies of forest growth have been conducted by Wadsworth (1951) and represent a 40 year record of tabonuco forest dynamics. In addition, the tabonuco forest has been the subject of studies of tree growth (Crow & Weaver 1977) and community composition (Crow & Grigal 1979), and the extensive data base has served in the development of simulation models of forest regeneration (Doyle 1981; Doyle et al. 1982).

The most detailed study of the tabonuco zone was the Rain Forest Irradiation Project of the U. S. Atomic Energy Commission, which took place from 1963 to 1968 (Odum & Pigeon 1970). The principal goals of this project were to determine the effects of gamma irradiation on a rain forest ecosystem, to examine the cycling of fallout elements, and to develop an understanding of vertical and horizontal forest structure and various system processes including nutrient cycling, energy flow, and forest regeneration mechanisms.

The Center for Energy and Environment Research (CEER) has continued to conduct studies of nutrient cycling and energy flow in tabonuco forest since the end of the Rain Forest Project in 1968. This research has been sponsored by the U. S. Department of Energy (AEC, ERDA) and the University of Puerto Rico. The initial phase of the current Rain Forest Cycling and Transport Project (1980-83) concentrated on the structure of terrestrial and aquatic food webs and their possible roles in the biotic control of ecosystem processes. The current phase examines nutrient import, export, and immobilization, decomposition, primary productivity, and forest regeneration as well as continuing work on food webs. The accumulated work of 50 years makes the tabonuco forest the best known of the four forest types in the Luquillo Mountains and probably the best known site in the tropics. In addition, the El Verde Field Station and research area has served as a focus for local and mainland ecologists, whose work has greatly enhanced knowledge of forest processes.

Research opportunities in the LEF

Unique scientific opportunities result from the size of the island of Puerto Rico, its mountainous topography, and its location relative to the trade wind belt and hurricane trajectories. For example, rainfall ranges from 500 to 5,000 mm in ecosystems separated by a three hour drive; within the LEF rainfall ranges from about 2,000 mm to 5,000 mm along a 1,000 m elevational transect. The diversity of rainfall conditions, complex topography, and variety of soil types in the LEF support a rich array of ecosystems with contrasting diversity of species and functional attributes that cannot be matched in continental sites where distance and access limit comparative research. The range of mature vegetation available for research in Puerto Rico is representative of many environments in tropical America. Using the life zone system of Holdridge as a guide, the six life zones in Puerto Rico (4 in the LEF) represent 40% of the land area in Central America (Budowski 1965).

Periodic visits by hurricanes and tropical depressions in the Caribbean and their inter-action with steep topography offer an opportunity to study long-term responses of complex ecosystems to natural disturbance, which is greatly enhanced in the LEF by the existence of long-term observation plots established by the Forest Service in the 1940's. These plots have changed dramatically in species composition and growth rates during the 30-40 yr since the last major disturbance (Crow 1980; Brown *et al.* 1983; Weaver 1986).

Scientific opportunities are enhanced by the fact that the island of Puerto Rico as a whole (including much of the lowlands of the LEF <u>but not its uplands</u>) was deforested early in this century (to about 10% forest cover) and has since recovered naturally to about 35% forest cover (Birdsey & Weaver 1982). Critical questions about succession, ecosystem recovery from human devastation, and the issues of how tropical diversity responds to human disturbance and management can be addressed in an island where research sites can be protected over long time periods. The intensive management of lands by the U.S. Forest Service in the LEF adds another dimension to the scientific opportunity at the site. Beginning in 1933 over 2,300 ha of plantations of dozens of exotic and native tree species were established in the LEF. Today the LEF has some of the oldest research plantations in the American tropics as well as an arboretum with over 100 tree species planted. Twenty mahogany provenances from central America (NW Mexico to Panama) and the West Indies are preserved in the arboretum. Seed collections are available and knowledge of tree establishment is much more advanced in Puerto Rico than in any other tropical research site (e.g., 412 tree species, including 100 native ones, have been tested; Marrero 1947).

In the LEF, the availability of long-term weather and growth records, an understanding of land use change, and a complex mix of ecosystems provide unique opportunities to study tropical moist forests under natural conditions, disturbed by periodic hurricanes, responding to previous human impacts, and managed with the purpose of restoring the land to production. Nowhere else under the U. S. flag is there such a mix of opportunity and background understanding for long-term ecological research. Furthermore, forest lands such as those in the LEF are the ones that are most likely to be deforested and used for agricultural production. Understanding montane moist tropical ecosystems should have priority if ecological research is to be of relevance to resolving the fiber and water needs of the growing human populations in the tropics.

Importance of Disturbance in the Luquillo Mountains

We are using a combination of experimental and observational studies to address questions about the response of the terrestrial and aquatic biota to disturbances of different scales, severities, and frequencies in five watersheds in the Luquillo Mountains. By response we mean both the impact of disturbance as well as the feedback from the biota to site quality following disturbance. The main questions addressed are:

• What is the distribution of different disturbance types within the landscape of the LEF, and how does the disturbance regime at a given site affect the structure and function of the ecosystem?

• What is the response of the biota to disturbances differing in scale, severity, and frequency, and how does this response affect a site's recovery toward mature forest?

These questions stem from the observation that the end results of secondary succession after different types of disturbance in the LEF are virtually indistinguishable despite quite different initial conditions. The type of disturbance that initiated succession at a site is difficult or impossible to determine through examination of the regenerated mature forest. We base our approach on the hypothesis that the mode of resistance of an ecosystem to disturbance is a function of the stressor (intensity, periodicity, sector of the ecosystem that it affects, and area affected). After disturbance of any severity, the path of site recovery is influenced by the physical and chemical properties of the soil, water, and atmosphere, by the activity of the biota, or by a complex interaction among all four (soil, biota, hydrosphere, and atmosphere).

The Role of the Biota in Recovery After Disturbance

Most tropical research has concentrated on interactions within the biota or the effect of environment on the biotic community. However, the biota's effect on site characteristics is also a key component in the post-disturbance recovery process. We hypothesize that the potential for a return to the previous level of productivity after disturbance is conditioned by the biota. This follows from the premise that different types of disturbance produce different types of environments conducive to different rates and pathways of recovery. Our research focuses on that period of time when the biota exerts its main influence over the physical environment (the recovery phase; *sensu* Bormann & Likens 1979). We expect that with increasing severity of disturbance the feedback function of the biota becomes more critical to the recovery process.

Some examples of biotic feedbacks that act during recovery illustrate the point: (1) The capacity of plants to retranslocate nutrients from senescent leaves prior to leaf fall affects litter quality, decomposition rates, and nutrient availability in the soil. Plants in some environments have high rates of retranslocation while those in others have low rates, and these are reflected in the ratio of nutrient use efficiency proposed by Vitousek (1982, 1984). Plants that exhibit high use efficiency ratios enhance nutrient recirculation and minimize potential losses due to leaching. Studies in Puerto Rico (Frangi & Lugo 1985) and Venezuela (Cuevas & Medina 1988) suggest that high efficiency ratios are associated with degraded sites and sites exposed to high leaching potential (Frangi & Lugo 1985). (2) Increasing complexity of root morphology, root functions, and spatial distribution of roots significantly increase the availability of nutrient pools to plants, enriching many substrates with organic matter, and improving the aeration and physical properties of soils. (3) Increased interception of rainfall by developing vegetation reduces soil erosion, leaching, and overland runoff. (4) The range of decomposition constants of complex biochemical materials (wood, bone, and shell) spreads nutrient releases over time. This provides stability to nutrient cycles in terms of storage and slow steady release. (5) As food web complexity increases through successional time, system resilience decreases (Pimm 1982). DeAngelis (1980) has shown theoretically that system resilience is inversely related to the "tightness" of nutrient cycling. Hence, as food web resiliency decreases during succession, the probability of retaining vital nutrients in biotic circulation increases (Odum 1969; Pimm 1982). High rainfall areas such as the LEF (average = 3775 mm/yr; Lugo 1986) are subjected to the mechanical impact of rain drops and winds, potential land movements, and constant leaching of nutrients. These potential stressors, if unchecked, can deplete soil nutrients, remove soil from the site, and lower site productivity. To the extent that the biota mitigates such a series of events, it represents a collection of mechanisms that conserve soil and nutrients and maintain the capability of the site to support biological productivity (Budowski 1965). Successional species are known to grow rapidly, bind nutrients in biomass, protect soil by closing the forest canopy, and moderate forest microclimates (Odum 1969; Budowski 1965; Marks 1974; Ewel 1980). However, these generalizations do not address the more important question of how the complexity of an ecosystem is rebuilt from different initial conditions. This issue can be addressed only through long-term study of specific sites that have been subjected to different severity, frequency, or scale of disturbance.

Conceptual Models for Ecosystem Study

In designing the Luquillo LTER program, we have taken advantage of the extensive research history of the forest by combining new approaches to ecosystem study with those that have traditionally proven effective in the LEF. A conceptual model of the main forcing functions and subsystems of a watershed in tabonuco (*D. excelsa*) forest provides a unifying focus for the proposed research (Fig. 9). The forcing functions of this ecosystem model are hurricanes, climate (including heavy rainfall events and resultant landslides), solar energy, geological substrate, and human management. The main subsystems are vegetation, animals, and soil and associated microbiota. The processes within the system include hydrologic flows, biotic interactions, and energy and nutrient fluxes, all of which are subject to disturbances generated by the forcing functions. Forcing functions, disturbances, subsystems, and flows are being studied as part of the LTER program. However, the measurements and experiments underway range widely in scale and detail depending of the hypothesis being tested.

We are using a patch dynamics model (Doyle 1982), as recommended for comparative studies of disturbance (Pickett & White 1985), to guide our research on disturbance and regeneration in the tabonuco forest. This model describes disturbance-mediated ecosystem processes by taking into account: (a) the frequencies, dispersion, and environmental characteristics of all types and sizes of disturbances; and (b) the recovery rates from all types and sizes of disturbances. The basic premises of the model are adapted from Levin & Paine (1974):

1.The community is a mosaic of different patch types, many of which originate as disturbances.

2.The patch is the fundamental unit of ecosystem structure. When recovery within individual patches is coupled to events generating patches, a bridge is built between patch processes and ecosystem processes.

The frequency, scale, and severity of disturbances affect the recovery process because there is a "continuum of biogeochemical, hydrological, and radiant energy responses at the forest floor, depending on the scale of the disturbance" (Bormann &

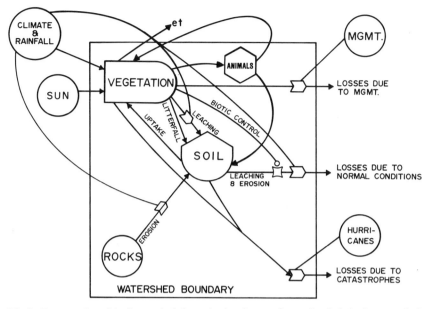

Fig. 9. Conceptual model of watershed dynamics in tabonuco forest. Symbols in the watershed model are after Odum (1983). Management is abbreviated **MGMT**, and evapotranspiration is abbreviated **et**

Likens 1979). This environmental continuum among disturbances induces a corresponding continuum of biological responses, which in turn influence the environment and ecosystem state (Bormann & Likens 1979) of recovering patches.

Our ultimate goal is to use our knowledge of these properties to predict the frequency and size-class distribution of different states - reorganization, aggrading, transition, steady state (Bormann & Likens 1979) in the forest mosaic, thus leading to an understanding of the structure and function of the system as a whole (Levin & Paine 1974).

Scaling up from the Ecosystem to the Landscape

The component investigations being conducted in the LEF are linked to the landscape level of ecosystem organization through a landscape model generalized to each cell of a geographic information system (GIS) covering the LEF. Whereas there is a relatively rich literature available for modeling forest stands (Shugart 1984; Dale & Gardner 1986), most of these models are based on growing a series of individual species in plots of about 0.1 hectare. There does not exist to our knowledge an explicit transfer of this approach to a geographically complex system except to solve the initial equations for one site vs. another (Shugart, personal communication). We have developed an explicit scheme for translating geographical information, derived from geographical space, into model parameter space (equivalent to ecological space) using a gradient approach (Whitaker 1975; Austin *et al.* 1984). For example, we can now predict micrometeorological conditions for many locations in the LEF landscape by integrating a GIS physical-specifications system with a statistical analysis that predicts meteorological data as a function of site location and related topographical characteristics (Wooster 1989). The parameters derived from this analysis plus other GIS-derived physical and biotic parameters that act as forcing functions operating on the ecosystem are being used to predict the behavior of individuals, populations, and ecosystems throughout the entire landscape.

References

Alvarez L, Alvarez W, Asaro F, Michel HV (1980) Extraterrestrial causes for the Cretaceous-Tertiary extinction. Science 208: 1095-1108

Austin MP, Cunningham RB, Fleming PM (1984) New approaches to direct gradient analysis using environmental scalars and statistical curve-fitting procedures. Vegetatio 55: 11-27

Benson WW (1982) Alternative models for infrageneric diversification in the humid tropics: tests with passion vine butterflies. Biological diversification in the tropics (GT Prance, ed.), pp 608-640. New York: Columbia University Press

Birdsey RA, Weaver PL (1982) The Forest Resources of Puerto Rico. US Department of Agriculture, Forest Service, Southern Forest Experiment Station, New Orleans, LA, Resource Bulletin SO-85

Bormann FH, Likens GE (1979) Pattern and Process in a Forested Ecosystem. Berlin and New York: Springer-Verlag

Brokaw NVL (1982) Treefalls: frequency, timing and consequences. The ecology of a tropical forest, seasonal rhythms and long-term changes (EG Leigh, AS Rand, DM Windsor, eds), pp 101-108. Washington, DC: Smithsonian Institution Press

Brown S, Lugo AE, Silander S, Liegel, LH (1983) Research history and opportunities in the Luquillo Experimental Forest. USDA Forest Service Southern Forest Experiment Station, General Technical Report SO-44, pp 128

Budowski G (1965) Distribution of tropical american rain forest species in the light of succession. Turrialba 15: 40-42

Covich AP (1978) A re-assessment of ecological stability in the Mayan area: evidence from lake studies of early agricultural impacts on biotic communities (PD Harrison, BL Turner II, eds). Pre-hispanic Mayan Agriculture. Albuquerque: University of New Mexico Press

Crow T, Weaver P (1977) Tree growth in a moist tropical forest of Puerto Rico. Forest Service Research Paper ITF-22, 17 pp. Available from: Institute of Tropical Forestry, Río Piedras, Puerto Rico

Crow TR, Grigal DF (1979) A numerical analysis of arborescent communities in the rain forest of the Luquillo Mountains, Puerto Rico. Vegetatio 40(3): 135-146

Crow TR (1980) A rain forest chronicle: a 30-year record of change in structure and composition at El Verde, Puerto Rico. Biotropica 12: 42-55

Cuevas E, Medina E (1988) Nutrient dynamics within amazonian forest II. Fine root growth nutrient availability and leaf litter decomposition. Oecologia (Berlin) 76: 222-235

Dale VH, Gardner RH (1986) Assessing regional impacts of growth declines using a forest succession model. J Environ Manage 24: 83-93

De Angelis DL (1980) Energy flow, nutrient cycling and ecosystem resilience. Ecology 61: 764-771

Deevey ES (1984) Stress, strain, and stability of lacustrine ecosystems. In: Lake sediments and environmental history (EY Hawroth, JWC Lund, eds), pp 203-229. University of Minnesota Press, Minneapolis

den Boer PJ (1986) The present status of the competitive exclusion principle. TREE 1(1): 25-28

Denslow JS (1980) Gap partitioning among tropical rain forest trees. Biotropica supplement 12: 47-55

Denslow JS (1987) Tropical rain forest gaps and tree species diversity. Annual Review of Ecology and Systematics 18: 431-452

Dobzhanski T (1950) Evolution in the tropics. Am Sci 38:209-221

Doyle TW (1981) The role of disturbance in the gap dynamics of a montane rain forest: An application of a tropical forest successional model. In: Forest succession: concepts and applications (DC West, HH Shugart, DB Botkin, eds.), pp 56-73. New York: Springer-Verlag

Doyle TW, Shugart HH, West DC (1982) FORICO: Gap dynamics model of the lower montane rain forest in Puerto Rico. Environmental Sciences Division, Publication No. 1879. Oak Ridge National Laboratory, Oak Ridge, Tennessee 378330

Doyle TW (1982) A description of FORICO, a tropical montane gap dynamics model of the lower montane rain forest of Puerto Rico. Environmental Sciences Division, Publication No. 1875. Oak Ridge National Laboratory, Oak Ridge, Tennessee 378330

Endler JA (1982) Pleistocene forest refuges: fact or fancy? In: Biological diversification in the tropics (GT Prance, ed), pp 641-657. New York: Columbia University Press

Ewel J (1980) Tropical successions: manifold routes to maturity. Biotropica 12 (supplement): 2-7

Ewel JJ, JL Whitmore (1973) The ecological life zones of Puerto Rico and the U. S. Virgin Islands. Forestry Service Research Paper ITF-18. Available from: Institute of Tropical Forestry, Río Piedras, PR

Ficher AG (1981) Climatic oscillations in the biosphere. In: Biotic crises in ecological evolutionary time (MH Nitecki, ed.), pp 103-131. New York: Academic Press

Foster DR (1988a) Disturbance history, vegetation dynamics, and community organization of the old-growth Pisgah Forest, southern New Hampshire. J Ecology 75: 105-134

Foster DR (1988b) Species and stand response to catastrophic wind in Central New England. J Ecology 75: 135-151

Frangi JL, AE Lugo (1985) Ecosystem dynamics of a subtropical floodplain forest. Ecol Monogr 55(3): 351-369

Giller PS (1984) Community structure and the niche. Chapman Hall

Goldammer JG, Seibert B (1989) Natural rain forest fires in eastern Borneo during the Pleistocene and Holocene. Naturwissenschaften 76: 518-520

Goldammer JG, Seibert B (1990) The impact of droughts and forest fires on tropical lowland rain forest of East Kalimantan. In: Fire in the tropical biota. Ecosystem processes and global challenges (JG Goldammer, ed.), 11-31. Ecological Studies 84, Springer-Verlag: Berlin-Heidelberg

Haffer J (1982) General aspects of refuge theory. In: Biological diversification in the tropics (GT Prance, ed.), pp 6-24. New York: Columbia University Press

Hartshorn GS (1978) Treefalls and tropical forest dynamics. In: Tropical trees as living systems (PB Tomlinson, MH Zimmerman, eds.), pp 617-683. Cambridge: Cambridge Univ Press

Ho MW, P Saunders, S Fox (1986) A new paradigm for evolution. New Scientist 109(1497): 41-43

Janzen DH (ed) (1983) Costa Rican natural history. Chicago: The University of Chicago Press

Jordan CF (1985) Nutrient cycling in tropical forest ecosystems. Chichester, GB: Wiley

Karr JR, KE Freemark (1985) Disturbance and vertebrates: an integrative perspective. In: The ecology of natural disturbance and patch dynamics (STA Pickett, PS White, eds.), pp 153-168. New York: Academic Press

Lanly JP (1982) Tropical forest resources. FAO forestry Paper 30. pp 106. FAO, Rome, Italy

Leigh EG Jr, Rand AS, Windsor DM (1982) The ecology of a tropical forest, seasonal rhythms and long-term changes. pp 468. Smithsonian Institution Press, Washington, DC

Levin SA, Paine RT (1974) Disturbance, patch formation, and community structure. Proceedings of the Natural Academy of Science. USA 71:2744-2747

Leighton M (1984) Effect of drought and fire on primary rain forest in eastern Borneo. In: Abstracts AAAS Annual Meeting (BC Klein-Melmuth, JL Hufnagel, eds.) New York

Lodge DJ, Asbury CE (1988) Basidiomycetes reduce export of organic matter from forest slopes. Mycologia 80: 888-890

Lugo AE (1978) Stress and ecosystems. In: Energy and environmental stress (JH Thorp, JW Gibbons, eds.), pp 62-101. Technical Information Center, U.S. Department of Energy. National Technical information Service, Springfield, VA

Lugo AE (1986) Water and the ecosystems of the Luquillo Experimental Forest. USDA Forest Service, Southern Forest Experiment Station. General Technical Report SO-63, New Orleans, LA

Lugo AE, Sánchez MJ, Brown S (1986) Land use and organic carbon content of some subtropical soils. Plant and Soil 96: 185-196

Lugo AE, Rivera-Battle CT (1987) Leaf production, growth rate, and age of the palm *Prestoea montana* in the Luquillo Experimental Forest Puerto Rico. J Trop Ecol 3: 151-161

Marks PL (1974) The role of pin cherry (*Prunus pennsylvanicus* L.) in the maintenance of stability in northern hardwood ecosystems. Ecol Monogr 44: 73-88

Marrero J (1947) A survey of the forest plantations in the Caribbean National Forest. MS thesis. School of Forestry and Conservation, University of Michigan, Ann Arbor, Michigan

Odum EP (1969) The strategy of ecosystem development. Science 164: 262-270

Odum HT, Pigeon RF (eds) (1970) A tropical rain forest: A study of irradiation and ecology at El Verde, Puerto Rico. US Atomic Energy Commission, NTIS, Springfield, VA

Officer CB, Hallam A, Drake CL, DeVine JD (1987) Late Cretaceous and paroxysmal Cretaceous/Tertiary extinctions. Nature 326: 143-149

Pickett STA, White PS (1985) Patch dynamics: A synthesis. In: The ecology of natural disturbance and patch dynamics (STA Pickett, PS White, eds.), pp 371-384. Orlando, Florida: Academic Press

Pimm SL (1982) Food Webs. New York: Chapman and Hall

Raup DM (1984) Death of a species. In: Extinctions (MH Nitecki, ed.), pp 1-19. The University of Chicago Press, Chicago

Sanford RL Jr, Saldarriaga J, Clark KE, Uhl C, Herrera R (1985) Amazon rain forest fires. Science 227: 53-55

Shugart HH (1984) A theory of forest dynamics. Springer-Verlag, New York

Sousa WP (1984) The role of disturbance in natural communities. Annual Review Ecology and Systematics 15: 353-391

Spepkoski JJ Jr, Raup DM (1986) Periodicity in marine extinction events. In: Dynamics of extinction (DK Elliott, ed.), pp 3-36. New York: John Wiley & Sons

Vitousek PM (1982) Nutrient cycling and nutrient use efficiency. American Naturalist 119: 553-572

Vitousek PM (1984) Litterfall, nutrient cycling, and nutrient limitation in tropical forests. Ecology 65: 285-298

Wadsworth FH (1951) Forest management in the Luquillo Mountains. Carib. For. 12: 93-132

Weaver PL (1986) Structure and dynamics in the colorado forest of the Luquillo Mountains of Puerto Rico. Ph D thesis, Michigan State University

White PS, Pickett STA (1985) Natural disturbance and patch dynamics: an introduction. In: The ecology of natural disturbance and patch dynamics (STA Pickett, PS White, eds.), pp 3-13. New York: Academic Press

Whitmore TC (1975) Tropical rain forests of the far east. Oxford Univ. Press (Clarendon) London and New York

Wooster KL (1989) A geographically-based microclimatological computer model for mountainous terrain with application to the Luquillo Experimental Forest in Puerto Rico. MS thesis. State University of New York. College of Environmental Science and Forestry

Tropical Forests in Transition
J. G. Goldammer (ed.)
© 1992 Birkhäuser Verlag Basel/Switzerland

Process-Oriented Models for Simulation of Growth Dynamics of Tropical Natural and Plantation Forests

Heiner Schäfer, Holger Krieger und Hartmut Bossel[*]

Abstract

A systems analysis of tree growth in a tropical rain forest was carried out to develop the simulation model FORMIX for representing inherent growth dynamics of tropical forests and assessing the consequences of logging strategies currently applied. Emphasis was put on a correct representation of the physiological processes mainly involved in the temporal development of biomass growth within a forest gap of a typical size of 100 - 400 m². On the gap level the model distinguishes between five canopy layers containing seedlings, saplings, poles, main canopy trees, and emergents. It comprises submodels for the light attenuation within the crowns, photoproduction, respiration, biomass turnover, deadwood losses, tree mortality, growth, and fructification. An imaginary forest was constructed connecting several of such gap models and including interrelations between them caused by fallen dead trees and seed dispersal. For simulation, the model was preliminarily parametrized using data for lowland dipterocarp forests in West Malaysia. Simulation runs showed that there is an internal regeneration cycle determining growth of tropical forests. Logging operations - especially their frequency and intensity - were judged in the light of this *eigendynamics*. In addition to this first application, the model can be used to determine gaps in empirical data, to integrate empirical results of different disciplines, and to check the consistency of given data sets.

---

[*] Environmental Systems Research Group, University of Kassel, Mönchebergstr. 11, D-3500 Kassel, Germany

During the last decades, large areas of the original forest in the tropics were converted to forest plantations. In order to provide accurate assessments of the development of such forest stands, generic dynamic simulation models (Treedyn, Treegrow) have been developed representing tree growth, and carbon and nitrogen dynamics in single species, even-aged forest stands. These process models contain detailed descriptions of tree-physiological (photosynthesis, respiration, growth and renewal of biomass, etc.) as well as soil-biological (decomposition, N-mineralization, humification etc.) processes. Several computer runs demonstrate the temporal development of the research stands investigated (acacia, eucalypt), from planting to maturity, as a function of diverse harvesting schedules, and as a result of various environmental conditions. Simulations also show the consequences of litter removal on soil fertility and hence on the productivity and stability of the forests. On the basis of the model results, some preliminary recommendations on future silvicultural measures guaranteeing sustainable timber yield (and fuel supply) are given.

Introduction

The world's tropical forests are being destroyed faster than ever; the yearly rate of its devastation increased dramatically from 94,000 km^2 (0.6 %) in the year 1980 to 168,000 km^2 (1.2 %) in 1990 (according to the most recent figures released by FAO [Anonymus 1990]). Blüchel (1990) and Reichholf (1990) estimate even a current annual loss of about 200,000 km^2. In addition to other causes, logging is - directly and indirectly - responsible for a significant part of tropical forest destruction (Colchester 1990); however, the degree of disturbance or disappearance and the reasons and ways of it vary from place to place (Steinlin 1989; Deutscher Bundestag 1990a; Oberndörfer 1990).

Overexploitation of tropical (rain) forests due to excessive logging, conicidental damages to young growth and understory vegetation as well as subsequently often occuring soil degradation and erosion are a severe problem not only in the locations under concern, but also on the regional and global scale. It endangers both the (ecological) balance of the far most complex and species-richest ecosystem of the world and the subsistence of indigenous people. Beyond that, it is still an open question, whether the short-term (economic) profit will in the long run also turn out to be a real net gain for the (social) economy of the tropical countries.

With respect to the following aspects of "sustainability", it is doubtful whether "sustainable" logging is possible at all: maintenance of all ecological functions of forests, maintenance of species diversity, maintenance of supply of other forest products, conservation of environment and habits of native people. Nevertheless, there is urgent need to apply at least those few existing concepts of "sustained yield management" and creating new "soft" and sustainable harvesting systems for secondary forests.

Since traditional instruments of forest inventory, assessment and planning - like descriptive growth approaches, yield tables and stand models based on regressions or simple growth functions - have failed to work when being confronted with stands composed of trees of diverse species, different age and various size and growth form, we tried to develop a more suitable mathematical model (FORMIX, see below; qualified for computer simulations) employing a process-oriented approach. This approach intends to "explain" (= to get a better insight in the functioning of) tree growth, stand development and forest dynamics, respectively, on the basis of physiological processes (photosynthesis, respiration, allocation etc.) and real parameters (activity rates, light extinction coefficients, temperature thresholds of bud-break and flowering etc.). The model structure itself contains comprehensive information about the structure and behavior of the system under research, and allows tentative conclusions concerning inherent dynamics (feedback loops etc.) and importance of particular components.

The main objective of our modelling efforts is the preparation of the integrated decision-supporting tool FORMAPS (see below) - to be used by forest scientists and foresters in responsible positions - for scenario simulation (and ensuing rating) of several silvicultural treatments and management strategies. The second major aim of these studies - which became more and more important as the systems analyses were carried out - is the stimulation, integration and coordination of present and future empirical research in order to collect a consistent data set describing the underlying phenomena and, thereby, to provide a reasonable set of model parameters.

Proceeding on the assumption that tree plantations will produce higher timber (or fruit etc.) yield than the previous original forest (Ruhiyat 1989; Gladstone & Ledig 1990) - a belief often proved to be an illusion (Zech *et al.* 1989; Grammel 1990; Sepp & Sepp 1990) - huge areas of primary or secondary forest in the tropics were successively converted into monoculture plantations of fast-growing exotic trees (e.g. pines, eucalypts, acacias etc.) (Lugo 1988; Boland 1989; Deutscher Bundestag 1990a). For the simulation of such single-species and rather homogenous stands, we included the (generic) models TREEDYN and TREEGROW (see below) in the FORMAPS FORest Management And Planning System.

In the following we will focus on the presentation of the models FORMIX and TREEGROW as well as on a short description of FORMAPS, which is still under construction.

FORMIX - A Dynamic Simulation Model for Lowland Dipterocarp Forest

Preface

Using a process-oriented modelling approach, the simulation model FORMIX was developed to investigate the temporal and spatial behaviour of lowland dipterocarp forests. In the light of the currently observed heavy exploitation of these forests, special emphasis was put on the simulation of their responses to logging operations, their potential recovery, and the conditions under which they may serve as future wood sources on a sustained basis. Apart from the model validation which was carried out using data for Pasoh Forest, Peninsular-Malaysia (Appanah *et al.* 1990) and Sepilok Forest, Sabah, Malaysia (Fox 1973), the model was only applied to forests which have already been under logging; the question of whether and how primary forests should be used for timber production is explicitly excluded. Moreover, the model should be used to examine the possibility of increasing the yield of already exploited and recovering forests in order to reduce - or even prevent - the conversion of new primary forest areas to timber production.

Model Structure

The evolution of the FORMIX model (current version: 2.0) for mixed lowland dipterocarp forests can be subdivided into three major modelling steps:

1. Development of the basic model using a vertical discretization of the forest into different crown layers, and process-oriented formulations for the physiological processes involved in tree growth within a forest gap.

2. Parameterization of the basic model for different physiognomic groups and coupling of the resulting models to gain the "staircase" model on the gap level.

3. Introduction of a horizontal discretization of a given stand into a number of potential gaps, application of the staircase model to all resulting forest cells simultaneously, and representing mutual interaction of the cells by random-driven processes results in the forest mosaic model.

The Basic Model

At the first modelling step, we tried to represent the dynamical behaviour of the vegetation of a tropical rain forest within a so-called "gap", being formed by quasi-random processes like windthrow, lightning, insect calamities etc. (causing the death of one or more dominating trees and - subsequently- an opening within the canopy). The basic unit of the FORMIX model is therefore similar to the gap-models of Botkin (1972, JABOWA models), Shugart (1984, FORET models) and a number of other models more or less directly derived from these (Aber *et al.* 1982; Solomon 1986; Dale & Gardner 1987; Kienast 1987). The main difference of the FORMIX model is the representation of forest growth by a number of physiological processes forming an explanatory model (like the model of Oikawa [1985]) and not by a number of pre-defined growth functions as used in the more descriptive approaches cited above. The advantage of this way of representing growth is that all model parameters have their counterparts in the real system (e.g. specific mortality rates, specific respiration rates etc.) and can therefore be measured more or less directly, while growth functions often employ complex mathematical formulations using parameters without (or with only indirectly contained) physiological meaning.

FORMIX subdivides the potential crown space vertically into five different canopy layers. According to the development stage of dipterocarp trees (which dominate most of the   forest sites under investigation), these layers were named "seedlings", "saplings", "poles", "main canopy", and "emergents" (cf. Hallé *et al.* 1978). Figure 1 illustrates the chosen stratification as applied to a lowland dipterocarp forest in Malaysia. Again the heights of the layer boundaries are model parameters in the above sense and can be measured in the real system; changing them could lead to an adaptation of the model to different site conditions. The overall structure of the basic model, including the path of the incoming radiation and its attenuation from the top of the canopy to the bottom of the stand, biomass transition from the seedling to the emergent layer, seed production as the new input for the lower-most layer, and anthropogenic influences, can be seen in Figure 2.

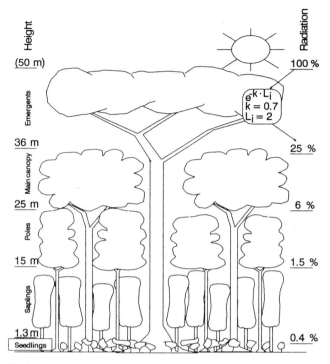

Fig.1. Schematic representation of the vertical structure of tropical rain forests and the corresponding reduction of photosynthetic active radiation received.

For each of the five crown strata, the wood biomass of the trees as well as the tree number (per hectare) are implemented as state variables and are determined by the following physiological processes (for the resulting mathematical formulations see Bossel & Krieger [1990a]).

Light attenuation: Each canopy layer is characterized by a unique relative position with respect to the other layers; this position determines the amount of light received. The light attenuation within the forest canopy is approximated by the Monsi-Saeki formulation of the Lambert-Beer law of exponential light attenuation (cf. France & Thornley 1984). This determines the incident radiation for each leaf layer which can be calculated as a function of the radiation above the canopy.

Photoproduction: The light response curve of leaves is approximated by a Michaelis-Menten formulation (rectangular hyperbola, cf. Thornley 1976). It provides the gross photoproduction rate as a function of the incident radiation. As each canopy layer may have several leaf layers, the photoproduction rate of each canopy layer at each point of time is calculated inserting the expression for the light received by each layer into the equation for the leaf photoproduction, and integrating formally over all leaf

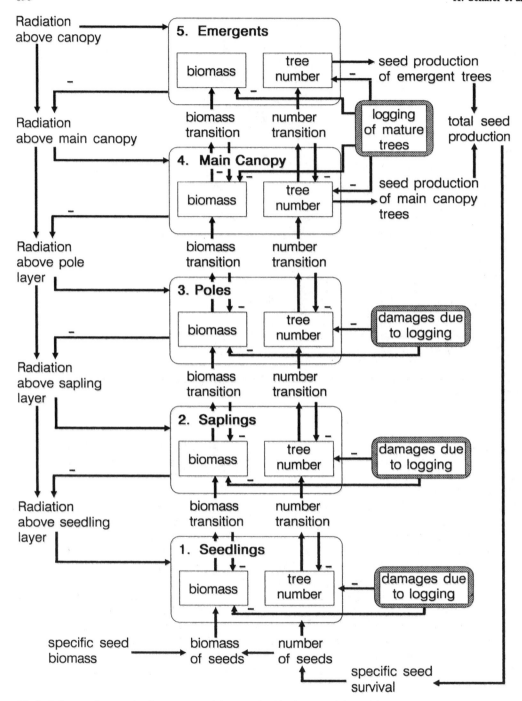

Fig.2. Influence diagram for the system modules contained in the FORMIX model

layers. The daily production is determined by time integration over all daytime hours; the annual production follows from an integration over all daytime hours of the year.

Respiration: Assimilate demand for maintaining the living biomass as well as energy needed to transform photosynthate into biomass is accounted for on two pathways: A certain amount is proportional to the current leaf biomass which is updated at each simulation step. This comprises also the demand for fine root maintenance and growth respiration assuming a functional balance between foliage and fine roots (cf. Schäfer *et al.* 1989). Another part of the respiration requirements can be derived directly from the standing wood biomass: maintenance of stemwood and other woody compartments like coarse roots and branches.

Biomass losses: All biomass compartments are assumed to have a fixed live span which results in turnover of leaves and fine roots as well as in losses of dead branches and coarse roots. These losses are lumped together as negative rates of the biomass state variable.

Mortality: Mortality of tree individuals manifests as loss rates of the tree numbers in the different canopy layers. The appropriate mortality rates have been derived on the basis of a given maximum survival time of individuals within the different layers.

Growth: As a result of photoproduction, respiration, and biomass losses caused by biomass turnover and deadwood losses, an evaluation of the assimilate balance leads to increment in (wood) biomass.

Transition: Tree-geometry parameters were used to derive stem diameter and height of an average tree for all height layers. When the trees of one layer reach a certain threshold height, they will be added to the next layer. To take the variance in tree height into account, the transition is modelled continuously, which means that at every instant of time only a few individuals are transferred to another layer. In addition, this transition reduces the average height of the next layer and delays further transition.

Seed production: Only trees of the main canopy and emergent layers are thought to be mature and to produce fruits at a given rate. According to a fructification scheme being derived from empirical observations of Ashton *et al.* (1988), these seeds are added to the seedlings pool after taking seed predation into account.

Finally, a compilation of all processes mentioned above and their mutual interactions leads to identical causal loop diagrams for each of the canopy layers (Fig. 3). In addition to the physiological processes presented in that figure, a logging module was implemented. Logging operation will decrease the number of stems and the wood biomass not only for the potential timber layers (emergents, main canopy), but - via logging damages - also for the lower layers.

Simulation Results with the Basic Model

As each layer consists of two state variables, the basic unit of FORMIX contains a total of ten ordinary differential equations per gap. Because of their non-linearity and their complex coupling via threshold functions, an analytic solution could not be obtained. The differential equation system was therefore solved numerically using a simple Cauchy-Euler integration routine and an integration stepsize of 0.1 year. Numerical experiments with more sophisticated routines and/or higher temporal resolution did not show significantly differing results. To minimize computational efforts - especially within the following long-term simulations - we therefore chose this simple algorithm.

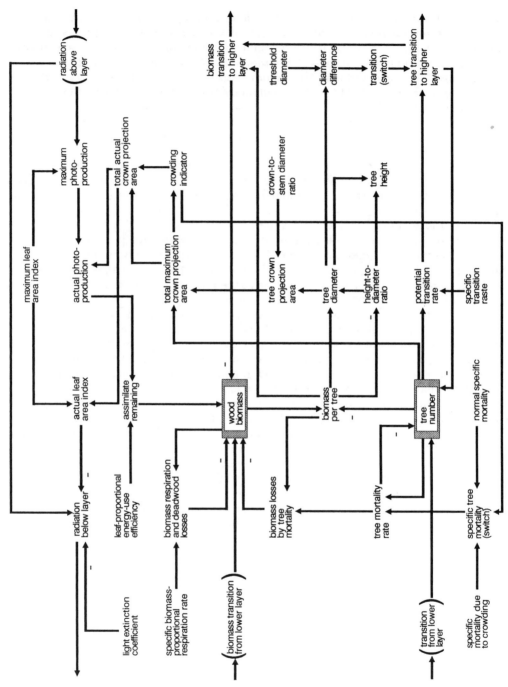

Fig. 3. Influence diagram for each canopy module of the FORMIX model

Before applying the model to a forest stand consisting of several gaps, we want to illustrate the temporal behaviour of the vegetation within one single gap especially under different management regimes. It will turn out that each gap cell has its own inherent dynamics even in undisturbed cases. The frequency of these so-called "eigendynamics" later on determines the reaction of the system to anthropogenic influences, and provides a basis for evaluating currently applied logging cycles. For comparability, all results are given as per-hectare data.

Standard Run

Figure 4 shows the results of the basic unit of the FORMIX model for standard conditions, i.e. without forest management. Biomass data for all height layers is given as time graphs in cumulative representation. To test the temporal development of the initial formation of the stand, we started with an artificial stand of 10,000 seedlings per hectare and no older trees shading them. Until the age of 60 years, seedlings pass the sapling and poles layer and enter the main canopy. After that time, the seedlings pool is refilled by fruiting of the - now present - mature tree. After about 100 years, the first individuals surpass the main canopy and reach the emergent layer. During this stage of development, the available light under the emergent and main canopy layer diminishes more and more - there is no chance for a pole layer to establish. Only the lower layers permanently contain a pool of individuals mainly driven by the seed production of the mature trees. Only after the emergent population starts to break down (appr. year 320), there is sufficient light to establish a new pole layer again followed by new main canopy and emergent trees. The initially observed transition cycle now repeats. The observed maximum biomass of about 450 t dm ha^{-1} corresponds to empirical observations of Kato *et al.* (1978), who estimated a total biomass of about 475 t dm ha^{-1} for a lowland dipterocarp forest in Pasoh, Peninsular Malaysia.

An evaluation of the assimilate balance during the simulation period (cf. Krieger & Bossel 1990b) revealed an annual gross production for a mature stand of about 65-70 t dm ha^{-1} yr^{-1}), which is comparable to the results of Kira (1978). Caused by the biomass turnover and the respiration demands a maximum of only 10 t dm ha^{-1} yr^{-1} can be observed for the biomass increment. We would like to state clearly, that these figures are not to be taken as a basis for calculating commercial values of a stand, because the basic model does not distinguish between commercial and non-commercial species. Additionally, model parametrization was preliminary and model results are based on the evaluation of the development of one single gap only! Finally, the biomass figures contain also the branch and coarse root fractions amounting to ca. 30%.

Reaction to Selective Logging

After being calibrated to reproduce reasonable results for undisturbed forests, we applied the basic model to the so-called "Selective Management System" (SMS) which is the dominating management regime for most of the currently exploited Malaysian dipterocarp forests. Logging operations according to the SMS remove all emergent trees, but leave a certain number of main canopy trees (32 per hectare [Thang 1987]). During logging operations damage to the pole, sapling, and seedling layers is unavoidable. In the model,

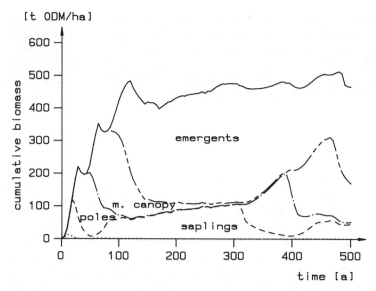

Fig.4. Temporal development of wood biomass in cumulative representation for the (undisturbed) standard run (·····: seedlings)

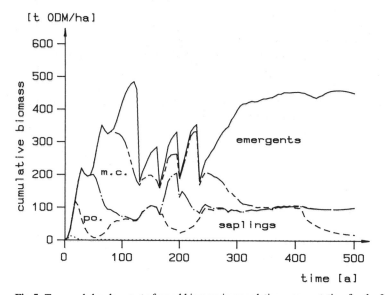

Fig.5. Temporal development of wood biomass in cumulative representation for the 35 years cutting cycle under SMS (·····: seedlings, po.: poles, m.c.: main canopy trees)

certain fractions of the lower canopy layers are therefore removed during the logging operations. The period of the logging cycle is 35 years. Underlying the SMS concept is the assumption that the remaining main canopy trees will grow into emergents during the 35 years, while poles will grow into main canopy trees, and that this cycle is sustainable. In the following, we compare results for different logging periods. As stated in the previous section, this comparison is preliminary and has to be judged on the basis of the chosen model parameters.

For the simulation of SMS logging, we again use the same initial conditions as in the previous case, scheduling the first logging at year 125 of forest development. The biomass development for the 35 year SMS cycle is shown in Figure 5. It is obvious that this approach produces neither a uniform timber assortment, nor a reliable and uniform harvest volume. The reason is that the cutting cycle is completely out of phase with any natural frequency of the forest system. A change (lengthening) of the logging period could lead to a better synchronization of logging and natural cycles, and would permit harvesting of a more or less constant assortment composition on a sustainable basis. The previous investigations indicate that a 100 year cycle would probably be in agreement with the natural frequency of the system.

The biomass development for a 100 year SMS cycle is shown in Figure 6. In this case we observe a repetition of the results every 200 years; i.e. the logging results are more or less identical at every second logging. At the 2nd, 4th, 6th etc. cuts, most of the trees harvested were emergents (approximately 230 t dm ha^{-1} of stem biomass). A similar volume can be harvested at the 1st, 3rd, 5th etc. cut; however, at these intervals the fraction of main canopy trees is somewhat larger.

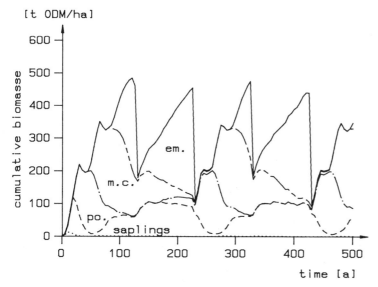

Fig.6. Temporal development of wood biomass in cumulative representation for the 100 years cutting cycle under SMS (·····: seedlings, po.: poles, m.c.: main canopy trees, em.: emergents)

Sensitivity Analysis

Some of the parameter values incorporated in the FORMIX model lack a solid empirical basis as in the past only little work has been done to determine light response curves, respiration rates, assimilate distribution patterns, and other important growth parameters for tropical moist forest species. Therefore, an extensive sensitivity analysis to investigate the influences of changes in the parameter set on the simulation results has been carried out (Krieger & Bossel 1990a). In addition to an evaluation of the model results with regard to changing parameters, this sensitivity test resulted in some recommendations for further empirical research in tropical rain forest ecosystems.

Summarizing, we judge the simulation results as being very robust against changes in parameter values influencing the biomass cycle. Changes in these parameters do not lead to unexpected reactions of the simulation model. The mortality parameters especially affect the results only slightly because of compensating positive and negative effects. Nevertheless, parameters involved in the photosynthesis process in particular may affect the total biomass gain of a given stand or a specific species composition. Therefore, these parameters can be used to adapt the model to different site conditions.

Moreover, the user may be interested in the specific wood assortment for a given forest situation. Here, the principle of mass conservation does not preclude an adjustment of the biomass distribution to the different diameter classes by means of parameter changes. Thus, especially the transition parameters in particular can be used to adapt the model to empirically derived diameter distributions.

The Staircase Model

After having studied the response of the basic model to different cutting regimes and changed parameter values, the different species being involved in the development of tropical lowland dipterocarp forests were subdivided into different "physiognomic groups" according to their maximum height. This was necessary because all trees modelled by the basic unit are assumed to have emergent potential and being able to reach the upper height layer. This is - of course - not the case in the real system! We have therefore added state equations describing the temporal development of stem numbers and tree biomasses for potential main canopy trees, understorey trees, small trees, and herbs and shrubs. The forest structure in the model is now represented by a 'forest staircase' as illustrated in Figure 7.

The main difference between the physiognomic groups is their response to the incoming radiation. The emergent trees   (represented by the dipterocarps) are shade-tolerant, i.e. their photoproductive capacity for lower radiation input is high compared to the light-preferring trees for which the initial slope of the appropriate light response curve is lower. On the other hand, the maximum photoproduction of the light-preferring trees is higher than that of the shade-tolerant ones. Caused by the different photoproduction parameters needed for the different physiognomic groups, the FORMIX parameter set was split up accordingly. The same holds for all other physiological parameters as respiration rates, wood density, mortality rates etc.

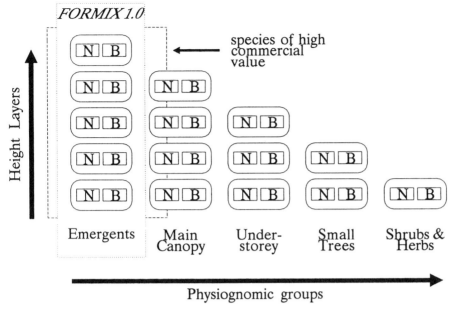

Fig.7. Compartmentation of tropical (humid) forests into physiognomic groups and height layers.

Each layer of the model forest now may contain trees of more than one "guild". All of them compete with each other for light. Thus, the calculation of the shading effects had to be modified. Corresponding to the different crown diameters of trees of one layer, the total crown area of each height class is determined by summing up the individual crown areas. This total crown area is then re-computed in terms of leaf biomass being used for evaluating the light attenuation of that particular layer. Additionally, the crowding index which describes the extent to which a crown layer is filled, is calculated by adding the individual crowding indices. The crowding index is then used to determine the transition rates from one layer to another. This prevents trees from growing into a layer which is already over-crowded.

Before applying the staircase model to a given spatial stand pattern (which then forms the forest mosaic model), we carefully tested its behaviour for the undisturbed case and its response to logging operations (cf. Bossel & Krieger 1990c).

The Forest Mosaic Model

For applying the FORMIX model to a given lowland dipterocarp forest, many of the single-gap staircase models have to be coupled to form a net of interacting spatial units. Within the resulting forest mosaic model, interactions between neighboring gaps are introduced via two different pathways:

The mortality of big trees (larger than 25 m) is not computed in proportion to the actual stem numbers as for the smaller trees, because the death of a bigger tree is not only an event influencing the tree number and biomass of the plot where it is located. Moreover, neighboring plots may be damaged by falling big trees. A random number generator determines the death of a big tree and the falling direction. Depending on the height of the falling tree, the place where its crown will hit the ground will be computed. At that location, existing trees will be damaged according to a given damage fraction (cf. Fig. 8). Tree numbers and biomasses will be diminished coincidentally.

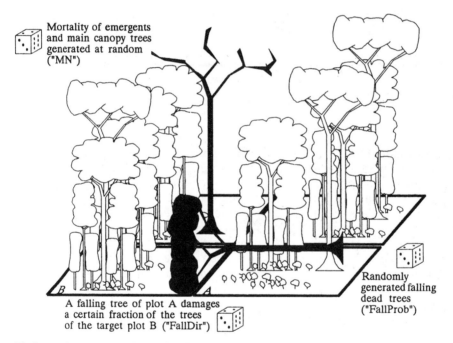

Fig.8. Random processes determining the mortality of large trees

For plots located at the edges of the forest sector currently under simulation, trees may fall outside of the given forest mosaic. Especially in the case where only a few forest plots are used in the simulation, this will cause erroneous figures in the other plots because damages caused by falling trees may eventually not be accounted for. To include these effects properly, we mirrored the damages at the opposite edges of the given forest pattern, i.e. we assume the forest surrounding the specific model forest to act in the same manner. To represent these effects, we apply damages to the right edge of the forest whenever a big tree at the left edge falls to the left and vice-versa.

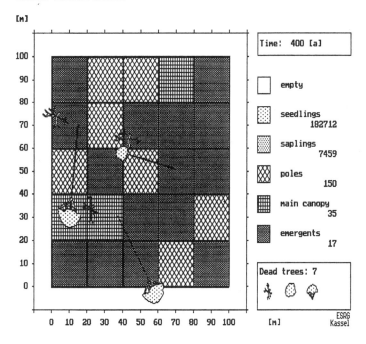

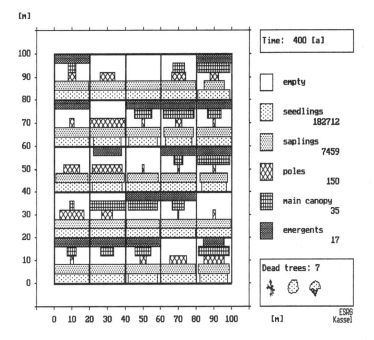

Fig.9. a) Top view of the 1-hectare test stand after 400 years of development. b) Layering of the test stand after 400 years of development

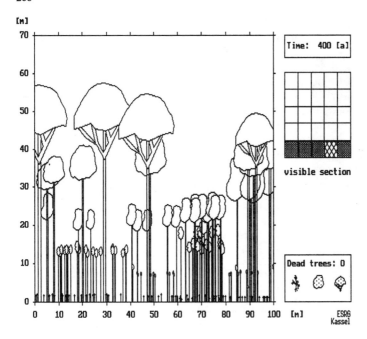

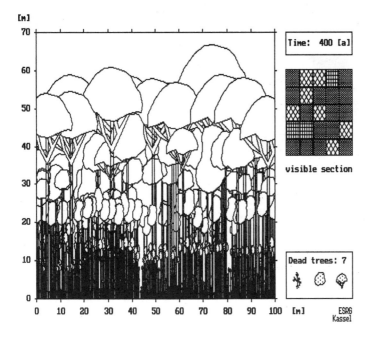

Fig.10. a) Vertical profile of a 20 x 100 m transect. b) Vertical profile of the whole (1-hectare) test stand

The number of seeds of a species group is introduced as a new set of state variables of the model. Corresponding to the seed production of mature trees of that group, and to the specific seed survival rate which accounts for seed predation etc., a given number of seeds is added to the actual seed number. Seed dispersal is driven randomly: A random number generator determines the time of a seed event and another one is used to calculate the wind direction at that particular instant of time. Species-specific parameters (like weight of seeds, maximum distance of seed dispersal etc.) are then used to determine the destination plot of the seeds. This means that not all of the seeds produced in a particular plot remain within this plot, but are distributed (more or less randomly) over the forest under examination.

The same mirror procedure as used in the random mortality module ensures accurate seed dispersal if the randomly chosen wind direction causes seeds to fall outside the given forest stand.

Simulation Results with the Staircase Model

Validation Run

For reasons of model validation, the FORMIX forest mosaic model was now applied to an "artificial" virgin forest starting with initial conditions as derived from inventories for lowland dipterocarp forests in Sandakan (Appanah *et al.* 1990) and Pasoh (Fox 1973). We evaluated the results of a 400 year simulation run both on the basis of diameter distributions produced by the model and by means of a graphical display routine developed to present FORMIX results in a more intuitive manner. The diameter distributions were in good agreement with empirical data (cf. Bossel & Krieger 1990c). In Figure 9, we show the chosen arrangement of potential forest gaps (20 m x 20 m each) and the development of this forest after 400 years of simulation. In Figure 9a, the hatching of the gaps characterizes the uppermost covered canopy layer. Additionally, the actual tree numbers for the different development stages as well as the number of big trees (main canopy trees and emergents) having died since the last recorded simulation step (here: 10 years ago) are given. Figure 9b gives more detailed information about the vertical structure of the forest canopy. Each layer is presented graphically by using its relative crown fill ratio. Several gaps with more than one (partially) established layer can be seen; small trees under the closed canopy are "waiting" to grow whenever an opening will appear. Forest profiles were generated and showed a well balanced mixture of trees at all stages of development (Fig. 10). On closer inspection of individual gaps, one can observe the process of gap-opening by falling large trees, of subsequent regeneration first of pioneers, then of dipterocarps and main canopy trees, of filling of the main canopy, and finally emergence of a few dominant trees.

As a further test of empirical validity, the basal areas and volumes in the equilibrium forest can be compared with observations in similar forests. At year 300, the simulation gives a total basal area of 53.8 m^2ha^{-1} for all trees, 26.4 for trees of greater than 10 cm diameter, and 11.5 for trees of greater than 60 cm diameter. The corresponding stem volumes are 530.9 m^3ha^{-1} for trees of all sizes, 412.3 for trees greater than 10 cm in diameter, and 237.2 for trees greater than 60 cm diameter. Since this includes all stemwood, the corresponding timber yield is smaller (assuming a log fraction of 0.8, the timber yield woud be 190 m³ha⁻¹). These numbers are in general agreement with observation. Appanah *et al.* (1990) quote a basal area for Pasoh forest of 36.9 m²ha⁻¹, excluding trees below 9.5 cm dhb. The biomass of stems only for a Pasoh plot was determined by Kira (1978) as 345.8 t dm ha⁻¹. Applying a specific weight of 0.65 (as used in the simulations), the corresponding volume would be 532.0 m³ha⁻¹.

We conclude from this simulation test of a virgin forest at equilibrium that the FORMIX model accurately describes natural forest development both with respect to general behavior (behavioral validity), as with respect to numerical quantities (empirical validity). It remains to establish validity also for the regeneration dynamics of logged forest.

Before applying the FORMIX model to simulate the response of a lowland dipterocarp forest to logging operations, we would again like to state clearly that the model should not be misunderstood as being a tool for developing optimal exploitation schemes for yet undisturbed tropical rain forests. On the contrary, the model should be used to ensure timber yield on a sustained basis from the forest sites already under exploitation in order to keep the area of additional primary forests being converted into logging areas as small as possible.

Response of the Forest Mosaic to Logging Operations

Using the Deramakot Forest Reserve (Sabah, Borneo) as an example, we would like to demonstrate the ability of the FORMIX model to simulate the reactions of a dipterocarp forest to logging operations and its usefulness as a tool for deriving new directives in forest management. As initial conditions we used data from a post-logging forest inventory carried out for that area approximately 10 years after logging (Anonymus 1987). The development of this forest was simulated for a period of 200 years without applying any further treatment. The simulations confirm the suspicion of poor regenerative potential of these forests.

Figure 11 illustrates the development of stemwood for the Deramakot case. The simulation was repeated several times in order to illustrate the influences of random effects (falling trees, seed events). In all cases, the maximum slope of the stemwood volume trajectory (i.e. the maximum volume increment) for the harvestable trees of 60 cm diameter (dbh) and above follows that of the total stemwood volume (comprising all trees) with a delay of about 60 to 70 years. This implies - whereas total stemwood increment is highest 40 years after logging - that re-logging is most reasonable and most economic at about 100 years after the first logging. Again, the currently applied 35-year logging cycle (cf. SMS logging system, above) must be judged as being out of phase with the model-inherent and - if the model were accepted to be valid - natural regeneration dynamics. A prolonged logging cycle would lead to a more efficient and sustained yield from lowland dipterocarp forests.

Discussion and Evaluation of the Results

Being a dynamic simulation model based on the eco-physiological processes of the natural forest, FORMIX has a major advantage over the statistics-based models currently still used in forestry: FORMIX represents a real-system structure and can therefore be structurally validated, while statistical models generally have no structural validity by

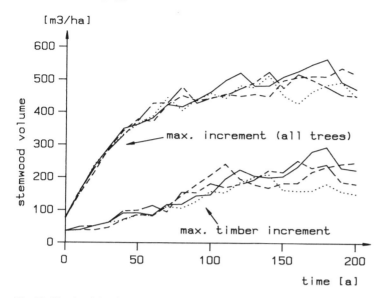

Fig.11. Simulated development of total stemwood volume (above) and harvestable timber volume (below, trees of 60 cm (dbh) and above) for the Deramakot units and four different simulation runs

design, and enforce behavioral and empirical validity by parameter fitting. In FORMIX, (almost) no parameter fitting is necessary (and none has been used); most parameters correspond to real system parameters.

The model explicitly integrates relevant tree geometric relationships, light attenuation in a multilayer multispecies forest canopy, empirical photosynthesis data etc. Although each of the five canopy layers in a forest gap is described by only the two state variables biomass and tree number for each of the competing species groups, the model contains the essential processes of forest growth and light competition and is therefore judged to amount to a structurally valid description of essential processes of the natural forest on the gap level as well as on the forest mosaic level.

Comparisons of simulation results of the FORMIX model with empirical data for Southeast Asian forests (Appanah *et al.* 1990; Krieger & Bossel 1991) as well as numerous plausibility and sensitivity tests have shown consistently that the FORMIX models in both the gap and forest mosaic versions produce forest response dynamics which are in good agreement with empirical observations. In the light of the preliminary parameter set, the model is therefore judged to be behaviorally valid.

The data required for the parametrization and validation of the FORMIX model correspond only partially to data routinely collected in forest science. The modelling experience suggests that empirical data collection efforts in the following areas would significantly contribute to a better understanding of the forest system and, subsequently, to a better model parametrization:

- light response curves for different physiognomic groups of forest trees (species groups)
- light attenuation for different canopy layers
- crown diameter and tree geometry data for different species groups
- carrying capacity of different sites in terms of basal area
- structure of different natural forests
- mortality and transition patterns of different canopy layers and species groups (guilds)
- partitioning of biomass as a function of development stage
- specific respiration rates of tree compartments as a function of temperature

Another serious shortcoming of FORMIX in its present developmental stage is the assumption of an adequate water and nutrient supply. This would limit the use of FORMIX to rainforest applications without seasonal dry spells or even droughts. However, the addition of soil water and nutrient (especially nitrogen) models is envisioned. Also, the model should be adapted to deal with sloping sites, especially to assess correctly the effects of soil and nutrient erosion on regeneration after logging operations. The biomass development after logging would then eventually be much more hampered than was observed from the current model.

TREEGROW - Simulation Model for Eucalypt Plantations

Preface

The natural climax community of several parts of (tropical) South China is the monsoon broad-leaved evergreen forest. Due to destructive human activities, starting at the beginning and becoming significant at the end of the last century, the original vegetation has disappeared almost totally. Subsequently, as a result of misuse and denudation, and especially during frequently occuring heavy rainfalls, the deeply weathered surface soils of that region were subjected to severe erosion. Such severely degraded land still covers hundreds of square kilometers in those regions.

Since the late fifties, local and regional governments have increasingly conducted afforestation campaigns for reclamation and improvement of the exploited or even useless areas. Two often planted species, introduced from Australia, are *Acacia auriculiformis* (A. Cunn. ex Benth.) and *Eucalyptus exserta* (F. Muell.) (cf. Boland 1989; Pinyopusarerk 1990).

In anticipation and within the framework of the Chinese-German Cooperative Ecological Research Project, CERP, administered by UNESCO, we have undertaken a systems analysis and computer-aided modelling of growth and nutrient cycling in an acacia and a eucalypt plantation, respectively, both established on originally barren land in Southeast China (a model for pure pine stands - omnipresent also in tropical regions all over the world - is just in preparation). Sites and data collection are described in Bossel *et al.* (1989) and Krieger *et al.* (1990).

The major purpose of these studies is to provide a tool for accurate assessments of (monospecies, even-aged) forest stand development under different growth conditions and varying silvicultural measures even if long-term yield observations are lacking.

Since the fully documented model TREEDYN, originally developed for the simulation of acacia plantations, but subsequently improved to a "generic" model, applicable to several species and different sites, is published already, for brevity we would like to refer to that article (Bossel & Schäfer 1989).

However, we will now concentrate on a brief description of the model TREEGROW (the complete documentation of which (Krieger et al. 1990) is available on request from the authors), followed by a presentation and discussion of some of the simulation results obtained.

Model Description

The modelling method used to develop TREEGROW does not attempt to describe a given forest state as exactly as possible, but tries to represent the most relevant dynamic processes involved in its development. The linking of all these processes leads to an explanatory model mapping adequately the development of a given forest at a given site as well as its reactions to changes in the environment. Moreover, the analysis and coupling of the physiological processes included assists in detecting critical parameters crucially influencing the system's behaviour.

In our process-oriented modelling approach, the 'average' tree modelled is subdivided into different biomass fractions (fulfilling different physiological functions and/or exhibiting differing activities). Each biomass fraction is represented by a state variable (quantified per hectar, see Fig. 12), the development of which is described by an ordinary differential equation. Ecophysiological processes like photoproduction, respiration, assimilate allocation etc. are specified by the flows of material between the state variables and model-inherent control variables influencing these flows. Soil properties are represented by additional state variables for the carbon and the nitrogen stores of litter and humus, and the plant-available nitrogen pool. In addition to this implementation of the (more or less continuous) flows of material and information, the simulation model also contains several time-discrete parts to handle i.e. the cutting of trees, fertilization events etc.

The number of state variables, and the complexity of the differential equation system employed prevent an analytical solution of the model. We therefore use a numerical integration routine employing the well-known Euler-algorithm. We have also tested more sophisticated numerical integration routines, but the accuracy of the results for the current model is improved only slightly, which encouraged us to use the simple algorithm to minimize the execution time.

Many of the functional relationships linking the state variables, as well as those between state variables and the surrounding environment, are taken from the TREEDYN model (see above). As a basis for the new model TREEGROW (essential structure given in Fig. 12), we took the appropriate simulation program now written in PASCAL and adapted this program in order to include the newly developed parts (modifications are documented in Krieger et al. [1990]). In addition to the model equations themselves and the integration algorithm, the (corrected) program contains several routines to calculate yearly carbon and nitrogen balances, to manage the simulation output, to interpolate table functions, etc.

In order to feed the TREEGROW model with information about site and species characteristics, and to guarantee easy modifications, the program collects the fixed model parameters, the initial values of the state variables, and the user defined cutting and fertilization scheme in separate units. An external file contains all information about the table functions of the model and can also be easily modified.

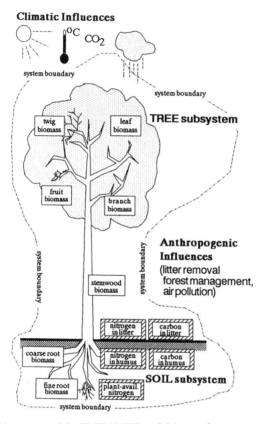

Fig. 12. Essential structure of the TREEGROW model (rectangles represent state variables)

The main distinction between TREEDYN and TREEGROW is the mode of assimilate distribution. With reference to the "sink strength approach", TREEDYN uses a hierarchical allocation "key" (with threshold values for servicing different demands), whereas TREEGROW combines a priority sequence (maintenance respiration needs and replacement of mortified biomass must be satisfied first) with an allocation "decision" based upon the current partitioning of biomass in comparision to a predetermined partitioning "goal" (cf. Fig. 13).

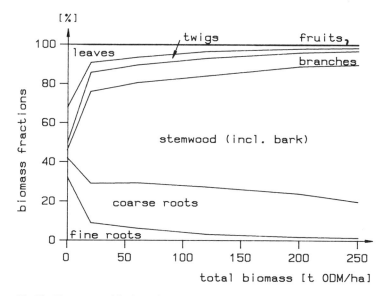

Fig. 13. Biomass partitioning scheme as used in the TREEGROW model. Percentage fractions were derived from destructive sampling of some 19 trees of various sizes

Simulation Results

Standard Run

Applying the parameter set for a *Eucalyptus exserta* stand listed and the adaptations described by Krieger *et al.* (1990), we ran the model for a simulation period of 50 years using a simulation stepsize of 0.02 years (approximately one week). Additionally we assumed an annual increment of the atmospheric carbon dioxide concentration of 0.24% and a synchronous rise in temperature of 0.16 % per year (future climate scenario "E" in German Bundestag 1989, pp. 412 ff., see below). In this "standard run", planting of saplings was accompanied by a tree-by-tree application of 2 kg humus per tree (entering the litter pool), which is equivalent to an amount of 208 kg Nha^{-1} (presuming a C:N ratio of 12).

The stem biomass increases along the typical saturation-type curve with superimposed annual dynamics (cf. Fig. 14, uppermost line), indicating a heavy drain of the assimilate pool by maintenance demands of the respiring compartment of the stems at maturity. After 50 years of simulation, a total biomass of 331.6 tons of organic dry matter per hectare (t dm ha^{-1}) was achieved. A small deviation appeared in case of omitted "start fertilization": a stand established in the "naked" soil accumulates 17.2 t dm ha^{-1} less.

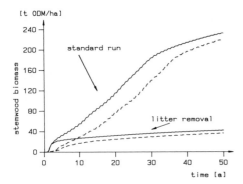

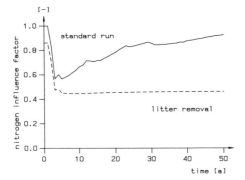

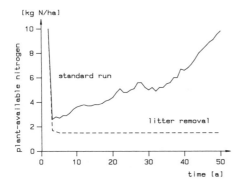

Fig. 14. (upper) TREEGROW simulation results for different environmental conditions (solid line: planting with humus application; dashed line: planting without humus application)

Fig. 15. (middle) Temporal development of the nitrogen influence factor (smoothed January values), which reduces potential photoproductivity to that quantity of biomass formation realizable with available nitrogen (fixed C:N ratios)

Fig. 16. (lower) Time course of mineral nitrogen (smoothed January values) in the upper 50 cm of soil (contains more than 95 % of all fine roots). Qualitatively comparable outcomes might be found for available fractions of other nutrients in such an impoverished substrate

Provided that the - measured only one time - nitrogen contents in the diverse biomass compartments will remain constant during the whole life cycle of the trees (an admissible simplification as long as concentrations are minimum values), the growth of the eucalypt stand is limited by inadequate supply of nitrogen (see Fig. 15).

After a strong peak at the beginning of the simulation, when the initially available soil nitrogen (cf. Fig. 16) is used up, nitrogen deficiency significantly affects photoproduction and - subsequently - harms leaf growth (negative feedback). Later on, the nitrogen situation slowly improves, as (external) nitrogen deposition occurs (postulated total nitrogen input amounts to 18.1 kg ha^{-1} in the first and to 25.0 kg ha^{-1} in the 50th year) - and accumulated litter and humus decompose, thereby continuously freeing nitrogen in a plant-available form.

Litter Removal

Figure 14 shows the temporal development of the stemwood biomass for a simulation characterizing the current situation at the research site in Xiaoliang (cf. Figs. 17 and 18). Since the dried leaves of *E. exserta* ("Queensland peppermint") are suitable for burning, all the above-ground litter is removed by the villagers for use as fuel (cumulative withdrawal within the simulation period: 190.0 t dm ha^{-1}). Total biomass accumulation after 50 years amounts to 74.4 t dm ha^{-1} (without humus fertilization: 65.7 t ha^{-1}), which is only about 22.5 % of the standing biomass of the untouched stand.

In this case, only the dead parts of the root system will feed the soil organic matter pool, leading to further humus erosion (whereas the standard run situation results in its accumulation). Plant-available nitrogen, which for the standard run approaches an annual mean of almost 10 kg N ha^{-1} (at the end of the 50 year period), is now reduced to less than 1.5 kg N ha^{-1} (cf. Fig. 16). To sum up, removal of the nutrient-rich litter not only deteriorates the physical, chemical, and hence the biological state of the soil in particular and the condition of the total ecosystem in general, but also diminishes the object of villagers primary interest: the total yield of burning material is much less in the unprotected case. Chinese forest scientists are familiar with these findings - which has been general knowledge in Central Europe for decades (Becker-Dillingen 1939; Rehfuess 1990) - but as long as the economic and social state of the rural population is not improved, villagers are dependant on raked litter, because they cannot afford another source of fuel for cooking.

Model results agree rather well with data from a survey carried out by some Chinese researches in an adjacent stand at an age of 20 years (Yu *et al.*, pers. comm.). Nevertheless, the figures given by Schneider *et al.* (1988) suggest an even higher production capacity for neighboring stands. This divergence from our simulations may result from better growth conditions due to higher initial N concentrations in those soils (soils at the Xiaoliang site were judged to be very heterogeneous), deeper rooting zone, and higher atmospheric N input than assumed as well as uncertainties concerning stand history. Beyond that, since N concentrations in biomass in our model decisively determine overall biomass formation (cf. sensitivity analyses in Krieger & Schäfer [1991]), lower N contents in trees than obtained for the sample tree would lead to higher production.

Fig.17. (left) Actual shape of the investigated eucalypt stand in Xiaoliang, Guangdong Province, South China

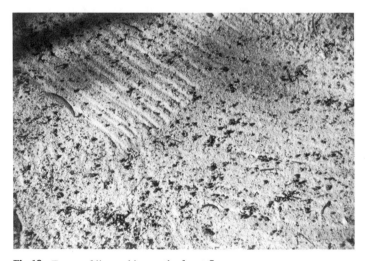

Fig.18. Traces of litter raking on the forest floor

Restriction to Coarse Wood Harvest

The figures in Table 1 illustrate on the one hand the response of stand productivity (and fertility) to repeated clearcutting and subsequent coppice growth (stocks normally will not regenerate more than four times). On the other hand, they clarify the difference between the actually prevailing way of total (aboveground) harvesting and coarse wood (stems and branches) withdrawal only. Taking out exclusively the nutrient-poor fractions conserves - and under presumed deposition rates even improves - the nitrogen capital of the system (cf. Krieger *et al.* 1990), thereby allowing a considerably higher biomass formation (cf. Fig. 19).

Tab.1. Carbon balance for repeated clearcutting after 48 years.
A: total (aboveground) harvesting and litter removal [t C ha^{-1}yr^{-1}].
B: coarse wood harvesting without litter removal [t C ha^{-1}yr^{-1}].

	A	B
Photoproduction	583.16	1008.45
Assimilate relocation	10.27	14.29
Maintenance respiration	339.72	540.32
Growth respiration	43.45	82.98
Harvesting: Stemwood	40.74	127.12
Harvesting: Branches	7.36	20.93
Harvesting: Twigs	3.68	0.00
Harvesting: Leaves	5.39	0.00
Harvesting: Fruits	0.05	0.00
Harvesting: Total	**57.22**	**148.05**
Litter removal: Stemwood	6.17	0.00
Litter removal: Branches	3.52	0.00
Litter removal: Twigs	3.59	0.00
Litter removal: Leaves	49.29	0.00
Litter removal: Fruits	1.01	0.00
Litter removal: Total	**63.58**	**0.00**
Total yield:	**120.80**	**148.05**

Impact of the 'Greenhouse Effect' on Stand Productivity

In Figure 20, we present some (preliminary) simulation results concerning a problem of pressing importance at the present time and especially in future, the world-wide change of climate. We included two isolated components of the actually rather complex phenomenon (Schönwiese & Diekmann 1989; Grassl & Klingholz 1990): increasing concentrations of CO_2 in the air and global warming. We run two scenarios based on varying assumptions, representing plausible upper and lower (= standard run) limits of potential future conditions (cf. German Bundestag 1989), and one "null-scenario", presupposing the hypothetical case of constant climate (perpetuation of present state). We assume a doubling of photoproduction by raising atmospheric (external) CO_2 concentrations from the current 354 to 700 ppmv (cf. Shugart *et al.* 1985; Strain &

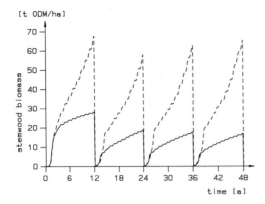

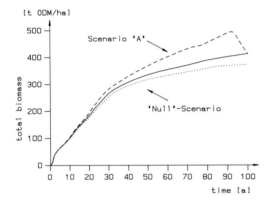

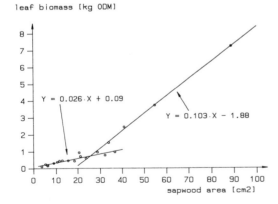

Fig.19. (upper) Stemwood accumulation for a multiple clearcutting scenario (solid line: total aboveground harvesting and continuous litter removal; dashed line: coarse wood harvesting and no litter collection)

Fig.20. (middle) Total biomass formation for the different 'greenhouse climate' scenarios (solid line: standard run = scenario "E", see text)

Fig.21. (lower) Relationship between cross-sectional area of (trunk) sapwood and leaf biomass of the sample trees

Cure 1986; leaf-internal partial pressure is simply assumed to increase in a 1:1 relation; altered stomatal conductance and transpiration is not considered yet since the coupling of the tree model to a soil-water submodel is still missing). Adaptation/acclimatization, as often observed in short-term fumigation experiments with high CO_2 doses (Solomon 1988; Deutscher Bundestag 1990a,b), is neglected (slowly increasing concentrations, of course, might create other responses!).

Standard run circumstances yield a little less than seven percent more standing biomass compared to the "null-scenario". The scenario "A" with high CO_2 and temperature rise (0.98 % and 0.41 % per year, respectively) first lead to greatest biomass formation, but later on to premature collapse of the stands due to 'respiration death' (elevated maintenance respiration and renewal demands exceed enhanced photoproduction; shortlived tissues like leaves and fine roots progressively diminish). However, special supplementary investigations revealed a rather tight relationship between leaf biomass and conductive (hydroactive xylem) area of stems (between breast height and first branching) (cf. Fig. 21). Therefore, a reduction of foliage (and feeder root) mass should be associated with a retrogression of (respiring!) sapwood mass. The not yet realized implementation of this functional relationship (necessitating an alternative allocation type based on "pipe model theory", e.g. Schäfer et al. [1989]) probably will delay the death of the trees for some years or even decades (sensitivity analysis has given proof of strong influence of heartwood formation on stand development, cf. Schäfer & Krieger [1991]).

Under the given environmental conditions, differentiation between the scenarios cannot occur until a stand age of about 20 years has been reached, since nitrogen limitation impairs any potential gain due to increased photosynthetic capacity (cf. Kramer 1981; for other constraints on growth see German Bundestag 1989; Krupa & Kickert 1989; Kickert & Krupa 1990; Peters 1990). Indeed, widening of C:N-ratios in biomass would allow higher production (see above), but possibly simultaneously hampered decomposition (cf. Attiwill 1986; Schäfer 1988) would decrease nutrient availability and subsequently reduce carbon assimilation (negative feedback).

Conclusions

The present way of forest use in the region under research is essentially a result of scarcity, especially a lack of fuel (closely connected with over-population). This problem has arisen in decades and will not be solved in short time. But it is to be hoped that some changes in forest management itself will offer the opportunity to create future silvicultural measures guaranteeing sustainable timber supply (and hence a much more suitable energy source than dried leaves). Due to the perseveringly low humus contents of the soil and the consequent deficiency of nitrogen (and other nutrients, too), the current practice of removing all the above-ground litter out of the forest strongly affects growth within the Xiaoliang eucalypt forest.

In addition to the primary effect of improving soil conditions at that site by protecting the forest (as now realized only for a small experimental plot), as a secondary effect total biomass yield itself is much higher, as improved soil conditions also improve the photosynthetic efficiency of the trees.

To provide the villagers with the vitally necessary material for burning, we recommend first of all a system of "rotation harvest", that is a strategy of removing only coarse wood (dbh greater than 10 to 15 cm) in selected areas, meanwhile conserving other stands until they are mature enough for felling. Since the nutrient content of wood is much lower than that of fallen leaves and twigs, more nutrients will be retained in the ecosystem, which, in the long run, allows a significantly higher and resource-saving energy output in comparison to the present exploitative use.

There is strong evidence that both leaf mass and total photoproductivity of eucalypt stands are intimately connected to the water availability at the respective site (Walter & Breckle 1983; Lugo *et al.* 1988; McMurtrie *et al.* 1988). An improved version of our model therefore will include a submodel for the calculation of water stocks and flows in the relevant compartments. The present version of TREEGROW suffers from its preliminary quantification; this points to the fact that more - and more accurate - measurements of the relevant eco-physiological parameters are urgently needed.

FORMAPS - A Forest Management and Planning System

The dynamic models describing the growth of tropical mixed forests (FORMIX) and plantations (TREEDYN and TREEGROW) form the basis in developing an integrated forest management and planning system (FORMAPS). Satisfying the requirement of representing the development dynamics of those forests, it should be able to act as a substitute for missing yield tables. Especially for mixed forests, it is still open to question whether yield tables could be produced for tropical forests at all. FORMAPS should additionally extrapolate the simulation results from the site level to the regional scale taken the given geographical, geological and climatic informations into account. Forest treatments (logging, fertilization, reforestation, road construction, etc.) must be aggregated to management scenarios which are then compiled as input data for the TREEGROW and FORMIX models. On the other hand, simulation results must be evaluated economically, using data bases containing information about quotation, costs of transport, road construction, planting etc. Finally, the integrated software package to be developed should contain a user-friendly interface enabling members of regional forest departments to use the model without being computer specialists. In particular, the FORMAPS management tool contains five major parts as shown in Figure 22 and briefly described below.

-       The simulation module contains dynamic models describing forest growth for complex mixed forests (FORMIX) as well as for monocultures (TREEGROW). Additional submodels describing soil water and nutrient relations should be coupled. All models should be 'generic' in a way that they employ a basic system structure which can then be adapted to different site conditions and species compositions choosing different parameter sets.

-       Model parameters as well as additional information about geography, soil conditions, climate, and (eventually available) forest inventory data are contained in the data base module. This module allows data collection, updating, modification, aggregation, etc. It is therefore data source for the other modules as well as linkage between them.

- On the basis of the geographical data base, the geographic information system (GIS) extrapolates the simulation results and superimposes the spatial information contained to available knowledge about road systems, slopes, watersheds, etc. It produces static and dynamic stand maps.

- The economic module evaluates the simulation results on a commercial basis.

- Finally, the interactive input/output system forms the interface between the user and the calculation modules within FORMAPS. It offers guidance through the system and a 'help facility' whenever questions occur, aggregates the user's input for further use by the other modules, and processes the simulation results producing interpretable numerical and graphical output. It supports modification and extension of the modules and integrates knowledge of different research disciplines in its common data base.

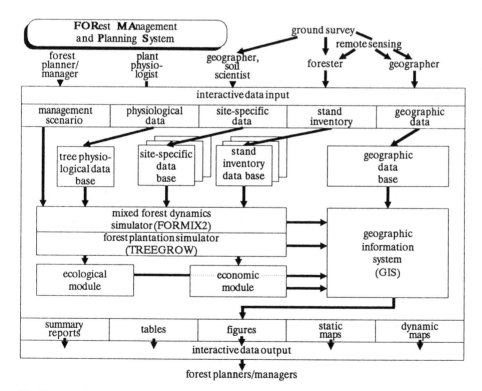

Fig.22. Overall structure of the Forest Management and Planning System (FORMAPS)

Acknowledgement

This work was sponsored by the Federal Ministry of Research and Technology of the Federal Republic of Germany under grant No. 325-4007-07 INT10 2 and the Deutsche Gesellschaft für Technische Zusammenarbeit GTZ under project No. 81.2181.601-100.

References

Aber JD, Hendrey GR, Francis AJ, Botkin DB, Melillo JM (1982) Potential effects of acid precipitation on soil nitrogen and productivity of forest ecosystems. In: D'Itri FM (ed): Acid Precipitation - Effects on Ecological Systems. Ann Arbor: 411-433

Anonymus (1987) Forest inventory for Deramakot Forest Reserve. Computer printouts, Sabah Forest Department, Sandakan, Sabah, Malaysia

Anonymus (1990) FAO gibt alarmierende Zahlen über Waldzerstörung bekannt. Allg Forst Z 45: 1272

Appanah S, Weinland G, Bossel H, Krieger H (1990) Modeling long-term responses of dipterocarp forests under different silvicultural regimes. J Trop For Sci (in print)

Ashton PS, Givnish TJ, Appanah S (1988) Staggered flowering in the dipterocarpaceae: New insights into floral induction and the evaluation of mast fruiting in the aseasonal tropics. Amer Natur 132: 44-66

Attiwill PM (1986) Interactions between carbon and nutrients in the forest ecosystem. Tree Physiol 2: 389-399

Becker-Dillingen J (1939) Die Ernährung des Waldes. Verlagsgesellschaft für Ackerbau, Berlin: 589 pp

Blüchel KG & Schutzgemeinschaft Deutscher Wald (eds) (1990) Tropischer Regenwald - Der Garten Eden darf nicht sterben. Pro Terra, München: 304 pp

Boland DJ (ed) (1989) Trees for the Tropics. ACIAR Monograph No 10. Canberra: 247 pp

Bossel H, Krieger H (1990a) Simulation of tropical natural forest dynamics: System structure, dynamic process model, and simulation results. Arbeitsberichte Heft 14, Wissenschaftliches Zentrum Mensch-Umwelt-Technik (WZ III). Gesamthochschule Kassel: 76 pp

Bossel H, Krieger H (1990b) Simulation of tropical natural forest dynamics. Ecol Modelling (accepted)

Bossel H, Krieger H (1990c) Dynamic simulation of natural tropical forest development for a forest management and planning system. GTZ report, October 1990

Bossel H & Schäfer H (1989) Generic simulation model of forest growth, carbon and nitrogen dynamics, and application to tropical acacia and European spruce. Ecol Modelling 48: 221-265.

Bossel H, Schäfer H, Wang Zhu-hao, Yu Zuo-yue, Ding Ming-mao, Li Zhi-an, Zhao Ping, Chang Wen-qi, Peng Shao-lin (1989) System analysis and simulation of carbon and nitrogen dynamics of an Acacia auriculaeformis stand in South China. Acta Botanica Austro Sinica 4: 235-251 (in Chinese)

Botkin DB, Janak JF, Wallis JR (1972) Some ecological consequences of a computer model of forest growth. J Ecol 60: 849-872

Colchester M (1990) The International Tropical Timber Organization: Kill or cure for the rainforests? The Ecologist 20: 166-181

Dale VH, Gardner RH (1987) Assessing regional impacts of growth declines using a forest succession model. J Environ Manage 24: 83-93

Deutscher Bundestag (ed) (1990a) Schutz der tropischen Wälder. 2. Bericht der Enquete-Kommission des 11. Deutschen Bundestages "Vorsorge zum Schutz der Erdatmosphäre". Zur Sache 10/90. Deutscher Bundestag - Referat Öffentlichkeitsarbeit, Bonn : 983 pp

Deutscher Bundestag (ed) (1990b) 3. Bericht der Enquete-Kommission des 11. Deutschen Bundestages "Vorsorge zum Schutz der Erdatmosphäre" zum Thema "Schutz der Erde". Bundestags-Drucksache 11/8030 vom 24.05.1990. Heger, Bonn: 935 pp

Fox JED (1973) A Handbook to Kabili-Sepilok Forest Reserve. Sabah Forest Record No. 9, Borneo Literature Bureau for Sabah Forest Department.

France J, Thornley JHM (1984) Mathematical models in agriculture. Butterworth, London: 335 pp

German Bundestag (ed) (1989) Protecting the Earth's Atmosphere: An International Challenge. German Bundestag - Publ Sect, Bonn : 592 pp

Gladstone WT, Ledig FT (1990) Reducing pressure on natural forests through high-yield forestry. For Ecol Manage 35: 69-78

Grammel R (1990) Ist eine nachhaltige Holznutzung im Amazonas-Regenwald möglich? Ber Naturf Ges Freiburg i Br 80: 143-168

Grassl H, Klingholz R (1990) Wir Klimamacher. Fischer, Frankfurt: 296 pp

Hallé F, Oldeman RAA, Tomlinson PB (1978) Tropical trees and forests. Springer, Berlin: 441 pp

Kato R, Tadaki Y, Ogawa H (1978) Plant biomass and growth increment studies in Pasoh Forest. Malay Nat J 30(2): 211-224

Kickert RN, Krupa SV (1990) Forest responses to tropospheric ozone and global climate change: An analysis. Environ Pollut 68: 29-65

Kienast F (1987) FORECE - A forest succession model for Southern Central Europe. Oak Ridge National Laboratory, ORNL/TM-10575, Environ. Sci. Div. Publ. No. 2989: 73 pp

Kira T (1978) Community architecture and organic matter dynamics in tropical lowland rain forests of Southeast Asia with special reference to Pasoh Forest, West Malaysia. In: Tomlinson PB, Zimmermann MH (eds): Tropical Trees as Living Systems. University Press, Cambridge (Mass): 561-590

Kramer PJ (1981) Carbon dioxide concentration, photosynthesis, and dry matter production. BioScience 31: 29-33

Krieger H, Bossel H (1991) Simulation der Waldlückendynamik tropischer Naturwälder mit einem vertikal und horizontal strukturierten Prozeßmodell. 4. Tagung der Sekt. Forstl. Biometrie und Informatik im Dtsch. Verb. Forstl. Forschungsanst. ("Klima und Wachstum"), Göttingen, 3.-5.7.1990. To be published in: Schriften Forstl Fak Univ. Göttingen & Niedersächs Forstl Versuchsanst

Krieger H, Schäfer H, Peng Shao-lin, Li Zhi-an, Chang Wen-qi (1990) Growth dynamics of a planted Eucalyptus exserta (F. Muell.) stand in South China - Adaptation of a generic simulation model. Arbeitsberichte Heft 12, Wissenschaftliches Zentrum Mensch-Umwelt-Technik (WZ III). Gesamthochschule Kassel: 64 pp

Krieger H, Schäfer H, (1991) Wuchsdynamik und Stickstoffökonomie südchinesischer Eukalyptusbestände - Datenerhebung, Analyse und Simulation. 4. Tagung der Sekt. Forstl. Biometrie und Informatik im Dtsch. Verb. Forstl. Forschungsanst. ("Klima und Wachstum"), Göttingen, 3.-5.7.1990. To be published in: Schriften Forstl Fak Univ Göttingen & Niedersächs Forstl Versuchsanst

Krupa SV, Kickert RN (1989) The greenhouse effect: Impacts of ultraviolet-B (UV-B) radiation, carbon dioxide (CO2), and ozone (O3) on vegetation. Environ Pollut 61: 263-393

Linder S, McMurtrie RE, Landsberg JJ (1985) Growth of eucalypts: A mathematical model for Eucalyptus globulus. In: Tigerstedt PMA, Puttonen P, Koski V (eds): Crop Physiology of Forest Trees. University Press, Helsinki: 117-126

Lugo AE (1988) The future of the forest. Environment 30: 17-45

Lugo AE, Brown S, Chapman J (1988) An analytical review of production rates and stemwood biomass of tropical forest plantations. For Ecol Manage 23: 179-200

McMurtrie RE, Landsberg JJ, Linder S (1989) Research priorities in field experiments on fast-growing tree plantations: Implications of a mathematical production model. In: Pereira JS, Landsberg JJ (eds): Biomass Production by Fast-Growing Trees. Kluwer Acad Publ: 181-207

Oberndörfer D (1990) Schutz der tropischen Regenwälder (Feuchtwälder) durch ökonomische Kompensation. Ber Naturf Ges Freiburg i Br 80: 225-261

Oikawa T (1985) Simulation of forest carbon dynamics based on a dry-matter production model. I. Fundamental model structure of a tropical rainforest ecosystem. Bot Mag Tokyo 98: 225-238

Peters RL (1990) Effects of global warming on forests. For Ecol Manage 35: 13-33

Pinyopusarerk K (1990) Acacia auriculiformis: an annotated bibliography. Winrock International, Bangkok /ACIAR, Canberra: 154 pp

Rehfuess KE (1990) Waldböden. (2nd ed) Parey, Hamburg/Berlin: 294 pp

Reichholf JH (1990) Der Tropische Regenwald. DTV, München: 207 pp

Ruhiyat D (1989) Die Entwicklung der standörtlichen Nährstoffvorräte bei naturnaher Waldbewirtschaftung und im Plantagenbetrieb, Ostkalimantan (Indonesien). Göttinger Beitr z Land- und Forstwirtsch i d Tropen u Subtrop 35: 206 pp

Schäfer H (1988) Auswirkungen der Deposition von Luftschadstoffen auf die Streuzersetzung in Waldökosystemen - Eine Fallstudie an den durch Stammablaufwasser stark säure- und schwermetallbelasteten Baumfuß-Bodenbereichen alter Buchen. Ber Forschungsz Waldökosysteme/Waldsterben Univ Göttingen A 37: 244 pp

Schäfer H, Krieger H (1991) Simulationsmodell zu Wachstum und Stickstoffhaushalt eines Eukalyptusbestandes in Südchina. Tagungsbericht zum 3. Herbstkolloquium der AG Biometrie und Ökologie, Deutsche Region der Internationalen Biometrischen Gesellschaft, Göttingen, 04.-05. Oktober 1990 (in print)

Schäfer H, Krieger H, Bossel H (1989) Using systems analysis to develop simulation models for managing forests under environmental pollution. In: Burkhart HE, Rauscher MH, Johann K (eds): Artificial Intelligence and Growth Models for Forest Management Decisions. (Proceedings of a IUFRO Meeting, Vienna, Austria, Sept. 18-22, 1989) School of Forestry and Wildlife Resources, Virginia Polytechnic Institute and State University, Blacksburg, Publication FWS-1-89: 322-332

Schneider TW, Wang Zhu-hao, Yu Zuo-yue, Ding Ming-mao, Chang Wen-qi, Yi Wei-min, Zeng Xiao-pin (1988) The structure and productivity of the eucalypt forest in South China. Working paper, Hamburg/Guangzhou: 12 pp

Schönwiese CD, Diekmann B (1989) Der Treibhauseffekt. Rowohlt, Reinbek/Hamburg: 215 pp

Sepp C, Sepp S (1990) Ein Forstprojekt im Wirkungsgefüge verschiedener Faktoren. AFZ 45: 51-53

Shugart HH (1984) Theory of Forest Dynamics. Springer, New York: 278 pp

Shugart HH, Antonovsky MY, Jarvis PG, Sandford AP (1985) CO2, climatic change and forest ecosystems. In: Bolin B et al (eds): The Greenhouse Effect, Climatic Change, and Ecosystems. SCOPE 29. Wiley, Chichester/New York: 475-521

Solomon AM (1986) Transient response of forests to CO^2-induced climate change: simulation modeling experiments in eastern North America. Oecologia (Berlin) 68: 567-579

Solomon AM (1988) Ecosystem theory required to identify future forest responses to changing CO$_2$ and climate. In: Wolff W, Soeder CJ, Drepper FR (eds): Ecodynamics. Springer, Berlin: 258-274

Steinlin H (1989) Tropenwälder. Freiburger Universitätsbl. 28 (105): 23-62

Strain BR, Cure JD (1986) Direct effects of atmospheric CO2 enrichment on plants and ecosystems: a bibliography with abstracts. - ORNL/CDIC-13, Oak Ridge National Laboratory/Carbon Dioxide Information Center, Oak Ridge: 199 pp

Thang HC (1987) Forest management systems for tropical high forest, with special reference to Peninsular Malaysia. For Ecol Manage 21: 3-20

Thornley JHM (1975) Mathematical Models in Plant Physiology. Academic Pr, London

Walter H, Breckle SW (1983) Ökologie der Erde. Bd. 1: Ökologische Grundlagen in globaler Sicht. Fischer, Stuttgart: 238 pp

Zech W, Elz D, Pancel L, Drechsel P (1989) Auswirkungen und Erfolgsbedingungen von Aufforstungsvorhaben in Entwicklungsländern. Weltforum, Köln: 348 pp

Tropical Forests in Transition
J. G. Goldammer (ed.)
© 1992 Birkhäuser Verlag Basel/Switzerland

A Finite-Element Model to Simulate Spacial Distributions of Populations of Large Mammals

Achmed Schüle[*]

Abstract

The composition of today's vegetation is a function of the overall biome composition and its development in the past. Historically, one of the major biome changes is to be seen in the disappearance of most of the megaherbivore species since the late Pleistocene. Saturated population densities of an estimated 2 megaherbivores per km^2 undoubtedly had a severe impact on the Pleistocene vegetation. The resulting greater biome diversity has to be taken into account when discussing the composition of today's natural forests.

In order to investigate the factors of influence on megaherbivore distributions a finite-element model allowing the calculation of distributions and migrations of big mammals has been developed. The underlying partial differential equations (PDE's) of the diffusion-reaction type are obtained by assuming a migrational strategy governed by the reproduction rate. This rate is calculated as a function of the food-per-head-rate depending on the various primary plant production rates and the number and features of the competitors for the same food source. A representation of the predation on megafauna by sabre-toothed cats is integrated by calculating encounter probabilities and killing rates.

In solving the finite-element-model a new numerical method is used that avoids the transport error usually arriving in finite differencing schemes. Its most important feature is the use of secondary grid points acting as transport buffers.

---

[*] Institute of Prehistory, University of Freiburg, Belfortstr. 22, D-7800 Freiburg, Germany

At the present stage the interactions with the vegetational food sources are limited to harvesting, neglecting overgrazing effects. By defining different primary production rates and geographic features, different biomes can be represented. Simulations of predator-prey systems show the important role of the spatial interactions. If the migrational stragtegy of the prey considers predational losses a stabilizing effect arises if the time steps used in solving are increased. This ample chaotic regime is reached for quite realistic time steps indicating the possible relevance of the effect. An important application of the model is the investigation of theories concerning anthropogenic overkill and its ecological consequences.

Introduction

The composition of the few natural forest biomes still remaining has to be explained by their past development. This includes the history of external influences, e.g. climatic changes which usually are conceived as open-loop control as well as changes in the behaviour of the biomes themselves. The latter can be treated as closed-loop controls, the main difference being the ability to maintain a given static or dynamic behaviour. There is strong evidence that a closed-loop-control approach should generally be preferred when investigating the behaviour of complicated ecological systems.

Discussion of anthropogenic changes are presently the main focus in this area. The beginning of anthropogenic changes have occured much earlier than generally supposed. Considering the world-wide changes in the respective biomes since the late Pleistocene, as far as they can be reconstructed, one particular change is most striking: The disappearance of the megafauna. In this context megafauna denotes animals with a body-weight exceeding 1 t in adult individuals. There are other definitions, e.g. 500 pounds (Martin 1975), but the size given here is better suited to explain the ecological role of such animals.

Recent investigations (Kortland 1976; Müller-Dombois 1981; Owen-Smith 1988) of the few extant relics of the rich Pleistocene megafauna make it clear that they exert a strong influence on the development of vegetation. Owen-Smith gives a detailed report of the mechanisms which one may expect at an assumed population density of two individuals per km^2. The beginning of the development is marked by the clearing of trees by browsing members of the megafauna, e.g. *Mastodon* and *Eremotherium* (browsing giant sloth) in Pleistocene North America initiating a succession of different animal and plant communities, which are in turn associated with different megaherbivore species. The result is a very heterogenous savanna-like vegetation extraordinarily rich in different habitats. Owen-Smith (1988) estimates that the Pleistocene vegetation "undoubtedly was in a severely disturbated stage". The high natural diversity of the Pleistocene biomes, that were largely shaped by the megafauna can be used to explain the richness of biotopes found in extant forest biomes, especially in rainforests.

Overkill-theories dealing with the anthropogenic extinction or decimation of the Pleistocene megafauna have been discussed for many years (Budyko 1967; Martin 1975, 1984). If they prove to be correct, one must consider whether man has not influenced the vegetation cover and, as a consequence, also the global climate throughout the Pleistocene by decimating the megafauna (W.Schüle 1990 a, 1990b).

The model presented here simulates communities of species containing megafaunas with special regard to the spatial distribution of the populations in order to simulate the interaction of different biotopes. The model is built as a two-dimensional finite element system allowing the numerical integration of the underlying system of coupled partial differential equations (PDE's). The model is designed as a first step towards a closed spatial simulation system of both vegetation and megafauna.

The Growth Rate as a Function of Trophic and Predatory Situation

Simulation systems based on stating and resolving ordinary differential equations (ODE's) were developed for game management (Meadows 1975; Goodman 1974), expenditure optimization in predator culling with stock breeding (Swart & Hearne 1989) and for fishery purposes (Steinberg 1986), just to mention a few.

The differential equations describing the growth or reduction of a species are derived by describing the trophic and predatory situation of the species. If both predatory and trophic situation are known, one may generally state:

$$\dot{n}_1 = \dot{n}_{1troph} - \dot{n}_{1pred}.$$

If the growth rate is plotted above the per-capita rate of food, three points are of special interest. The first denotes the maximum death rate of a population when the available amount of food is zero. The second is a "break-even point" and describes the per-capita rate at which the population is neither growing nor decreasing. The third point characterizes the food amount beyond which the growth-rate of the species no longer increases.

This approach is characterized by limited growth and death rates respectively. This feature is important for stability reasons, as migrations which are faster by orders of magnitude easily result in extreme situations where growth and death rates take unrealistically high values. The function linking the three points has to meet few clauses, namely monotone gradient and constancy. The simplest procedure is to define the sectors between two points as straight lines (Fig.1). It can also be defined as an hyperbolic function or other kinds of functions, which may be desirable for stability reasons.

The available amount of food per species is calculated as the sum of all accessible food resources considering their respective nutritive values. Values describing the probability of an actual use are comprised in the formulation describing the trophical affluence. To obtain a basis for the calculation of such values a model has to be developed. For a predator this can be done as follows: An area with one predator and one prey is considered. The simplest assumption regarding the type of their movement on the area is that of stochastic behaviour.

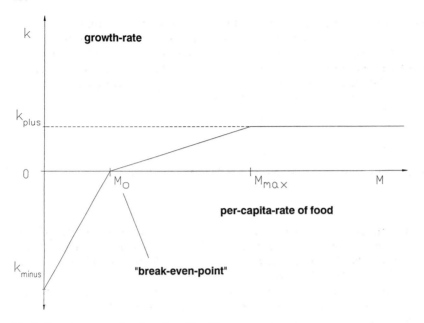

Fig.1. Growth rate as a function of trophic affluence

Figure 2 shows the model. It is assumed that predator and prey are characterized by their respective mean velocities and that the prey furthermore carries a radius in which the predator perceives the prey. If the predator moves with the velocity v_2, the prey with the velocity v_1 and if the prey carries a radius of the extension r_1, the encounter probability in an area of size A is represented by:

$$w_{12} = 2 \cdot (v_1 + v_2) \cdot r_1 / A .$$

The predation is successful in the case of an encounter in a certain percentage c, which can be calculated rather closely by observation. Such values are found in the specific literature for a number of predators, e.g. lions, hyenas (crocuta) and wild dogs. The total food amount FL_j available to the predator j together with the mass Mkg_i of the hunted species i, the loss factor d and the caloric eqivalent e for flesh then becomes:

$$FL_j = d \cdot e \cdot \sum_i (c_{ij} w_{ij} n_i Mkg_i) .$$

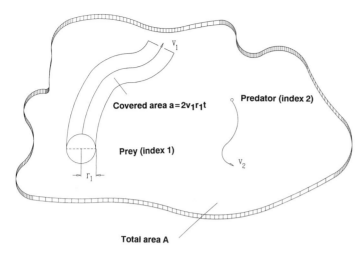

Fig.2. Model for the determination of encounter probabilities

Loss factors have been determined in a number of cases (Brain 1970; for man: Lee 1979; Hawkes *et al.* 1982).

Stochastic movement types are encountered in nature mainly alternating with deterministic behavior. Among the factors having influence on it are geographic properties, e.g. the increased encounter probability of predator and prey at waterholes in arid zones. On the other hand in the case of mammals both predator and prey show strategies which are aimed at influencing these probabilities, inasmuch as the prey avoids areas of increased predator encounter probabilities and the predator seeks such areas. To which degree these strategies neutralize each other has to be determined in each case by the observation of the behaviour of the respective species.

There are several reasons why the model of stochastic movement is applied in spite of this. The model allows a simple calculation of encounter probabilities which are the basis for further estimations. At the same time important operating mechanisms are introduced into the model: e.g. it becomes obvious that the formation of herds is of major importance to the prey because it decreases encounter probablities as they no longer increase proportionally but degressively with the number of prey. Furthermore the importance of mobility and, thereby, of the adopted energetic level and the physical characteristics of a species for its survival and finally, for the entire ecosystem enter into the calculations.

The consideration of predational losses in the balancing equation of a species is also covered by the determination of predational probabilities. It can be defined as a similar term as in the case of meat food:

$$\dot{n}_{ipred} = n_i \sum_j c_{ij} w_{ij} n_j.$$

Here the sum of the predators j is calculated, caloric contents do not occur.

In the case of plant food mean concentrations can be used. The amount of food M_i withdrawn by species i at a mean concentration Q of the food in the considered area A then becomes:

$$M_i = 2Qr_iv_i$$
$$= Q \cdot a_i.$$

with

   a_i = the area covered by an individual of the species i
          per time unit

If the food source is exploited by more than one animal the probability to find an area not yet harvested decreases. In the case of intraspecific competition it is described by the recursive formulation

$$p = A'/A = (A-(n-1) \cdot p \cdot a)/A,$$

with   A: entire area   A': area not yet harvested

In the case of one species i the probability p_1 is found to be described by:

$$p_i = 1/(1 + a_i/A \cdot (n_i-1)).$$

The expression (n-1) becomes n for large n. If several species exploit the same source the expression

   $a_i(n_i-1)$ is substituted by
   $\sum_i(a_i n_i)$,

a sum of the I species participating in the exploitation of the resource. We have thereby found a way to express the competition between species of different physical characteristics, in this case of different covered regions a. As an alternative the amounts actually withdrawn can be used as the basis for the calculation (see below).

The maximum amount I_{gpik} that species $_i$ can withdraw from resource k then becomes:

$$I_{gpik} = p_i a_i Q.$$

The amounts actually withdrawn are obtained by taking a second function as a basis, which shows the amount actually withdrawn as a function of the trophic situation. Such functions were first described by Holling (1959) and are known as Holling-types I to III. The simplest (type I) employes two significant values describing the maximum gradient and the maximum value of the withdrawal function (Fig. 3). They are employed in the exploitation of vegetational and flesh resources.

With the aid of the specific growth rate function from Figure 1 and by summarization of the food resources k of a species the formulation

$$\dot{n}_{itroph\_pf} = f(\sum_k I_{gpik}) \cdot n_i = f(PFL_i) \cdot n_i,$$

is obtained for the vegetational food, with the term containing the sum of all plant species k and the available food amount I_{gpik} above all species which feed on plant species k.

If the food resource of species i contains both vegetational (PFL) and flesh (FL) resources, then a sum has to be taken:

$$\dot{n}_{i\_troph} = f(PFL_i + FL_i) \cdot n_i.$$

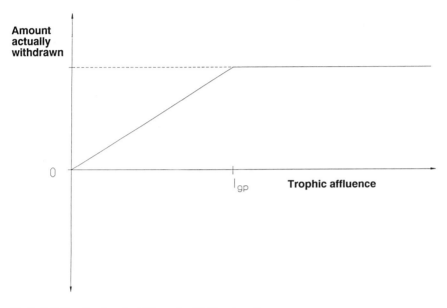

Fig.3. Satiation function for killing rates (Holling-type I)

The Transport Problem

Migrations occur in order to improve the fitness of the population. They require the comparison and evaluation of differences in growth rates of neighbouring areas either with or without regard of losses caused by predators. Populations thus follow the gradient of the growth or the reproduction rates, while modifying them by consumption of food resources and by attraction of predators.

Mathematically the direction of migration and the amount of the increase of the 'landscape' formed by the growth rate upon the area can be expressed by the gradient of the scalar field $U(x,y,t)$. In the simplest case a vector field $\underline{F} = f(x,y,t)$ of the population flux may be assumed, which can be defined as:

$$\underline{F}(x,y,t) = C(x,y,t)(grad\ U(x,y,t)).$$

The function C is used for several purposes. Its most important one is cutting the flux density at a certain value, as the gradient of a scalar field can become infinite. Further possible functions of C concern the trophic situation of the migrating populations or geographic factors influencing migrational speed.

With a predefined vector field describing the speed $\underline{V}(x,y,t)$, which is variable only directionwise to guarantee the mobility and the transported population density $q_t(x,y,t)$ the flux can be determined at location x,y.

$$\underline{F}(x,y,t) = \underline{V}(x,y,t) \cdot q_t(x,y,t).$$

The value calculated for the determination of the encounter probability, which denotes a constant result, may be used here as the value of abs $|\underline{V}|$. Thus an advective formulation of the transport problem has been established. It makes it possible to describe the fluxes not by the velocity during the migration but by the density of migrating populations travelling at a fixed speed. This means a considerable simplification for transport in the model. One error characteristic of this class of problems is also avoided: the so-called transport error. It occurs because on the grid per time dt unit a quantity is transported over the grid-spacing dx which is only true for

$$dx = v \cdot dt$$

with the given velocity v (Press *et al.* 1989). One method for reducing the transport error is known as "upwind differencing" (Roache 1976).

In our case annuling of the transport error is achieved by the introduction of secondary grid points, their spacing corresponding to the given time step dt and the now fixed velocity v so that the above relation is fulfilled. It is the ensuing decoupling of grid-spacing and the duration of the time step which allows the elimination of the transport error while maintaining the accuracy of the calculation. The transport is performed by shifting the densities accumulated at the secondary grid points according to the sign of the gradient of the growth rate point by point. The transported densities correspond to the value of the calculated flux. A further advantage is a cut-down in computation time, because the time-consuming calculations for the description of the gradient are carried out on the original grid.

The described strict management of migrational movement also allows the application of highly convergent methods of numerical integration in the determination of transported population densities. Present aspirations are towards an application of the Bulirsch-Stoer method (Stoer & Bulirsch 1980).

The mentioned application of highly convergent functions suggests the strict requirements the numerical procedure has to meet in describing the relatively fast migrations. The first point to be considered is the intended retardation between the change causing a migration and its actual impact on the growth-rate-distribution. It can be considered by a suitable "prognostics" approach because the needed information on the future development is almost completely present in the system.

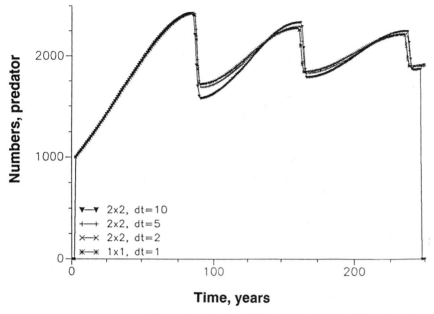

Fig.4. Predator-prey system oscillations described by ODE's (1x1) and finite differencing schemes

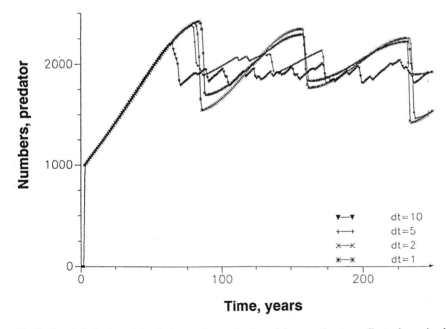

Fig.5. Chaotic behavior arising by incomplete evaluation of the growth-rate gradient when using longer time steps

Simulation Results

The implementation of the described approach was carried out in Pascal on a 32-Bit PC with coprocessor. In spite of the mentioned cut in computation time the calculations for realistic applications are still taking days, so that a further cut-down in time needed remains a major target.

If one considers the development of populations in the course of calculations with different paramenters, the behaviour for the exact calculation converges to the behaviour of the system of differential equations if only one cell is used as a basis and corresponding migrations do not occur (Fig. 4). For an exact calculation the Runge-Kutta method of the second degree employed up to now requires the neccessity of determining the growth rate gradient every 24 hours when assuming a grid spacing of 160 km. The necessary time step length decreases approximately with the grid spacing. Because of the prognostical approach described above the determination of the growth-rate-gradient is accomplished with a chronological outlook of eight days.

Beginning from a step size dt of 48 hours the periodical behavior is impaired and is transformed into a stable narrow-banded chaotic regime for dt = 120 hours (Fig. 5). Periodical oscillations with minima endangering the population occur no longer. This stabilizing effect arises because the predators cannot evaluate the movement of their prey exactly and suffer stochastically distributed losses in areas which are poor in or free of prey.

Similar effects occur if the information on the gradient of the growth-rate function is superimposed by a small stochastic signal or is multiplied with a stochastic factor approaching 1. This corresponds to an incomplete evaluation of the gradient of the growth-rate function. A chaotic regime is also observed if the transported amounts are not real values, but rather can only be expressed as whole numbers. If unprognosted values are used for the gradient of the growth-rate chaotic behaviour sets in even faster.

The establishing chaotic regime is deterministic but is not a property of the underlying system of PDE's (Steele 1974; Levin 1976; Haaken 1977). Thus, the techniques used in the determination of its behaviour have to be chosen carefully and generally should not be taken without precaution from the theory of nonlinear systems.

Talking about real predator-prey systems, it does not seem to be realistic to assume an exact evaluation of the gradient of the growth rate, because here the information is not propagated over the neccessary distances and is not evaluated with the neccessary exactness. This seems to indicate that a deterministic, chaotic regime arising by the inexact evaluation of the growth rate gradient is of importance for the stability of real predator-prey systems.

The simulation of invasion phenomena by predators is a good application for the simulation system. Figures 6 and 7 show results of such a simulation. It deals with the invasion of a predator into a biotope inhabited by an autochthonous predator and two different herbivores, one of which is a megaherbivore of 2 tons body weight. Its migrational strategies are not aimed at avoiding losses by predation. It is interesting that the effects of the predatorial invasion are nearly unnotable for some time, and that the collapse of the megafauna occurs suddenly. The autochthonnous predator becomes extinct shortly afterwards because of a lack of food as the population of the smaller herbivore is also affected by the new predator after an short interim peak. An oscillating regime with chaotic elements is finally established between the new predator and the small herbivore.

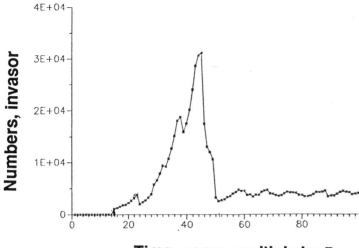

Time, years, multiply by 5

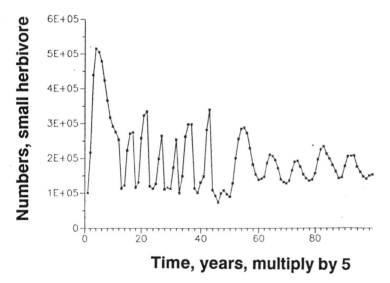

Time, years, multiply by 5

Fig.6. Population development in a system comprising four species (invader above, small herbivore below)

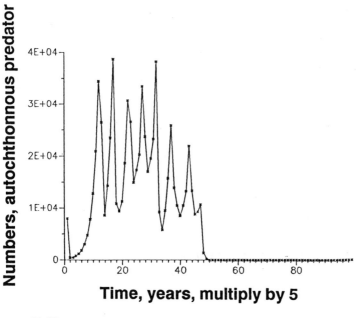

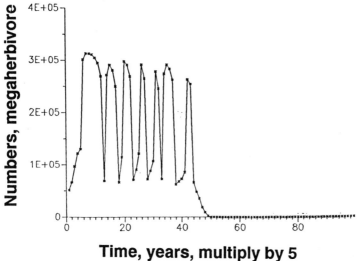

Fig.7. Population development in a system comprising four species (aboriginal predator above, large herbivore below)

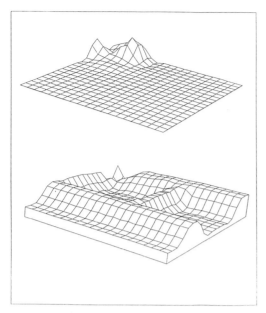

Fig.8. Spatial patterns formed by an invading carnivore (upper) and its prey (lower), 25 years after start of the invasion

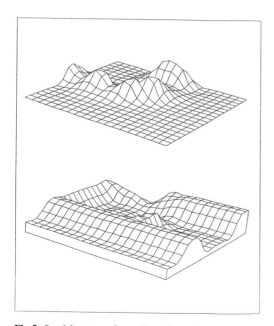

Fig.9. Spatial patterns formed by an invading carnivore (upper) and its prey (lower), 50 years after start of the invasion

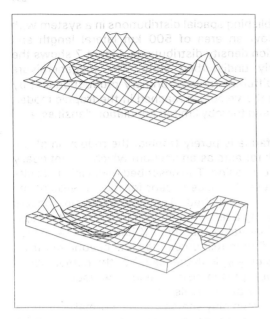

Fig.10. Spatial patterns formed by an invading carnivore (upper) and its prey (lower), 75 years after start of the invasion

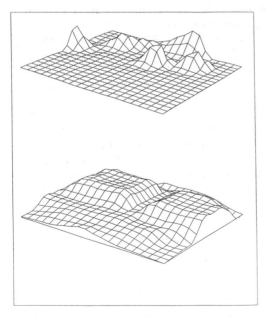

Fig.11. Spatial patterns formed by an invading carnivore (upper) and its prey (lower), 85 years after start of the invasion

Figures 8-11 give an insight into the establishing spacial distributions in a system with two species during an invasion. They show an area of 500 km lateral length and 250,000 km^2 with the establishing population density distributions. Figure 7 shows the distribution of both species in an nearly undisturbed state. The megaherbivore distribution is in this case determined by different rates of primary production and by geographically determined modifications of the velocities reached in the trophic model. The influence of zones with limited mobility and thereby limited population densities, e.g. mountains, can be represented in that way.

As the migrational strategy of the megafauna is purely trophic, the reduction of the population density caused by the new predator acts as an vacuum which is continually refilled from the areas not yet affected by the invasion. The described mechanism results in an metastable phase, in which no changes take place except for the increase of the invading population. Even the invasion is nearly halted. The final expansion occurs relatively fast, with the invasion front exhibiting a tendency to split into isolated groups. Analogous to the prediction of the "marginal value theorem" (Charnov 1974) which deals with the optimum exploitation of distributed resources the zone beyond the front is not free of prey and the density of prey is only little decreased. Yet the comparability of the two models is limited, because the model presented here regards various biotopes, an even distribution of resources and several trophic levels.

Figure 11 shows that areas which are populated only sparsely under normal conditions may act as refuges during the last phase of the extinction.

Outlook

The statement described above describes the vegetation as a constant source exploited by animals in a competitive situation. Repercussions like the destruction of resources or the influence on the primary production by grazing (Belsky 1986, 1987) as well as seasonal changes are disregarded at this point of the development of the system.

However, the consideration of the qualitatively changed behaviour when establishing feedback loops between fauna and flora is the main objective of the system described. Therefore, how a model of the flora can be integrated, is of particular interest. This will be accomplished through the definition of successions which occur according to the intensity of browsing, grazing and destruction of the vegetational cover by members the megafauna. Thus, anthropogenic influences on the overall biome composition can be investigated. Simulations of this type allow first estimations of the anthropogenic effect on the CO_2 fluxes and the accumulation of greenhouse gases in the atmosphere (primarily methane). One may also expect further insights in to the composition of late Pleistocene floral and faunal associations.

References

Allee WC (1931) Animal aggregations. A study in general sociology. Chicago: University of Chicago Press.

Belsky AJ (1986) Does herbivory benefit plants? A Review of the Evidence. American Naturalist 127: 870-892

Belsky AJ (1987) The effects of grazing: confounding of ecosystem, community, and organism scales. American Naturalist 129: 777-783

Brain CK (1970) New finds at the Swartkrans Australopitecine site. Nature Lond. 225: 1112-1119

Budyko MI (1967) On the causes of the extinction of some animals at the end of the Pleistocene. Iszvestija Akademii Nauk SSSR Serija Geograficeskaja 2: 28-36

Charnov EL (1974) Optimal Foraging, the Marginal Value Theorem. Theoretical Population Biology 9: 129-136

Goodman MR (1974) Study notes on System Dynamics. Cambridge, Mass.: MIT Press

Haken H (1977) Synergetics. An introduction. Berlin, Heidelberg, New York, Tokyo: Springer

Hawkes K, Hill K, O'Connel JF (1982) Why hunters gather: Optimal foraging and Ache of eastern Paraguay. American Ethnologist 9: 379-398

Holling CS (1959) Some characteristics of simple types of predation and parasitism. Can. Ent. 91: 293-320

Kortland A (1976) Netherlands Journ Zoology 26: 449-51

Lee RB (1979) The Kung San: Men, women and work in a foraging society. Cambridge: Cambridge University Press

Levin SA (1976) Dispersion and population interactions. American Naturalist 108: 207-228

MacNaughton SJ (1983) Serengeti grassland ecology: The role of composite environmental factors and contingency in community organisation. Ecol Monogr 53: 291-320

Martin PS, Klein RG (eds.) (1984) Quarternary Extinctions. Tucson, Arizona: The University of Arizona Press

Martin PS, Mosiman JE (1975) Simulating overkill by paleoindians. American Scientist 63: 304-313

Meadows D (1975) Formulation of a model of deer population of the Kaibab plateau, (Lectures 2 and 3). In: Fourth Annual Advanced Studies Institute on Social System Dynamics. Hanover, N.H.: Dartmouth College

Mueller-Dombois D (1981) Crocon distortion and elephant distribution in the woody vegetation of Ruhunu National Park. Ecology 53: 208-226

Owen-Smith N (1988) Megaherbivores. Cambridge: Cambridge University Press

Press WH, Flannery BP, Teukolsky SA, Vetterling WT (1989) Numerical Recipes. The art of scientific computing. Cambridge: Cambridge University Press

Roache PJ (1976) Computational fluid dynamics. Albuquerque: Hermosa

Schüle W (1990a) Landscapes and Climate in Prehistory: Interactions of wildlife, man, and fire. In: Fire in the tropical biota. Ecosystem processes and global challenges. J.G. Goldammer (ed.), 273-318. Berlin, Heidelberg, New York: Springer

Schüle W (1990b) Human evolution, animal behaviour, and Quarternary extinctions. A paleo-ecology of hunting. HOMO 41: 229-250

Steinberg MN (1986) Using system dynamics to evaluate policies for managing New Yorks hard clam fishery: Some unexpected insights. Proceedings of the 1986 International System Dynamics Conference. Sevilla, Spain

Steele JH (1974) Spatial heterogenity and population stability. Nature 83: 248

Stoer J, Bulirsch R (1980) Introduction to Numerical Analysis. New York: Springer-Verlag

Swart J, Hearne JW (1989) A mathematical model to analyze predation and competition problems in a sheep-farming region. System Dynamics Review 1: 35-50

Tropical Forests in Transition
J. G. Goldammer (ed.)
© 1992 Birkhäuser Verlag Basel/Switzerland

The Role of the Tropics in the Global Carbon Budget: Impacts and Possible Developments

Gerd Esser[*]

Abstract

The Osnabrück Biosphere Model was used by the author to investigate possible consequences of deforestation, atmospheric CO_2 increase, and climate change, in the tropics in a global context. The extensive agricultural cultivating systems in the tropics must be intensified to counteract the increasing losses of natural land. At present, the losses of carbon due to deforestation are probably balanced by additional carbon storage as a consequence of the CO_2 fertilization effect. The expected temperature increase will presumably show positive feedback to carbon losses from litter and soil. The model results are in agreement with recent data, but a convincing validation is still lacking.

Introduction

About 5.5×10^9 humans are living on the earth at present. The population density and and the state of development and industrialization of human communities are very uneven in the world. Despite the regional problems of high population density or

*Institute for Plant Ecology, Justus-Liebig-University, Heinrich-Buff-Ring 38, D-6300 Giessen, Germany

industrialization which are observed in many countries, the global population as a whole has begun to destroy the boundary conditions of human life. The processes on which this assumption is based, some of which were already discovered long ago, include:

- The destruction of the stratospheric ozone layer as a consquence of complex interactions of human emissions from traffic, agriculture, chemical industry, and energy plants (Molina & Rowland 1974; Chubachi 1984; Farman et al. 1985);

- The toxification and acidification of terrestrial and aquatic systems and of the air, including the increase of the atmospheric CO_2 concentration through burning of of fossil fuels (Smith 1872; Odén 1868; Keeling 1986; Friedli et al. 1986);

- The climate change induced by the enhanced greenhouse effect of anthropogenic trace gases (Arrhenius 1896; Ramanathan 1987; Wuebbels & Edmonds 1988);

- The deforestation, degradation, and erosion of land (Marsh 1874; Richards et al. 1983).

This list is probably incomplete, since we may become aware of processes which are not yet discovered.

Places of highest anthropogenic emissions to the environment rarely coincide with places of the strongest impacts of those emissions. The tropics have always been one of the most vulnerable parts of the global system. For example, severest consequences of the expected climate change may be expected in the semiarid tropics (i.e. the Sahel) due to changes in the amount and distribution of precipitation. However, the major sources for greenhouse gases are in some developed countries (fossil fuel burning) and in the humid tropics (deforestation).

The development and acceptance of response strategies would require a global consensus, and national sacrifices. All response strategies must take in account that the world population will double in the next few decades. The highest growth rate of populations is mainly found in developing countries in the tropics (Keyfitz & Flieger 1991). Therefore, the tropics will most probably become a region of concentrated impacts to the environment with global consequences as well.

In this paper the author presents a systems analysis of the deforestation/climate/ carbon cycle related processes with special emphasis on the tropics. This analysis is based on a global dynamic model which considers the major globally relevant mechanisms. Those include (1) deforstation and its consequences on phytomass, litter, and soil organic carbon; (2) changes of atmospheric CO_2 concentration and their consequences on the biospheric production and storage of carbon; (3) feedback effects of climate change on mechanisms (1) and (2).

The Model

In terms of systems science, the global carbon cycle is considered as a 'dynamic system' consisting of carbon pools (atmosphere, ocean, phytomass, litter, soil organic carbon, fossil resources), and fluxes between the pools. Control variables (climate, soil fertility, human impact) regulate the fluxes. The pools are balanced by their respective fluxes. Such a system reacts dynamically, i.e. actions taken on by one system flux influence all the others. For example, tropical deforestation influences the uptake of CO_2 into the ocean. Such a system structure may be easily transformed into mathematical formulations and used as a computer model. The author used the Osnabrück Biosphere Model (OBM, Esser 1986; Esser 1991) to investigate the consequences of deforestation, the rise in atmospheric CO_2, and climate change.

The OBM is a dynamic model of the terrestrial carbon cycle, which is regionalized on a global 2.5 degree grid. The reasons which required the regionalization of the model were: (1) non-linearity of the model's equations; (2) human impacts acting on different regional natural vegetation complexes; (3) yields in agriculture depending on regional socio-economic influences in addition to natural ones; (4) complex regional patterns of change in the driving forces of the model. For the model application, the results of which are presented here, the model was coupled with the box-diffusion ocean model suggested by Oeschger et al. (1975). The method of calculation for the principal model variables is explained in more detail in Table 1. For a detailed description of the structure, equations, and the data sets used to run the latest model version see Esser (1991).

Results

Importance of the Tropics in a Global Context

It is surprising to learn about the relative importance of the tropics in a global context. Let us consider — very schematically — those regions to be the tropics which are enclosed by the parallels of latitude of 20° south and 20° north. These boundaries enclose only 30% of the global land area of 132.9×10^6 km² (without Antarctica). The following results are given for the reference year 1980. This tropical belt receives more than 50% of the precipitation over land on an annual average. The net primary productivity (*NPP*) of the natural and seminatural vegetation of this belt (i.e. the net annual carbon flux atmosphere to green plants) amounts to about 23×10^9 t · yr^{-1} carbon, which is slightly less than 60% of the respective global value. The carbon stored in this belt's living phytomass is roughly 400×10^9 t or more than 60% of the global phytomass. About 26% of the global plant litter and 31% of the soil organic carbon are found in this belt, in total shortly 500×10^9 t of carbon in the litter and soil organic carbon.

Tab.1. Principal biospheric variables of the Osnabrück Biosphere Model and their computation (from Esser (1990) modified). For further explanations see Esser (1991)

biospheric variable	calculated from
net primary productivity	temperature, precipitation, soil fertility, agricultural yield, conversion factors yield to productivity, land-use areas, CO_2-fertilization
land-use changes in the period 1860-1980	statistical data on country basis, remote sensing
land-use changes after 1980	scenarios considering: land-use density in 1970, natural productivity, soil fertility, increase of agricultural areas 1950-1980; options: preservation of natural vegetation, minimum-fertility for economic uses
cleared phytomass	land-use changes, natural phytomass, crop phytomass
soil fertility	empirical factor for soil types
conversion factor yield to productivity	empirical factor for major field crops
CO_2-fertilization	atmosph. CO_2-concentration, soil fertility
phytomass	net primary productivity, litter production
litter production	residence time of carbon in respective phytomass compartment, phytomass pool
litter pool	litter production minus depletion
litter depletion	depletion coefficient, litter pool
litter depletion coefficient	temperature, precipitation, material depleted
soil organic carbon production	litter production, lignine content
soil organic carbon	production minus depletion
soil organic carbon depletion	temperature, precipitation, soil organic carbon pool
leaching of dissolved and particulate org. C	precipitation
atmosphere	balanced by: fossil emissions, ocean exchange, net primary production, depletion fluxes of litter and soil organic carbon, burnt biomass
ocean	box diffusion ocean, 1 mixed layer, 43 deep sea boxes

Tab. 2. Comparison of the productivities of natural vegetation and agricultural crops for some tropical and extratropical countries. The productivities of the agricultural crops were calculated from the yields (FAO Production Yearbooks) by use of conversion factors given by Aselmann & Lieth (1983). Values refer to the weight of dry matter (for carbon multiply by 0.45). From Esser (1990)

country	agricultural productivity $[g \cdot m^{-2} \cdot yr^{-1}]$	natural productivity $[g \cdot m^{-2} \cdot yr^{-1}]$	ratio agric./natural
Zaire	180	1960	0.10
Kenya	180	1300	0.13
Niger	150	890	0.17
Kampuchea	310	1800	0.17
Bolivia	280	1500	0.19
Brazil	310	1620	0.19
Spain	510	750	0.68
FR Germany	1130	1190	0.95
Belgium, Luxemburg	1290	1210	1.07

In contrast, this belt lacks almost any importance for human nutrition, on a global view. Only about 10% of the productivity of the global agricultural areas and plantations stems from this belt, and this minor contribution is mainly consumed by the native population of the countries itself. One of the reasons for the lack of importance of the tropics for agricultural production is the very low relative productivity of agriculture in most of the relevant countries, which in fact is the reason for the relatively high land consumption for agricultural purposes. As pointed out in Table 2 the low-input agriculture of many developing countries results in an agricultural productivity of only 10-20% of the potential productivity (that of natural systems) which in contrast is achieved in high-input agriculture, i.e. in the European Community. From a technical point of view the very high relative productivity of the EC countries could also be achieved in the tropics, but this would require a high input of capital into the agricultural systems and therefore requires high prices of the food products. It could be a contribution of the developed countries to subsidize the prices for agricultural products in tropical countries, i.e. raise the prices for food products to be consumed by the native population to a level where high-input agriculture becomes profitable. If this could finally be achieved without harming the world's economics during the transition, there would be a reduction of the actual land needs for agriculture of up to 80-90%. The destruction of the natural vegetation and soils could then be retarded if not prevented, despite the future population increase. Although the potential negative side of pesticide and fertilizer application can not be denied, intensifying agricultural production processes in the tropics may prove to be the only way to preserve the remnant natural systems.

Carbon Dynamics in the Tropics

Changes in the sizes of major carbon pools of the terrestrial biosphere in the tropics, i.e. living phytomass, dead phytomass (litter), and soil organic carbon, are the result of processes which change the fluxes related to those pools: (1) The CO_2 fertilization effect enhances the net primary productivity; (2) deforestation is a flux which diminishes the living phytomass and the productivity as well; (3) the changing climate may primarily influence the production and depletion processes of litter and soil organic carbon.

It was already discussed that deforestation not only reduce the phytomass (through reduction of the residence time) but also the net primary productivity to less than 20% of its natural state. As a consequence the input fluxes into the litter and soil organic carbon pools are reduced as well. Since the depletion coefficients are basically unchanged, the pools are reduced due to lower input. On the other side, reforestation does not restore the production of litter and soil organic carbon immediately, since immature forests produce less litter, although their net primary productivity may be as high or even higher than that of mature forests. Thus reforestation of old fallow land may even reduce the litter and soil carbon pools during the first decades.

The CO_2 fertilization effect is a very complicated process, which is largely unknown in the tropics mechanistically. The OBM considers this effect by use of functions which were derived from the results of laboratory and field experiments with field crops, and with a limited number of meadow plants and forest species mainly of the temperate zone. Its application to the tropics may be considered arbitrary. Theoretically, the following effects of a rising atmospheric CO_2 level may be important: (1) direct effect on the quantum efficiency of photosynthesis through changes of the activity of ribulose-bisphosphate- carboxylase/oxygenase as a consequence of higher intra-cellular CO_2 partial pressure; (2) higher carbon-fixation to transpiration ratio through increasing stomatal resistance; (3) nutrient availability to plants may limit the phytomass increase although the net primary productivity may be enhanced by effects (1) and (2). This latter effect may be of special importance in the tropics due to the nutrient-poor soils, mainly Ferralsols, Acrisols, and Podzols in large areas. The OBM considers influences of soil fertility on the CO_2 fertilization effect empirically.

The processes are interacting. The advantage of a model is that the contribution of each process to pool changes which are observed in model experiments is easily detectable (sensitivity analyses). Results of such a deconvolution of different contributions to the observed changes are shown in Table 3. Column (a) demonstrates the zonal integrals of the annual fertilization effect. It is highest in the humid tropics. If we again take the belt 20° south to 20° north, its carbon sequestering due to the fertilization effect amounts to about 60% of the global value. In total, 1.25×10^9 t carbon were additionally sequestered in the global phytomass, of which 0.76×10^9 t between 20° north and 20° south.

Tab.3. Zonal integrals of the phytomass change due to the fertilization effect alone (a), due to fertilization effect and land-use changes together (b), and the total biospheric balance including phytomass, litter, and soil (c). The difference (b - a) is the net effect of deforestation, afforestation, and land-use changes alone. Values are in 10^6 tons of carbon per year as integrals of $10°$ latitudinal zones for the reference year 1980. Negative values are losses from the biosphere. From Esser (1991)

hemisphere	latid. zone	(a)	(b)	(b - a)	(c)
north	70-80	1.1	1.0	-0.1	5.6
	60-70	40.4	34.9	-5.5	64.2
	50-60	80.7	62.6	-18.1	10.6
	40-50	102.5	171.1	68.6	143.9
	30-40	67.5	178.1	110.6	116.9
	20-30	80.5	-113.6	-194.1	-50.8
	10-20	82.3	-95.4	-177.7	-71.5
	0-10	233.9	79.5	-154.4	144.7
south	10-0	295.0	180.5	-114.5	215.0
	20-10	147.7	67.5	-80.2	115.4
	30-20	90.5	-102.3	-192.8	-57.3
	40-30	19.4	-20.9	-40.3	-31.0
	50-40	9.3	1.8	-7.5	1.6
	60-50	1.1	0.9	-0.2	1.9
total		1251.9	445.7	-806.2	608.2

In column (b) of Table 3 the phytomass change due to deforestation, reforestation, land-use changes, is included in addition to the fertilization effect. It is quite obvious that in regions with high deforestation rates net losses from the phytomass pool occur, although the fertilization effect alone may be high. Globally the 1.25×10^9 t · $^{-1}$ sequestered by the fertilization effect are reduced to 0.45×10^9 t · yr^{-1}. The difference (b-a) then is the net direct change of phytomass based on deforestation, reforestation and other land-use changes. Globally, 0.8×10^9 t · yr^{-1} were emitted from the living phytomass by land-use changes and deforestation. In the belt 20° south to 20° north the emissions were about 0.5×10^9 t · yr^{-1}. The highest deforestation rates occur between the 30° latitude circles of both hemispheres. They add up to 0.9×10^9 t · yr^{-1} released for the tropics and subtropics together. This is about 16% of the emissions into the atmosphere from fossil sources in the same year (Marland *et al.* 1989). In contrast, in the belt 30° to 50° north a net fixation of carbon is modeled, due to afforestation in those regions, namely the eastern and southeastern U.S.A. It amounts to 0.2×10^9 t · yr^{-1}.

The carbon release from deforestation has frequently been estimated in the past. The use of deforestation rates and the changes in carbon per unit area prior and after deforestation (i.e. estimates are not based on dynamic model calculations) gave as flux to the atmosphere $0.6-2.5 \times 10^9$ t · yr^{-1} of carbon in 1980 (Houghton 1990). The broad range is due to uncertainties in the area deforested, the carbon per unit area, and the fate of the carbon after clearing. The figure given by the OBM is close to the lower end of this range.

If the consecutive effects of CO_2 fertilization and land-use changes, respective deforestation on litter and soil organic carbon are considered as well (see Table 3, column (c)), then the global carbon balance of the terrestrial biosphere is 0.6×10^9 t · yr^{-1}. This means that, despite the deforestation, the biosphere was a small sink for carbon in 1980.

Clearly, this will change in the near future for several reasons: (1) since 1980, the deforestation rates have probably doubled; (2) the reduction of woody phytomass as a consequence of deforestation, forestry, forest grazing, and burning will diminish the fertilization effect, since medium to long-term storage of carbon in living plants is only due to woody material; (3) the temperature increase will lower carbon sequestering due to the enhanced respiration; (4) soil and nutrient constraints will become increasingly more limiting.

Biospheric Carbon Balance in Transition, and Validation of the Model Results

We will now discuss the results of the OBM for an extended time period, and the feedback effects of a changing climate. These investigations require a transitional model experiment. Since the model rests on very crude assumptions and working hypotheses, as we have pointed out earlier, it is especially important to find possibilities to prove the model results by use of independent experimental results. A transitional model run can be used to predict changes of the atmospheric CO_2 concentration. This value can be determined experimentally for time periods of several hundred years with sufficient reliability. Therefore, and because those measurements were not used for the model development, they can serve for model validation.

Between the year 1860, which is commonly referred to as "preindustrial", and 1980 the fertilization effect of CO_2 has caused additional C-fixation in phytomass of about 70×10^9 t. The losses due to deforestation were somewhere around 100×10^9 t globally. Therefore, during that period the biosphere was a net carbon source of 30×10^9 t.

In the period 1950 - 1980, the carbon lost from phytomass by deforestation sums up to 25×10^9 t C. As a consequence of the CO_2 fertilization, 35×10^9 t C were bound. Thus, altogether the phytomass was a net sink for C. Prior to 1950, the fertilization was rather small — the atmospheric CO_2 concentration in 1950 was about 312 $\mu l \cdot l^{-1}$ — that the deforestation losses strongly prevailed.

In Table 4 a comparison is given of the results of three scenarios for the period 1860 - 1980. The first scenario assumes an invariable climate in this period, the second a temperature increase of 0.8 °C, and the third scenario assumes that no CO_2 fertilization effect exists.

The question is which scenario comes closest to the measured data as represented by the Mauna Loa records and the results of polar ice core measurements.

The model runs with standard climate and with the increased temperature brought resembling results. Eventually, a positive feedback of the increased temperature may be concluded, since the atmospheric CO_2 in this scenario rises 2 $\mu l \cdot l^{-1}$ more than with invariable climate. But this result is clearly insignificant. The existence of a large fertilization effect has long been controversial. If a fertilization effect is ignored in the models a CO_2 concentration close to 260 $\mu l \cdot l^{-1}$ has to be assumed for the year 1860 to get the measured value of 340 $\mu l \cdot l^{-1}$ in 1980. In contrast, measurements of air in ice cores from antarctic glaciers suggest 283 ±3 $\mu l \cdot l^{-1}$ for 1860 (Friedli et al. 1986), which is in excellent agreement with the results of the model experiments which consider CO_2 fertilization. Moreover, the modelled increase of +37 $\mu l \cdot l^{-1}$ for the Mauna Loa period 1958-1980 is much higher than the measured, if a CO_2 fertilization effect is ignored. The other two scenarios are similar to the Mauna Loa value. But the amount of CO_2 uptake by the ocean is still uncertain. If it is underestimated at present, then a weaker CO_2 fertilization effect would be sufficient to explain the measured results.

Tab.4. Net changes of global carbon pools due to three scenarios for the period 1860-1980 (from Esser 1991). Standard climate means that the climate was invariable, temperature increase relates to a change of the mean annual temperature coupled to the atmospheric CO_2 to yield +0.8 °C in the period 1860-1980, no CO_2 fertilization assumes that NPP is uninfluenced by the atmospheric CO_2 level. Values are net changes in Gt and Gt·yr^{-1}, respectively. Negative prefix indicates losses of the respective pool to the atmosphere. The CO_2 values are in $\mu l \cdot l^{-1}$. Mauna Loa means ΔCO_2 for the period 1958-1980 at the Mauna Loa observatory, Hawaii (Keeling, 1986). Ice core value after Friedli et al. (1986)

	standard climate	temperature increase	no CO_2 fertil.
CO_2 1860	285	283	261
antarctic ice cores 1860		283 ± 3	
ΔCO_2 1958-1980	+22.6	+23.3	+37.4
Mauna Loa 1958-1980		+23.2	
phytomass	-23	-20	-83
litter	+1	-0.5	-5
soil organic C	-5	-12	-26
ocean	+76	+78	+112
atmosphere	+114	+117	+164
fossil source		-163	

At present, it is not possible to estimate the reliability of the model predictions. The models must be considered as working hypotheses rather than results which can be proven in terms of statistical confidence. Therefore, more independent data which have not been used for the calibration of the model functions should be used for attempting to falsify the model results. Those data include the fractionation of carbon isotopes. Especially the high seasonal dynamics of the carbon cycle could be used to prove the models via atmospheric CO_2 time and space gradients, since several carbon fluxes which compensate over a year or several years, are not in phase on a shorter time scale.

Recently, Tans et al. (1990) concluded from independent calculations using observed atmospheric concentrations of CO_2 and boundary layer concentrations in the ocean, that the observed north-south atmospheric concentration gradient could be only maintained if sinks of CO_2 were greater in the extratropical northern than in the southern hemisphere. We can compare their suggestion with the results of the OBM. The extratropical northern hemisphere ($> 20°$ N) is a net sink of about 0.3 Gt C annually, while the similar southern latitudes are a source of about 0.08 Gt C. It can not be excluded at present that the northern hemispheric sink might be even larger than calculated by the OBM, since this model does not yet consider the possible fertilization effect of anthropogenic immissions besides CO_2, i.e. NO_x compounds. On the other side, measured $\delta^{13}C/\delta^{12}C$ ratios in the atmosphere do not support this hypothesis (Keeling et al. 1989).

Conclusions

The tropics have played a major role in the global change of the past. Deforestation and other land-use changes and the presumed fertilization effect of the increasing atmospheric CO_2 are especially important in the tropical regions. They have partly compensated in the past. It might be expected with a high degree of security that the destruction of tropical ecosystems will dramatically increase in the future, due to the high population increase in those countries. One of the major reasons is the low relative productivity of agriculture in most developing coutries in the tropics, in comparison to the productivity of the natural vegetation.

Deforestation has led to emissions of about 100×10^9 t C in the period 1860 - 1980. This is about 60% of the emissions from fossil sources in the same period. At present (1980) the emissions from deforestation of tropical and subtropical regions are 0.9×10^9 t $\cdot$ yr^{-1} C, which is only 16% of the annual fossil emissions. This underlines the importance of greatly reducing the burning of fossil carbon. For the future it might be expected, that due to the population growth in tropical countries their consumption of fossil fuel and the needs of areas for agricultural use will greatly increase, if no substantial support is to come from developed countries.

The models used to investigate the global change are still highly hypothetical and their reliability is not yet proven. Techniques must be developed which allow better validation of those models.

Acknowledgments

This paper is based on results which were achieved from research activities sponsored by the German Science Foundation (DFG), the German Federal Environmental Agency (UBA), the German Federal Ministry of Research and Technology (BMFT), and the Commission of the European Communities (CEC). I also wish to thank all colleagues who promoted and encouraged the work by their assistance and critical discussions.

References

Arrhenius S (1896) On the influence of carbonic acid in the air upon the temperature of the ground. PhilMag 41: 237

Aselmann I, Lieth H (1983) The implementation of agricultural productivity into existing global models of primary productivity. In: Degens. Kempe. Soliman. eds Transport of carbon and minerals in the major world rivers. Part 2 Mitt Geolog-Paläontolog Inst Univ Hamburg SCOPE/UNEP Sonderband Heft 55: 107-118.

Chubachi S (1984) A special ozone observation at Syowa Station, Antarctica, from February 1982 to January 1983. In: Atmospheric Ozone. D Reidel Dordrecht: 285

Esser G (1986) The carbon budget of the biosphere — structure and preliminary results of the Osnabrück Biosphere Model (in German with extended English summary). Veröff Naturf Ges zu Emden von 1814. New series vol 7: 160 pp and 27 figures

Esser G (1990) Modelling global terrestrial sources and sinks of CO_2 with special reference to soil organic matter. In:

Bouwman AF ed. (1990) Soils and the greenhouse effect. J Wiley & Sons Ltd Chichester New York Brisbane Toronto Singapore. pp 247-261

Esser G (1991) Osnabrück Biosphere Model: construction, structure, results. In: Esser G. Overdieck D. (1991) Facets of Modern Ecology. Elsevier Sci Publ Amsterdam New York (in press)

Farman JC, Gardiner BG, Shanklin JD (1985) Large losses of total ozone in Antarctic reveal seasonal ClOx/NOx interaction. Nature 315: 207-210

Friedli H. Lötscher H. Oeschger H. Siegenthaler U. Stauffer B (1986) Ice core record of the $^{13}C/^{12}C$ ratio of atmospheric CO^2 in the past two centuries. Nature 324: 237-238.

Houghton RA (1990) The global effects of tropical deforestation. Environ Sci Technol 24: 414-422

Keeling CD (1986) Atmospheric CO_2 concentrations — Mauna Loa Observatory, Hawaii 1958-1986. NDP-001/R1 Carbon Dioxide Information Centre Oak Ridge Tennessee (regularly updated)

Keeling CD, Bacastow RB, Carter AF, Piper SC, Whorf TP, Heimann M, Mook WG, Roeloffzen H (1989) A three-dimensional model of atmospheric CO_2 transport based on observed winds: 1. Analysis of observational data. In: Peterson DH (ed) Aspects of climate variability in the Pacific and the western Americas. Geophysical Monograph 55: 165-236

Keyfitz N, Flieger W (1991) World population growth and aging — Demographic trends in the late twentieth century. The University of Chicago Press. Chicago and London

Marland G, Boden TA, Griffin RC, Huang SF, Kanciruk P, Nelson TR (1989) Estimates of CO_2 emissions from fossil fuel burning and cement manufacturing, based on the United Nations energy statistics and the U.S. Bureau of Mines cement manufacturing data. Carbon Dioxide Information Analysis Center. Environmental Science Division Publication No 3176. Prepared for the U.S. DOE by Oak Ridge National Laboratory. ORNL/CDIAC-25 NDP-030

Marsh GP (1874) The earth as modified by human actions. Sampson Low London and New York

Molina MJ, Rowland FS (1974) Stratospheric sink for chloro-fluoro-methanes: Chlorine atom catalyzed destruction of ozone. Nature 249: 810-814

Odén S (1968) The acidification of air and precipitation and its consequences in the natural environment. Bulletin No 1 Swedish National Research Council Stockholm

Oeschger H, Siegenthaler U, Schotterer U, Gugelmann A (1975) A box diffusion model to study the carbon dioxide exchange in nature. Tellus 27: 168-192

Ramanathan V (1987) Climate-chemical interactions and effects of changing atmospheric trace gases. J Geophys Res
    25: 1441-1482
Richards JF, Olson JS, Rotty RM (1983) Development of a data base for carbon dioxide releases resulting from
    conversion of land to agricultural uses. Institute for Energy Analysis Oak Ridge Assoc Universities,
    ORAU/IEA-82-10(M); ORNL/TM-8801
Smith RA (1872) Air and rain: the beginnings of a chemical climatology. Longmans Green London
Tans PP, Fung IY, Takahashi T (1990) Observational constraints on the global atmospheric CO_2 budget. Science 247:
    1431-1438
Wuebbles DJ, Edmonds J (1988) A primer on greenhouse gases. Report for United States Dept of Energy TR040,
    DOE/NBB-0083

Modeling the Response of Terrestrial Vegetation to Climate Change in the Tropics

Thomas M. Smith, Jackson B. Smith Jr. and Herman H. Shugart[*]

Abstract

The conservation and management of tropical ecosystems must consider the temporal and spatial dynamics of vegetation. An understanding of the patterns and processes of ecosystems as they relate to environmental gradients is of particular importance in the face of potential global climate change as a result of increasing atmospheric levels of CO_2.

Three classes of models relating vegetation pattern to climate and their application to climate change research are discussed.

The potential consequences of global climate change on the distribution of vegetation in the tropics are examined using the vegetation-climate classification model of Holdridge. The distribution of major biome-types was simulated under both current climate and four climate change scenarios based on general circulation models. The changes in global climate patterns have a major influence on the distribution of tropical ecosystems. All four scenarios predict a decrease in the areal coverage of desert. The scenarios differ, however, in their predictions of forest distribution. Differences among the scenarios are due to the general uncertainty with regard to predictions of precipitation patterns in the tropical zone.

[*] Department of Environmental Sciences, University of Virginia, Charlottesville, VA 22903, USA

Introduction

The impacts of timber harvest and land clearing for agricultural development in the tropics have led to a major decline in distribution of tropical forest ecosystems (Myers 1980). The importance of these ecosystems in the global carbon and hydrologic cycles, as well as their role in the maintenance of global biodiversity, has raised awareness for the conservation and management of these systems. The conservation and management of these ecosystems can not ignore the dynamic nature of vegetation distribution both in time and space. Paleoecological records attest to the dynamic nature of the distribution of tropical forests over the past 20,000 years with past changes in global climate patterns (Peteet 1987). These changes in forest distribution occured over thousands of years, with species migrating with changing climate patterns on a regional to continental scale (Davis 1982, 1984, 1989).

The current increase in atmospheric levels of greenhouse gases has the potential to alter global climate patterns over a much shorter timescale than that seen in paleo-records (Hansen et al. 1988). This potential for change in the global climate pattern could have major implications for the distribution of terrestrial vegetation (Emanuel et al. 1985; Prentice & Fung 1991; Smith et al. 1992a, 1992b), and consequently on the global carbon cycle (Sedjo & Solomon 1989; Prentice & Fung 1990; Smith et al. 1992a).

There is a need to develop an understanding of the potential impacts of climate change on the distribution of vegetation in the tropics, not only to determine the implications on the global carbon and hydrologic cycles, but also for the management and conservation of tropical fauna and flora. The conversion of areas of natural vegetation into agricultural and urban use has resulted in much of the floral and faunal diversity being dependent on a network of conservation and management areas. Due to this fragmentation of the landscape, the potential for species migration is limited. Therefore, there is a need for the development of a framework to predict long-term, large scale vegetation dynamics. This need is important not only in the face of possible climate change, but for long-term management and development of conservation policy. The objective of this chapter is (1) to examine some of the methodologies currently available for relating climate and vegetation at a regional to global scale, and (2) to present some preliminary analyses of the potential impacts of climate change as predicted by general circulation models (GCM's) on the distribution of vegetation in the tropics.

Models for Relating Vegetation and Climate

There is a wide array of models which have been developed to relate both the spatial and temporal dynamics of vegetation to climatic and other environmental factors. These models address spatial and temporal scales ranging from CO_2 and water flux from single leaves to the global distribution of biomes. Three general categories of these models which are currently being applied to climate change research will be discussed: (1) Climate-Vegetation Classification Models, (2) Canopy Process Models, (3) Demographic Process Models.

Climate-Vegetation Classification Models

Perhaps the simplest of models for relating vegetation pattern to climate at a global scale is the approach of climate-vegetation classification. Assuming that the broad-scale patterns of vegetation (e.g., biomes) are essentially at equilibrium with present climate conditions, one can relate the distribution of vegetation or plant types with biologically important features of the climate. Global bioclimatic classification schemes (von Humbolt 1867; Grisebach 1838; Köppen 1900, 1918, 1936; Thornthwaite 1931, 1933, 1948; Holdridge 1947, 1959, 1967; Troll & Paffen 1964; Box 1978, 1981; Prentice 1990) are essentially climate classifications defined by the large scale distribution of vegetation. Although similar in concept, the wide variation in both the terminology used to describe categories of vegetation and the climate variables identified as important in influencing plant pattern make comparisons among models difficult.

Bioclimatic classification models have a history of application in simulating the distribution of vegetation under changed climate conditions, both for past climatic conditions associated with the last glacial maximum (Manabe & Stouffer 1980; Hansen *et al.* 1984; Prentice & Fung 1990) and predictions of future climate patterns under conditions of doubled CO_2 (Emanuel *et al.* 1985; Prentice & Fung 1990; Smith *et al.* 1992a, b). However, classifications are equilibrium models, and as such, can not explicitly address temporal vegetation dynamics associated with changed climate patterns.

Canopy Process Models

Canopy process models (e.g., Running & Coughlan 1988) simulate the flux of CO_2 and water from plant canopies over timescales of seconds to a day. In general, these models are extentions of leaf-level models of photosynthesis (e.g., Farquhar *et al.* 1980) and transpiration (e.g., Penman 1948; Monteith 1973) applied to whole canopies. The models do not consider individual plants, but view the canopy as a single, multi-layer unit with a fixed structure (i.e., leaf area). Photosynthesis and transpiration are simulated by estimating microclimatic variation and stomatal conductance for the canopy (or canopy layers).

These models are generallly used to estimate seasonal patterns of CO_2 and water flux, and associated estimates of primary productivity. Running *et al.* (1989) have used a canopy process model to simulate seasonal variation in primary productivity across a range of sites in North America. The simulated patterns of productivity closely matched the remotely sensed values of NDVI (normalized difference vegetation index; Tucker 1979) for the sites, an index believed to be related to photosynthetic activity (Tucker *et al.* 1985).

The physiologically rich nature of this class of models makes them well suited to examining the response of forest canopies to short-term changes in climate (i.e. seasonal to yearly) and other environmental factors. However, they are not able to address the longer-term consequences of possible changes in species composition and forest structure.

Although canopy process models have generally been used to simulate fluxes given a defined canopy structure, recent appications have used this class of model to predict canopy structure from site factors and the prevailing climatic conditions. The approach is based on the assumption that an equilibrium exists between climate, soil water-holding capacity and maximum leaf area in water limited ecosystems. Given this assumption, it is then possible to solve for maximum sustainable leaf area under a given set of site conditions and climate (Woodward 1987; Nemani & Running 1989).

Woodward (1987) developed an approach for predicting leaf area and associated physiognomy using a model of plant energy balance. The Penman-Monteith (Penman 1948; Monteith 1973) evapotranspiration model is a biophysical model used to simulate the physiology of water use at the canopy level. Using a set of parameters describing the environment of the canopy, combined with a functional relationship between leaf environment and stomatal conductance, the model predicts evapotranpiration for a given leaf area and climatic conditions. By solving the model iteratively for varying values of leaf area, Woodward used the model to solve for the maximum leaf area which could be sustained under the climatic conditions at any given location.

This approach provides a process based alternative to the vegetation-climate classification models described above. By using this approach to predict leaf area under current and changed climate conditions, it is possible to predict changes in the leaf area which can be sustained under the changed climate conditions (Woodward 1987; Smith *et al.* 1992b). The comparison of current and changed leaf area index (LAI) can then be used to infer potential changes in the composition and structure of vegetation which may relate to the predicted shifts in LAI.

Like the Holdridge System, the energy balance-based approach of Woodward (1987) represents an equilibrium solution to a dynamic process. The predicted patterns of LAI under current and changed climate are equilibrium solutions to the corresponding spatial changes in climate patterns. The model does not explore the temporal dynamics of vegetation reponse to changed climate, rather it assumes that vegetation can respond by increasing/decreasing leaf area to eqilibrate with new climate conditions, even though this may require major shifts in species or even life-form composition.

Demographic Process Models

The use of vegetation-climate classification models to evaluate plant response to climate change discussed above implicitly assumes a time-scale sufficient for vegetation migration and eventual equilibrium of vegetation to the new "changed" climate patterns. In contrast, the canopy process models fuction over a short time scale and are able to examine changes in plant carbon and energy over a time scale of days to perhaps decades. However, simulating the temporal response of vegetation to changing climate conditions requires the explicit consideration of plant demographic processes. There are numerous models of vegetation dynamics which simulate the demographics of plant populations (Shugart & West 1980). One such class of demographic process models are "gap models".

Forest gap models simulate the establishment, growth, and mortality of individual plants on a plot scaled to the maximum size of the plant species being simulated (Shugart 1984). These models have been developed for a wide range of forest and grassland ecosystems. Although the models differ in their inclusion of processes which may be important in the dynamics of the particular site being simulated (e.g., hurricane disturbance, flooding), all gap models share a common set of characteristics and demographic processes.

Each individual plant is modeled as a unique entity with respect to the processes of establishment, growth, and mortality. This allows the model to track species- and size-specific demographic behaviors. The model structure includes two features important to a dynamic description of vegetation: (1) the response of the individual plant to the prevailing environmental conditions, and (2) how the individual modifies those environmental conditions (i.e., the feedback between vegetation structure/composition and the environment).

Gap models have been applied to examine the response of forested systems to climate changes, both in the reconstruction of prehistoric Quaternary forests (Solomon *et al.* 1980, 1981; Solomon & Shugart 1984; Solomon & Webb 1985; Bonan & Hayden 1990; Bonan *et al.* 1990), as well as, in the projection of possible consequences of future climate change (Solomon *et al.* 1984; Solomon 1986; Pastor & Post 1988; Bonan *et al.* 1990; Urban & Shugart 1989; Overpeck *et al.* 1990). In contrast to the two modeling approaches discussed in the earlier sections, the gap model approach is high resolution in that it can predict species composition, vegetation structure and associated productivity and standing biomass through time, however, it is limited in spatial scale. That is, it is limited in the spatial extent to which the results can be extrapolated. The reason for this limitation is that the information required to parameterize/initialize a model which can address changes in these state variables (e.g., species composition and productivity through time) relate to site specific features such as topographic position, soil characteristics, land-use history, history of disturbance, and present vegetation structure, all of which may vary over short distances. The application of fine resolution models to provide total coverage over broad regions would be virtually impossible due to both computational and data limitations. As an alternative, sampling approaches have been put forward to provide large scale coverage over broad environmental gradients (Solomon 1986; Bonan 1990a, 1990b; Smith *et al.* 1992b).

A Preliminary Analysis of the Potential Impacts of Climate Change on the Distribution of Vegetation in the Tropics

The purpose of this analysis is to explore the possible implications of changes in global climate patterns as predicted by General Circulation Models (GCM's) on the distribution of vegetation in the tropical zone. We will focus on large-scale continental patterns using the climate-vegetation classification model developed by Holdridge (1947). As discussed above, climate-vegetation classification models are essentially correlations between current vegetation and climate patterns. They are equilibrium models and do not address temporal dynamics.

Therefore, the results represent changes in the climate zones associated with certain vegetation types or biomes, rather than changes in the vegetation per se. Despite these limitations, the models provide a means of interpreting changes in climate patterns as they relate to current vegetation patterns.

Application of Holdridge Life-Zone Classification to Climate Change in the Tropical Zone

The Holdridge Life-Zone Classification System is a bioclimatic model relating the distribution of natural vegetation associations to climate indices. The features of the Holdridge Classification are summarized in Figure 1. The life zones are depicted by a series of hexagons formed by intersecting intervals of climate variables on logarithmic axes in a triangular coordinate system. Two variables, average biotemperature and average annual precipitation, determine the classification. Average biotemperature is the average temperature over a year with the unit temperature values (i.e., daily, weekly or monthly) that are used in computing the average set to 0°C if they are less than or equal to 0°C.

In the Holdridge Diagram (Fig. 1), identical axes for average annual precipitation form two sides of an equilateral triangle. A logarithmic axis for the potential evapotranspiration (PET) ratio (effective humidity) forms the third side of the triangle, and an axis for mean annual biotemperature is oriented perpendicular to the base. By marking equal intervals on these logarithmic axes, hexagons are formed that designate the Holdridge Life Zones. Each life zone is named to indicate a vegetation association.

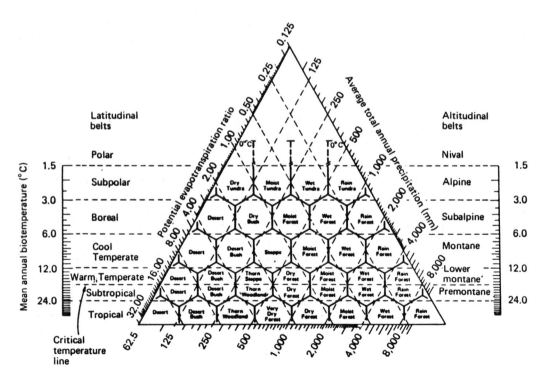

Fig. 1. Holdridge climate-vegetation classification scheme (from Holdridge 1967)

The potential evapotranspiration is the amount of water that would be released to the atmosphere under natural conditions with sufficient water throughout the growing season. The potential evapotranspiration ratio is the quotient of PET and average annual precipitation. Holdridge (1959) assumes, on the basis of studies of several ecosystems, that PET is proportional to biotemperature. The Holdridge Classification is therefore dependent on the two primary variables, annual precipitation and biotemperature.

One additional division in the Holdridge System is based on the occurrence of killing frost. This division is along a critical temperature line that divides hexagons between 12° and 24°C into Warm Temperate and Subtropical Zones. This line is adjusted to reflect regional conditions. The complete Holdridge Classification includes 37 life zones.

The expected current distributions of Holdridge Life Zones for the tropics (latitudinal belt 23.5° N to 23.5° S) were mapped using a climate data base of mean monthly precipitation and temperature at a 0.5° (latitude and longitude) resolution (Leemans & Cramer 1990). Simulations of current and $2xCO_2$ climates from four GCM's (Tab. 1) were used to construct climate change scenarios. Changes in mean monthly precipitation and temperature were calculated for each GCM scenario for each computational grid element by taking the difference between simulated current and $2xCO_2$ climates. These data from each GCM were interpolated to 0.5° resolution and changes in monthly precipitation and temperature were then applied to the climate data base to provide a change scenario. The altered data bases corresponding to each of the four GCM scenarios were then used to reclassify the grid cells (0.5°) using the Holdridge System.

Tab. 1. General circulation models used to construct climate change scenarios

| | Change in Mean Global: | | |
GCM	Resolution (lat/lon)	Temperature (°C)	Precipitation (%)
[1] Oregon State University (OSU)	4 x 5°	2.84	7.8
[2] Geophysical Fluid Dynamics Laboratory (GFDL)	4.5 x 7.5°	4.00	8.7
[3] Goddard Institute for Space Studies (GISS)	7.8 x 10°	4.20	11.0
[4] United Kingdom Meteorological Office (UKMO)	5 x 7.5°	5.20	15.0

[1] Schlesinger & Zhao 1988 [2] Manabe & Wetherald 1987 [3] Hansen *et al.* 1988 [4] Mitchell 1983

Maps and summary statistics of changes in the distribution of major biome-types under the four climate change scenarios are shown in Figure 2 and Table 2 respectively. The biome types are aggregates of the life zones and are defined in Table 2.

In general, there is a qualitative agreement between the GFDL, GISS and UKMO scenarios for changes in areal coverage of the four general classes of biomes. The three scenarios result in a decrease in the areal coverage of desert and mesic forest, with a corresponding increase in the extent of grassland and dry forest ecosystems. In contrast, the OSU scenario predicts a decrease in the extent of desert, grassland and dry forest biomes, with a resulting increase in the areal coverage of mesic forest (Tab. 2).

The changes presented in Table 2 represent changes in the areal coverage of biomes for the geographically defined tropical zone between 23.5° N and 23.5° S latitude only. In the global context, there is a much larger increase in the extent of tropical mesic forest for the OSU scenario as defined by the Holdridge Classification (Smith *et al.* 1992a, b). In addition, there is a net global increase in tropical mesic forest for the GISS scenario. These global increases are due to the expansion of the tropical zone as defined by biotemperature in the Holdridge System (see Fig. 1). Under the warmer climate conditions predicted by the GCM's, many areas currently classified as subtropical and warm temperate forest are reclassified as tropical forest. In general, the global warming results in a poleward shift in all forest zones with the subsequent expansion of the boreal forest zone into the region currently occupied by tundra (Smith *et al.* 1992a, b).

Tab.2. Changes in the areal coverage of major biome types* under current and changed climate conditions

	CURRENT Area (km²x10³)	OSU	GFDL	GISS	UKMO
Desert	815.6	-106.5	-94.0	-191.2	-164.8
Grassland	734.3	-70.4	95.2	212.5	148.7
Dry Forest	1267.9	-193.2	154.2	152.4	630.9
Mesic Forest	2195.6	373.9	-151.6	-169.7	-610.9

*
Desert:
   Polar Desert, Boreal Desert, Cool Temperate Desert, Warm Temperate Desert, Subtropical Desert, Subtropical Desert Bush, Tropical Desert, Tropical Desert Bush
Grassland:
   Cool Temperate Steppe, Warm Temperate Thorn Steppe, Subtropical Thorn Steppe, Tropical Thorn Steppe, Tropical Very Dry Forest
Dry Forest:
   Warm Temperate Dry Forest, Subtropical Dry Forest, Tropical Dry Forest
Mesic Forest:
   Moist, Wet and Rain Forest for Boreal, Cool Temperate, Warm Temperate, Subtropical and Tropical temperature Zones

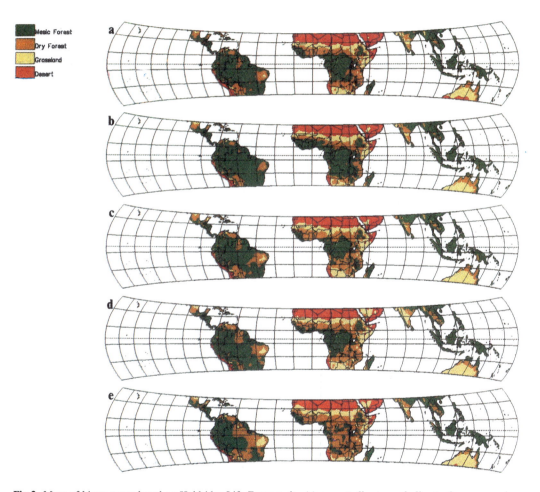

Fig. 2. Maps of biome types based on Holdridge Life Zones under (a) current climate, and climate change scenarios based on the (b) Oregon State University, (c) Geophysical Fluid Dynamics Laboratory, (d) Goddard Institute for Space Studies, and (e) United Kingdom Meteorological Office general circulation models. The resolution is 0.5° latitude x 0.5° longitude. Key relating biome types to Holdridge Life Zones are shown in Table 2

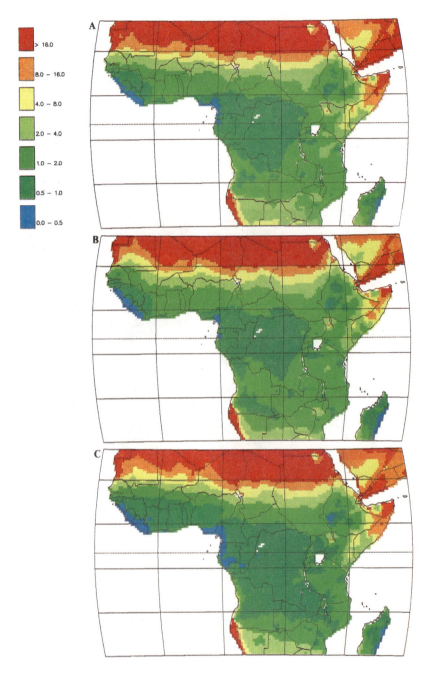

Fig.3. Maps of annual PET-ratio (potential evapotranspiration/precipitation) for tropical Africa under (a) current climate, and climate change scenarios based on the (b) United Kingdom Meteorological Office, and (c) Oregon State University general circulation models. Classes of PET-ratio correspond to divisions on PET-ratio axis of Holdridge Diagram in Figure 1

The changes in coverage of the biome types presented in Table 2 are the outcome of a dynamic process of spatial changes in the climate pattern, and associated spatial changes in the distribution of life zones. These spatial dynamics can be described as a matrix of transitions between types (Tab. 3). Rows of the matrix show transitions from that biome type (i.e., aggregated life zone) to the specified type in the column headings. The diagonal elements show the area occupied by the biome type under current climate which does not change (to another biome type) under the new climate conditions. Therefore, the sum of the elements in each row is the current coverage for that biome type, while the sum of the elements in each column is the coverage for that type under the changed climate conditions.

The decrease in the extent of desert seen in all four scenarios is largely a function of the shift from desert to grassland along the southern boundary of the Sahara Desert and in the Arabian Peninsula (Fig. 2). In addition to this shift from desert to grassland, the increase in the extent of grassland in the GFDL, GISS and UKMO scenarios is a result of the shift from grassland to dry forest in the lower Sahel, and to a lesser degree in eastern Brazil.

The increase in coverage of dry forest in the GFDL, GISS and UKMO scenarios is primarily due to a drying of mesic forest. This decline in mesic forest cover is widespread in both South America and central Africa.

In contrast to the other three scenarios, the decline in grasslands in the OSU scenario is a function of the shift from grassland to dry forest in both South America and Africa. This shift is a result of an overall increase in precipitation in the tropical zone. This increase in rainfall is also responsible for the decline in dry forest and subsequent increase in mesic forest cover in the OSU scenario.

These results suggest large scale shifts in the vegetation of the tropics under changing global climate patterns. The changes in vegetation pattern are primarily a function of changes in patterns of moisture availability. Unless precipitation is sufficient to offset the increased evapotranspirative (ET) demand from increasing temperatures, plant moisture stress will occur. If increased precipitation is greater than the increase in ET demand resulting from the higher temperatures, productivity would increase, and with time the site could possibly change to a more mesic vegetation type (e.g., grassland to dry forest).

Although the Holdridge Classification relates life zones to PET-ratio (potential evapotranspiration/precipitation) this ratio is assumed to be linearly related to biotemperature (i.e., biotemperature*58.93). To determine if biotemperature is providing a sufficient index of the PET-ratio under the changed climate conditions, we calculated PET for each 0.5°x0.5° land cell of tropical Africa under current climate and the four GCM-based scenarios using the Priestley-Taylor model of potential evapotranspiration (Priestley & Taylor 1972).

Maps of the PET-ratio for tropical Africa under current climate and the OSU and UKMO scenarios are presented in Figure 3. The values of the PET-ratio were classed to correspond to the divisions along the corresponding axis of the Holdridge Diagram (Figure 1). In general, the patterns of calculated PET-ratio match the shifts in life zones shown in the biome maps of Figure 2. The expansion of mesic forest in western Africa under the OSU scenario corresponds spatially to the decrease in the PET-ratio seen in Figure 3c. Likewise, the transition from mesic to dry forest throughout western and central Africa under the UKMO scenario is paralleled by corresponding increases in the PET-ratio (Fig. 3b).

Tab.3. Transitions between biome types for the four GCM-based climate change scenarios. Matrices show the changes in areal coverage between biome types. Values are in $km^2 x 10^3$ (D-Desert; G-Grassland; DF-Dry Forest; MF-Mesic Forest)

OSU

To:	D	G	DF	MF	Total
From: D	703.3	103.8		2.9	810.0
G	2.0	529.9	202.3		734.2
DF		28.7	809.0	430.2	1267.9
MF	.3	1.5	63.3	2130.5	2195.6
Total	705.6	663.9	1074.6	2563.6	5007.7

GFDL

To:	D	G	DF	MF	Total
From: D	711.9	94.9	3.3	810.1	
G	6.5	648.3	78.4	1.1	734.3
DF		85.2	1087.9	94.8	1267.9
MF	.3	.6	255.9	1938.8	2195.6
Total	718.7	829.0	1422.2	2038.0	5007.9

GISS

To:	D	G	DF	MF	Total
From: D	620.6	179.4	4.1	5.9	810.0
G	1.8	653.0	77.4	2.1	734.3
DF		112.9	995.5	159.4	1267.8
MF		.3	343.3	1852.0	2195.6
Total	622.4	945.6	1420.3	2019.4	5007.7

UKMO

To:	D	G	DF	MF	Total
From: D	622.1	168.2	3.0	17.6	810.9
G	7.2	573.7	145.3	8.1	734.3
DF	5.0	121.9	984.9	156.2	1268.0
MF	13.9	17.7	764.5	1399.1	2195.2
Total	648.2	881.5	1897.7	1581.0	5008.4

Discussion

The results of the potential impacts of climate change in the tropics presented in this chapter suggest large scale changes in the current patterns of vegetation distribution. However, these results have two major sources of uncertainty. The first source of uncertainty is associated with the GCM model predictions.

Although all of the GCM's predict some degree of warming in the tropics, the models vary widely in their predictions of precipitation patterns. This variation is most apparent in the qualitative difference between the OSU and UKMO scenarios for the tropical zone. The purpose of the GCM models is to examine the sensitivity of the global climate system to changes in the major forcing functions, such as atmospheric concentrations of CO_2.

The spatial resolution of the models is very coarse (see Table 1) due primarily to computational limitations. As such, the scale at which climate is defined is, in most cases inappropriate for examining associated vegetation patterns at anything less that the continental scale. However, they are the best estimates of the spatial variation in climatic patterns, and provide a more realistic approach to assessing the sensitivity of global vegetation to climate change than applying global average temperature and precipitation changes homogeneously.

The second source of uncertainty is in the models relating vegetation and climate. The results discussed above must be viewed in light of the limitation of the methodology. As with any classification scheme, the Holdridge model is an abstraction of the actual vegetation pattern. The Holdridge Life Zone model is a climate classification rather than a classification based on actual vegetation distribution, such as the system developed by Box (1981).

The approach also assumes that the vegetation unit or biome structure moves as a fixed unit in time and space. This assumption may not hold, especially under conditions where the changed climate has no current analogue.

The Holdridge Classification, like all climate-vegetation classification models, is correlative and based on a limited set of variables. Although the bioclimatic indices used in the classification may do a sufficient job of bounding present vegetation patterns, the actual patterns are a function of additional factors not explicitly considered in the model (e.g., soils) which may vary differently (both temporally and spatially) under the changed climate conditions.

Perhaps most importantly, the results represent equilibrium solutions for both climate (i.e., $2 \times CO_2$) and vegetation dynamics. In reality, the vegetation would most likely be unable to track the true transient climate dynamic. Although changes in the climate pattern as suggested by the GCM simulations may occur on a timescale of decades to a century, the response of vegetation and soils to those changes may occur at different and varying timescales. In areas where biomass values decrease due to moisture stress (i.e., higher PET-ratio) the changes may occur quickly as the environmental conditions become such that the present vegetation can no longer be supported (e.g., forest to grassland).

In contrast, increases in biomass may require much longer periods of time. In some cases the present vegetation may show increased growth or recruitment under the more favorable conditions. However, major shifts of vegetation type (e.g., dry to mesic forest) are dependent on the movement of species across the landscape and the ability of new species to invade existing communities. These changes in vegetation would operate on timescales related to the lifecycle or longevity of the component species. In the case of many forest species this may be on the order of centuries.

Predicting the temporal dynamics of vegetation response of changing environmental conditions requires a modeling approach which explicitly considers the demographic and landscape processes influencing dispersal, establishment and competition. Approaches such as the gap models discussed earlier (see: Demographic Process Models) are able to simulate changes in the structure and composition of vegetation on a given site with changes in environmental conditions. The application of this class of models to tropical systems is hindered by the difficulties in model parameterization. High species diversity combined with the lack of basic data on the life-history characteristics and physiological response of even dominant species to such environmental factors as temperature and soil moisture limit the application of demographic models to tropical forest ecosystems.

The growing concern over the possibility of changes in the global climate system as a function of increasing concentrations of atmospheric CO_2 has caused ecologists to address focus on fundamental questions concerning the distribution and function of ecosystems. In most cases this focus has shown our lack of understanding of key patterns and processes. The need for understanding these processes and patterns, and the development of predictive models relating plant distribution and ecosystem function to environmental gradients is not only essential in the face of possible anthropogenically-induced climate change, but for rational management and conservation policy.

References

Bonan GB (1990a) Carbon and nitrogen cycling in North American boreal forests. I. Litter quality and soil thermal effects in interior Alaska. Biogeochemestry 10: 1-28

Bonan GB (1990b) Carbon and nitrogen cycling in North American boreal forests. II. Biogeographic patterns. Canadian J For Res 20: 1077-1088

Bonan GB, Shugart HH, Urban DL (1990) The sensitivity of some high-latitude boreal forests to climatic parameters. Climatic Change 16: 9-29

Bonan GB, Hayden BP (1990) Using a forest stand simulation model to examine the ecological and climatic significance of the late-Quaternary pine-spruce pollen zone in eastern Virginia, U.S.A. Quat Res 33: 204-218

Box EO (1978) Ecoclimatic determination of terrestrial vegetation physiognomy. Ph.D. dissertation, 381 pp., Univ. of N.C., Chapel Hill, N.C.

Box EO (1981) Macroclimate and Plant Forms: An Introduction to Predictive Modeling in Phytogeography, Junk: The Hague

Davis MB (1982) Quaternary history and the stability of forest communities. In: Forest Succession: Concepts and Application (DC West, HH Shugart & DB Botkin, eds.) New York: Springer-Verlag

Davis MB (1984) Climatic instability, time lags and community disequilibrium. In: Community Ecology (J Diamond and TJ Case, eds.) pp 269-284. New York: Harper and Row

Davis MB (1989) Lags in vegetation response to greenhouse warming. Climatic Change 15: 75-82

Emanuel WR, Shugart HH, Stevenson MP (1985) Climatic change and the broad-scale distribution of terrestrial ecosystem complexes. Climatic Change 7: 29-43

Farquhar GD, von Caemmerer S, Berry JA (1980) A chemical model of photosynthetic CO_2 assimilation in leaves of C3 plants. Planta 149: 78-90

Grisebach A (1838) Über den Einfluß des Climas auf die Begrenzung der natürlichen Floren. Linnaea 12: 159-200

Hansen J, Lacis A, Rind D, Russell G, Stone P, Fung I, Ruedy R, Lerner J (1984) Climate sensitivity: Analysis of feedback mechanisms. In: (JE Hansen & T Takahashi, eds.) Climate Processes and Climate Sensitivity, Geophys. Monogr. Ser., vol. 29, Maurice Ewing Ser., vol. 5

Hansen J, Fung I, Lacis A, Rind D, Russell G, Lebedeff S, Reudy R, Stone P (1988) Global climate changes as forecast by the GISS-3-D model. J Geophys Res 93: 9341-9364

Holdridge L R (1947) Determination of world formulations from simple climatic data. Science 105:367-368

Holdridge L R (1959) Simple method for determining potential evapotranspiration from temperature data. Science 130: 572

Holdridge L R (1967) Life Zone Ecology. Tropical Science Center, San Jose Humboldt A von (1867) Ideen zu einem Geographie der Pflanzen nebst einem Naturgemälde der Tropenländer. Tübingen

Humboldt A von (1867) Ideen zu einer Geographie der Pflanzen nebst einerm Naturgemälde der Tropenländer. Tübingen

Köppen W (1900) Versuch einer Klassification der Klimate, vorzugsweise nach ihren Beziehungen zur Pflanzenwelt. Geogr Z 6: 593-611

Köppen W (1918) Klassification der Klimate nach Temperatur, Niederschlag und Jahreslauf. Petermanns Geogr Mitt 64: 193-203

Köppen W (1936) Das geographische System der Klimate. In: Handbuch der Klimatologie (W Köppen & R Geiger, eds.) vol. 1, part C. Berlin: Gebr Borntraeger

Leemans R, Cramer W (1990) The IIASA climate database for land area on a grid of 0.5° resolution. WP-41, International Institute for Applied Systems Analysis, Laxenburg

Manabe S, Stouffer RJ (1980) Sensitivity of a global climate to an increase in CO_2 concentration in the atmosphere. J Geophy Res 8: 5529-5554

Manabe S, Wetherald RT (1987) Large scale changes in soil wetness induced by an increase in carbon dioxide. J Atm Sci 44: 1211-1235

Mitchell JFB (1983) The seasonal response of a general circulation model to changes in CO_2 and sea temperature. Q J Roy Met Soc 109: 113-152

Monteith JL (1973) Principles of Environmental Physics. London: E Arnold

Myers N (1980) The present status and future prospects of tropical moist forests. Environ Conservation 7: 101-114

Nemani RR, Running SW (1989) Testing a theoretical climate-soil-leaf area hydrologic equilibrium of forests using satellite data and ecosystem simulation. Agr For Met 44: 245-260

Overpeck JT, Rind D, Goldberg R (1990) Climate-induced changes in forest disturbance and vegetation. Nature 343: 51-53

Pastor J, Post WM (1988) Response of northern forests to CO_2-induced climate change. Nature 334: 55-58

Penman HL (1948) Natural evaporation from open water, bare soil and grass. Proc Royal Soc London, Series A, 193: 120-145

Peteet D (1987) Late Quaternary vegetation and climatic history of the montane and lowland tropics. In: pp. 72-76 (C Rosenzweig & R Dickinson, eds.) Climate-Vegetation Interactions. University Corporation for Atmospheric Studies: Boulder, CO

Prentice KC, Fung I Y (1990) Bioclimatic simulations test the sensitivity of terrestrial carbon storage to perturbed climates. Nature 346: 48-51

Prentice KC (1990) Bioclimatic distribution of vegetation for GCM studies. J Geophy Res Priestley, CHB & Taylor RJ 1972. On the assessment of surface heat flux and evaporation using large-scale parameters. Monthly Weather Review 100: 81-92

Priestley, CHB, Taylor RJ 1972. On the assessment of surface heat flux and evaporation using large-scale parameters. Monthly Weather Review 100: 81-92

Running SW, Coughlan JC (1988) A general model of forest ecosystem processes for regional application: Hydrologic balance, canopy gas exchange and primary production processes. Ecol Modelling 42: 125-154

Running SW, Nemani R, Peterson DL, Band LE, Potts DF, Pierce LL, Spanner MA (1989) Mapping regional forest evapotranspiration and photosynthesis by coupling satellite data with ecosystem simulation. Ecology 69: 40-45

Schlesinger M, Zhao Z (1988) Seasonal climatic changes induced by doubled CO_2 as simulated by the OSU atmospheric GCM/mixed layer ocean model. Oregon St. U., Corvallis, OR, Climate Research Institute

Sedjo RA, Solomon AM (1989) Climate and forests. In: Greenhouse Warming: Abatement and Adaptation, (eds., Rosenberg NJ, Easterling WE, Crosson PR & Darmstadter J), Resources For The Future, Washington, D.C.

Shugart HH (1984) A Theory of Forest Dynamics. New York: Springer-Verlag

Shugart HH, West DC (1980) Forest succession models. BioScience 30: 308-313

Smith TM, Leemans R, Shugart HH (1992a) Sensitivity of terrestrial carbon storage to CO_2-induced climate change: Comparison of four scenarios based on general circulation models. Climatic Change. (in press)

Smith TM, Shugart HH, Bonan GB, Smith J B (1992b) Modeling the potential response of vegetation to global climate change. Adv Ecol Res 22 (in press)

Solomon AM, Delcourt HR, West DC, Blasings TJ (1980) Testing a simulation model for reconstruction of prehistoric forest-stand dynamics. Quat Res 14: 275-293

Solomon AM, West DC, Solomon JA (1981) Simulating the role of climate change and species immigration in forest succession. In: Forest Succession (DC West, HH Shugart & DB Botkin, eds.), pp 154-177. Springer-Verlag: New York

Solomon AM, Shugart HH (1984) Integrating forest-stand simulations with paleoecological records to examine long-term forest dynamics. In: State and Change of Forest Ecosystems: Indicators in Current Research (GI Agren, ed.), pp 333-357, Report Number 13. Swedish University of Agricultural Science, Upsala, Sweden

Solomon AM, Webb T III. (1985) Computer-aided reconstruction of late-quaternary landscape dynamics. Ann Rev Ecol Syst 16: 63-84

Solomon AM, Tharp ML, West DC, Taylor GE, Webb JM, Trimble JL (1984) Response of unmanaged forests to CO_2-induced climate change: Available information, initial tests and data requirements. Tech Report TR009., U.S. DOE Carbon Dioxide Research Division, Washington D.C.

Solomon AM (1986) Transient responses of forests to CO_2-induced climate change: Simulation modeling experiments in eastern North America. Oecologia 68: 567-569

Thornthwaite CW (1931) The climates of North America according to a new classification. Geogr Rev 21: 633-655

Thornthwaite CW (1933) The climates of the earth. Geogr Rev 23: 433-440

Thornthwaite CW (1948) An approach toward a rational classification of climate. Geogr Rev 38: 55-89

Troll C, Paffen KH (1964) Karte der Jahreszeitenklimate der Erde. Erkund Arch Wiss Geogr 18: 5-28

Tucker CJ (1979) Red and photographic infrared linear combinations for monitoring vegetation. Remote Sensing of the Environment 8: 127-150

Tucker CJ, Townshend JRG, Goff TE (1985) African land cover classification using satellite data. Science 227: 369-374

Urban DL, Shugart HH (1989) Forest response to climate change: A simulation study for Southeastern forests. (pg. 3-1 to 3-45). In: The Potential Effects of Global Climate Change on the United States (J Smith and D Tirpak, eds.), EPA-230-05-89-054, US Environmental Protection Agency, Washington, D.C.

Woodward FI (1987) Climate and Plant Distribution. Cambridge: Cambridge Univ. Press

Subject Index

B I R K H Ä U S E R
L I F E S C I E N C E S

Claude Martin
WWF International, Gland

The Rainforests of West Africa
Ecology - Threats - Conservation

Translated by Linda Tsardakas

1990. 235 pages, 52 color-
and 106 b/w-illus. Hardcover
ISBN 3-7643-2380-9 (English edition)

Also available in German
ISBN 3-7643-1987-9 (German edition)

Man is far from having discovered all the secrets held by Africa's rainforests. But we know more than
is generally believed: This book surprises its reader with an exciting and comprehensive look at the
ecology and utilization of African rainforests as well as the possibilities and prospects for their
protection.
For the first time, the rainforest is seen as a whole, the enormous biological diversity of these forests
is documented in text and with numerous photographs. The reader is offered a varied palette of
information: How eight different monkey species share the forest from the floor to the tops of the trees,
how the forest elephant is responsible for the seed dispersal of certain tree species – these questions
are treated just as are the traditional hunting and gathering culture of forest people and the importance
of the rainforest from their point of view. But the reader also learns the details of tropical timber
exploitation and the often dubious role industrialized countries play in that respect. There are still
possibilities for better protection: Interesting forest conservation projects in West Africa could soon
become of worldwide importance.

*«New books on the Amazon seem to come out every month, but a brief search in the library of the
Oxford Forestry Institute reveals that the most recent book on West Africa's rainforests was
published more than 30 years ago. This alone makes Claude Martin's book an important
publication, indeed a mandatory purchase for many libraries and environmental organisations; it
is also one to be recommended to a wider public. It is a highly ambitious work combining history,
natural history, ecology, fearsome critiques of the timber trade and a prognosis for the
conservation of this ravaged biome. It is a lot to fit into 230 pages but Martin succeeds in doing so
gracefully. The text is light and readable and accompanied by his own excellent photographs...»*

Oliver Tickell
in *New Scientist*

Please order through your
bookseller or directly from:
Birkhäuser Verlag AG
P.O. Box 133
CH-4010 Basel /
Switzerland
Fax 0041 / 61 721 79 50

Orders from the USA or Canada
should be sent to:
Birkhäuser Boston Inc.
c/o Springer Verlag New York
Inc.
44 Hartz Way
Secaucus, NJ 07096-2491 / USA

Birkhäuser

Birkhäuser Verlag AG
Basel · Boston · Berlin

B I R K H Ä U S E R
LIFE SCIENCES

Advances in Life Sciences

Species Conservation:
A Population-Biological Approach

Edited by
Alfred Seitz, *Univ. of Mainz, Germany*
Volker Loeschcke, *Univ. of Aarhus, Denmark*

1991. 292 pages. Hardcover. ISBN 3-7643-2493-7 (ALS)

Contents:

Please order from your bookseller or directly from:
Birkhäuser Verlag AG
P.O. Box 133
CH-4010 Basel / Switzerland
Orders from the USA or Canada should be sent to:
Birkhäuser Boston Inc.
c/o Springer Verlag New York Inc.
44 Hartz Way
Secaucus, NJ 07096-2491 / USA

Birkhäuser

Birkhäuser Verlag AG
Basel · Boston · Berlin